PSYCHIATRY AND THE COMMUNITY IN NINETEENTH-CENTURY AMERICA

PSYCHIATRY AND THE COMMUNITY IN NINETEENTH-CENTURY AMERICA

The Recurring Concern with the Environment in the Prevention and Treatment of Mental Illness

RUTH B. CAPLAN

IN COLLABORATION WITH GERALD CAPLAN

Basic Books, Inc., Publishers   NEW YORK   LONDON

Dedicated to the memory of

Jack David Siebenberg

1915–1964

FOREWORD

Milton Greenblatt *

How better can we judge our times than in the tribunal of history?
Only by appreciation of all that has happened in the past can the
present scene be fully understood and evaluated. Humanity itself
presents a rich case history with its contemporary events developed
on a baseline extending infinitely into the past. In its chronicles, the
historian encounters unlimited challenge.

Ruth B. Caplan, assisted by her distinguished father, Gerald Caplan, has furnished us with the historical background necessary to
evaluate the present state of treatment for mental disorder. The
penetrating scholarship of the daughter and the clinical wisdom of
the father, himself greatly involved in setting psychiatry's pattern
for the future, make a rare combination. Together they have produced a rich and lively document with many new and revealing
views of the past, heretofore unnoticed or below our threshold of
significance. Our present knowledge of the importance and relevance of socioenvironmental factors in the cause and treatment of
mental disorders makes it possible for us to see and appreciate a
broader and deeper background of socioenvironmental practice and
experience in nineteenth-century psychiatry than we had ever suspected. Much that we think is new in our practices we find to be
a revival, in an altered form, of what went on before, enacted upon
a more modern stage.

The author holds our attention with many arresting themes. Per-

* Commissioner, Massachusetts Department of Mental Health; Professor of Psychiatry, Tufts University School of Medicine; Lecturer in Psychiatry, Harvard
Medical School and Boston University School of Medicine.

haps the most moving one has to do with the high level of humanism, individual care, and attention accorded the mentally ill patient in hospitals of the early 1800's under the banner of "moral treatment." The dignity of the patient was preserved and enhanced, and the conditions of his living were extraordinarily rich and culturally impressive compared with the subsequent era of custodialism that dominated for so long, and even compared with the level of care and attention that prevail today in our public mental hospitals. How moral treatment declined and finally succumbed to a new philosophy of mass incarceration at lowest per capita cost in ever larger institutions is a fascinating tale. The great influx of poor foreigners after 1860, and the social and psychological barriers erected against them, is a story of discrimination highly reminiscent of racism today. The lesson of history is that, whenever and wherever man is set against man in society outside our hospital walls, the same attitude is to be found within our institutions, militating against effective treatment and ultimate cure of our mentally ill. This is the climate in which philosophical doctrines such as the "survival of the fittest" were ill-applied to the social scene, and were allowed to flourish and become the rationalization for further callous neglect, thus compounding errors and visiting upon the twentieth century the legacy of chronicity with which so many of us are now struggling.

Much that was embodied in moral treatment sprang from the warm regard of the early settler for his neighbor. It depended on small-group living, was nourished by close interpersonal contact, and included, by its very nature, a concern with continuity of care. When this was lost, everything was lost. The later, almost accidental, discovery of "tent therapy," which the author so interestingly discloses, and whose success was dependent primarily on narrowing the gap between staff and patients and on raising the dignity of the individual, unfortunately did not result in any generalization of the humanistic principle involved. Indeed, from the writings of that period it is even doubtful whether the idea of humanism was ever fully recognized as the main effective therapeutic ingredient of the "new" modality.

Today we glory in the fact that the public is becoming concerned and interested in the proper care of the mentally ill. Major pronouncements of the federal government, backed by huge financial outlays for research, demonstration, training, building, and staffing, plus massive inducements to entice states into commitment of resources to fight mental illness and retardation, have suddenly made our specialty legitimate, even desirable. Yet, for many decades in the past, psychiatry was *déclassé*, a pariah in the family of medicine, scorned for its claims of expertness, and custodian of the most hapless and hopeless patients in the world.

How psychiatry tried to overcome this dreadful period is revealed by the story of a stalwart band of superintendents who separated themselves sharply from the general public, supported each other and their leaders through crises with almost religious dedication, and drew strength from their autocratic powers as heads of asylums and hospitals. But the guild they established was professionalism at its worst. It resisted collaboration with the citizens, it defended practices that had no substantial scientific foundation, and it even squelched criticism arising from within.

Now, at last, after many terrible vicissitudes, psychiatry is being accepted in the family of medical specialties; our many systems of treatment of mental illness and retardation are seeking ways to return to the community. Environment and the very fabric of our social life are being studied for their contribution in a public health sense to the behavioral misfortunes of our people. But, along the way, many pathways have been explored; some were blind alleys, others led directly into our times. We recall with amusement that one physician prescribed for a mentally ill boy a "course of the larger mammals," that is, a period of living in the zoo alongside elephants and other large mammals in order to restore his troubled mind. The theory was that the larger mammals, with their slow and lumbering ways, would act as tranquilizers. One is not sure that this concept is totally dead, but one could venture a prediction that it will not be resurrected for some time. On the other hand, at the turn of the century Adolf Meyer, with brilliant insight, outlined in one or two small paragraphs the whole concept of community psychiatry in all its breadth and depth that prevails today.

Thus, insight into the past, perspectives on today, and thoughts for tomorrow are found in this rich historical narrative; and not the least of our pleasures in reading this book are the generous quotations directly from leaders of American thought, who, whatever the merits of their ideas, have not been surpassed by any of our modern writers in their beauty of expression and command of phrase.

Is there anything new under the psychiatric sun, the reader will ask. Yes, indeed. Though rooted in the past, much that we think and do today is nevertheless in sharp discontinuity with former times. For example, although the ideas about community psychiatry are not new, the doing is new, and today we are attempting to accomplish on a grand scale what could hardly have been imagined by our forebears. And in the almost infinity of variations in which we are projecting new programs, we are certainly very different from the nineteenth century. Partnership with the people is proceeding in a way that would have seemed impossible to the members of the old psychiatric guild. Our beginning attempts to work with a whole army of experts in urban living, for example, would have seemed strange if not wonderful to our conservative ancestors.

There is one great development of our times that stands like a polished structure over and above all our past, namely, our monumental efforts, fostered, financed, and guided by the federal government, to establish the whole edifice of psychiatry and behavioral pathology on a solid scientific foundation, aided and abetted by remarkable advances in research methodology and technology. Surely this is a far cry from the almost slavish dependence of the nineteenth century on reports and dicta emanating from Germany, where scientists were held in awesome esteem by our American fathers. What is also heartening is to know that America has freed itself from narrow reliance on the methods and techniques of the laboratories of neurology and pathology and has included a large range of social, psychological, and behavioral approaches and propositions as appropriate grist for the scientific mill. We hope that in the not-too-distant future we will be on much firmer ground than ever before in terms of security in and certainty about what we teach and are able to hand down to our successors.

Finally, history teaches us caution and respect for our unknowns and our probable errors. However enthusiastic we may be about our "new" day, the chances are probably not good that present concepts and practices will survive intact for fifty or a hundred years. Society is changing faster than ever; it is difficult to foresee what structure and form it will take tomorrow. But of this we may be certain: our methods of care and treatment of the psychiatrically ill will keep pace with the various social reorganizations we can expect to take place.

We would hope that our changing world of the future and the

many developments in psychiatric services generated to keep up with its needs will be recorded, evaluated, and analyzed with the same perceptiveness and integrity that the Caplans have applied to their exciting research into the nineteenth century.

INTRODUCTION

This book was originally intended to be a history of mid-twentieth-century American psychiatry. The authors felt that the rapid growth and change in this field since World War II had created a need for historical perspective and for maintaining contacts with the traditions of the profession. We hoped, therefore, to examine the origins and development of progressive psychiatric practices of our own day, such as milieu therapy, catchment areas, and community-based programs of prevention and after-care, and participation by psychiatrists in such nonpsychiatric institutions as schools, the Army, and the Peace Corps. We also hoped to trace the social, economic, and political currents that had produced the Mental Health Study Act of 1955, the report of the Joint Commission on Mental Illness and Mental Health in 1961, the 1963 Kennedy Message, and the ensuing federal legislation that provided funds for a network of community mental health centers across the country.

Our book, however, does not deal directly with any of these topics. The sources we examined drew us further and further back into the nineteenth century, into the history of the Association of Medical Superintendents of American Institutions for the Insane (now the American Psychiatric Association) and into the early volumes of the *American Journal of Insanity* (now the *American Journal of Psychiatry*). Most of the material was found in primary sources, in *Journal* articles, obituaries, asylum notices, accounts of Association meetings, and the books and records of individual nineteenth-century psychiatrists. What emerged was so unexpected that we abandoned all our preconceived plans. The material took command and molded the book into one quite different from what we had originally envisioned.

This book, however, is not merely an account of nineteenth-rather than twentieth-century American practice. A history of the field from 1800 to 1900 might be expected to deal with the development of, and gradual disenchantment with, a system of massive public and private mental hospitals. It might chronicle American psychiatry's absorption of contemporary European, and particularly German, models of nosology and patient care. And it might summarize the theories of such contemporary leaders of the profession as Benjamin Rush, John Gray, Isaac Ray, and Adolf Meyer.

Although this book treats of all these matters, the original vantage point of late twentieth-century psychiatry has remained and has given the material a particular focus. The emphasis is on "environment," a term used here to encompass two main areas: changing professional theories about the possible role of physical and social surroundings in creating and curing insanity; and the relationship of psychiatrists to their own milieux—that of their treatment wards, that of the lay community, and that of the psychiatric guild.

When one traces these themes through American psychiatry of the last century, one realizes that many of the theories considered most revolutionary today have emerged and disappeared over and over in the past: the concept of the therapeutic community and the realization of the dangers of overcrowded and impersonal chronic-stay institutions; the idea of isolating the social and physical factors that place a segment of the population in danger and of then attempting to protect the mental health of that group; the concept of after-care; the realization of the need to establish co-operation and consultation with other community caregivers; the development of a repertoire of varied and flexible treatment modalities; and even plans, expressed by the Association of Medical Superintendents in 1864 and by Adolf Meyer in 1909, that closely approximate the pattern of a catchment area served by a comprehensive network of local facilities. These examples may be multiplied at length.

That such ideas should arise at all is not, perhaps, surprising. Human needs are fairly constant from one age to another, and they may be expected to evoke similar responses from intelligent and humanitarian professionals. More puzzling are the reasons that governed the decline of these theories; and one of our major preoccupations has been a search for these.

We will try, in particular, to show the complexity and drama of psychiatric history, to chronicle the interaction between the theories of psychiatry and the ideals of the general culture, and between professional judgment and lay zeal, whether expressed in voluntary aid societies, in furious exposés, or in governmental action.

In one sense, therefore, this book may be a history of mid-twentieth-century psychiatry, after all. It is so, however, only obliquely in showing contemporary psychiatrists their own work in the ironic perspective of another century. Some direct implications of this history for community psychiatry will be further examined in the Epilogue by Gerald Caplan.

Finally, this book has been written both for psychiatrists and laymen. This has entailed certain editorial difficulties—how often should parallels between nineteenth- and twentieth-century ideas be made explicit? There was a danger of either overstating the obvious for psychiatrists or puzzling readers unfamiliar with contemporary American practice. We hope that, on the whole, we have reached a balance between these two positions; but in case we have not, we apologize for any confusion over apparently esoteric ancedotes or for irritation over labored explanations.

R. B. C.
G. C.

Boston
March 1969

ACKNOWLEDGMENTS

We acknowledge with pleasure our gratitude to the following:

Bellenden R. Hutcheson, Chief of the Commonwealth of Massachusetts Department of Mental Health Training Unit at the Harvard Laboratory of Community Psychiatry, who, with the support of Harry S. Solomon, Commissioner of Mental Health, provided the administrative framework within which the research was carried out. The research was partially financed by NIMH Grant Number MH-09214. Oscar Handlin advised on historiographic methodology and helped in the initial planning. Norris Hansell studied the first draft and prepared a detailed critique, which was the basis for a revision of the manuscript. Jack R. Ewalt, Leston L. Havens, and Robert S. Weiss also gave invaluable advice. Ann Caplan gave encouragement and support throughout and read the final draft.

CONTENTS

PART THREE

Late Nineteenth Century: Reformers and Their Impact

PART FOUR

*The Turn of the Century: The Revitalization of
Psychiatry*

PART FIVE

Epilogue

PART ONE

Early Nineteenth Century:

Moral Treatment

Chapter I

BACKGROUND AND THEORY
OF MORAL TREATMENT

During the first half of the nineteenth century, American psychiatrists were fascinated by the idea that the physical and social environment might play the key role in determining mental health and illness. They therefore attempted to manipulate the milieux not only of their hospital wards but also of the lay community in order to provide a therapeutic rather than a pathogenic experience. This goal was akin to that of modern community psychiatry, and the methods used to achieve it were often strikingly similar.

Preoccupation with adverse effects of the physical and social environment was characteristic of much nineteenth-century thought, as examination of contemporary European and American literature will demonstrate. Sir Walter Scott, for instance, showed that different cultural, climatic, and topological regions produce different patterns of values, speech, and action. Gothic novelists described brooding, haunted landscapes, and houses blighting the fate of their inhabitants. Dostoevski, Balzac, Dickens, and other Realists held that a city exerts great pressures on its inhabitants and distorts traditional values, family ties, and social obligations. Thus, the environment in their stories no longer appears as a mere painted backdrop for action but becomes instead as much a living character as the human actors in the books.

This view of the mutative powers of environment gained particular popularity in America, where it was supported by an eighteenth-century philosophical thesis held by Jeffersonians like Benjamin Rush, one of the earliest American psychiatrists. They held that, because all men were created members of the same species, differences among them must stem from accidental causes of environment. Hence, it was felt that inequalities of physical and mental faculties might be redressed by exposure to optimum conditions of temperate climate, democratic government, and a life regulated by the precepts of "right reason" and liberal education.

Concern about physical and social pressures on individuals was heightened by the experiences on which the early public health movement was based—the increased visibility of urban squalor and the consequent awareness of the plight of dislocated rural poor, crowded and exploited in manufacturing centers. Charitable societies worked to establish hospitals and orphanages, to lobby for sanitary and labor codes, and to crusade for prison reform, prohibition of alcohol, and improving the lot of the insane. Although sanitation of the physical environment became the growing preoccupation of nineteenth-century public health, sanitation of both the physical and social environment became the goal of physicians concerned with alleviating and preventing mental illness.

Early in the century the practitioners of *moral treatment* formed the most articulate and organized group dealing with the mentally disturbed. They made up the original membership of the Association of Medical Superintendents of American Institutions for the Insane, which later became the American Medico-Psychological Association and then the American Psychiatric Association. They were also the founders and major contributors to the early volumes of the *American Journal of Insanity*. In its purest form moral treatment was short-lived. At the height of its development it was practiced by only a few American asylum superintendents, and its benefits were extended to merely a fraction of the insane. Modern historians have, nevertheless, seen it as a prophetic movement because many of its practices resemble those of progressive programs of our own day. Moral treatment was, moreover, the original spur to the development of widespread institutionalization of the insane; and for nearly a century it remained the model of asylum management. It contained, even in its earliest forms, assumptions and procedures that shaped the practice of nineteenth-century American psychiatry and its relations with patients and with the surrounding community.

Several broad ideals characterized this system. Insanity was believed to be a readily curable physical disease. Its victims were removed to hospitals where they were provided with an individualized regimen of work and recreation, with religious and educational services, and with the supports and restrictions of group living. They were cared for by well-disciplined attendants and by a sympathetic, omnipresent superintendent, who attempted to cure them by both medicinal and "moral," or what would now be called psychological, means.

Moral treatment was developed in the late eighteenth century by Phillippe Pinel in France, Vincenzo Chiarugi in Italy, William Tuke in England, and Benjamin Rush in the United States. In that era of intellectual ferment, liberal treatment of the insane was corollary to humanistic and humanitarian philosophies, which sowed rebellion against concepts of religious predestination and political and social subjugation in Europe and America.

In this period, moreover, a pervasive sense of religious humanism substituted a rule of love for man's fearful relationship with God. Equitable interactions among men, and particularly the alleviation of the burdens of the unfortunate, were a major tenet of this faith.[1] Thus it is no coincidence that many of the earliest and most generous patrons and practitioners of moral treatment in America were religious New Englanders. Among these were Puritans who held that wealth must be used to succor the unfortunate rather than for vain show or luxury; and there were Quakers and Unitarians who believed that the fatherhood of God and the brotherhood of man ennobled all fellow human beings and made them equal. Thus humanitarian service became an obligation for all. Typical products of this environment were such pioneers in the humane treatment of the insane as Horace Mann, Dorothea Dix, Pliny Earle, Isaac Ray, and Amariah Brigham.

The system was also supported by an innovative climate in science and medicine, which encouraged the curious to explore the causes of natural phenomena and human behavior. The eighteenth and early nineteenth centuries valued meticulous observation and rational deduction, replacing much superstitious heritage by naturalistic formulations. Thus, reflective persons could study insanity as a disease rather than as divine retribution or demonic possession.

Moral treatment received early impetus from events surrounding the supposed insanity of George III of England. The king's condition gave rise to a series of active Parliamentary inquiries, the results of which were publicized in Europe and America. His sufferings, both from his disease and from his treatment at the hands of rough attendants, inspired deep compassion. Because of the royal disorder, fashionable doctors who would never have specialized in the care of such troublesome and hopeless cases felt suddenly obliged to study insanity,[2] particularly as fashionable people, reading the latest treatises on the subject, began to suffer from "nerves" and "bilious conditions." [3] At the same time, governmental investigations uncovered a shocking chronicle of abuse in madhouse management. These discoveries coincided with the revolutionary efforts of Pinel, Tuke, and Rush and with the testimony at the 1784 Parliamentary inquiry by Thomas Willis, an occasional attendant on the king's illness, in which he claimed to have cured nine out of ten of those who came to his private asylum.[4] There was thus, at the turn of the nineteenth century, a convergence of popular indignation, an appropriate philosophical climate, growing medical interest, and several concrete examples that seemed to prove that, with humane treatment, insanity may be cured.

In this context certain laymen and physicians working in institutions for the insane developed the system that they called moral treatment. It was based upon a contemporary philosophy known as Ideology, which emphasized the role of environment in molding personality and mental functioning. First set forth by the Abbé Etienne de Condillac, the theory was later reworked by such major figures as John Locke. It proposed that all operations of the mind depend upon the action of sensations upon the brain surface. These sensations transmitted from the outside world become the basis of all ideas, inducing such orderly mental motions as thought and understanding.[5] In derangement caused by delirium or insanity, however, this cerebral motion becomes disorganized so that the brain fails to receive or react appropriately to environmental cues, producing instead disordered judgment, delusions, hallucinations, and memory lapses.

In this school of psychological medicine, insanity was invariably linked with brain damage. Most practitioners posited a dualism between brain and intellect, which formed an extension of their more familiar terminology differentiating body and soul. The intellect was a spiritual potential, which became act through the medium of the brain, just as volition becomes act through the medium of the limbs. If the brain were diseased, the intellect would be denied its avenue to act, just as paralysis of a limb would frustrate volition. The intellect itself, however, could never be diseased, because sickness is on a continuum with death, and the intellect, like the soul of which it is part, is immortal and hence immutable. As Amariah

Brigham, first superintendent of Utica State Hospital in New York, wrote:

To say otherwise is to advocate the doctrine of the materialists, that the mind, like our bodily powers, is material, and can change, decay, and die. On this subject, the truth appears to be, that the brain is the instrument which the mind uses in this life, to manifest itself, and like all other parts of our bodies, is liable to disease, and when diseased, is often incapable of manifesting harmoniously and perfectly the powers of the mind.[6]

In 1812, in *Medical Inquiries and Observations upon the Diseases of the Mind,* the only textbook of psychiatry produced in America before 1883, Benjamin Rush had placed the seat of insanity in the blood vessels of the brain.[7] Later physicians considered damage to the central nervous system as an additional cause of lesions and of other changes in the texture of the cortical surface. Such physiological damage might be caused directly, by malformation, head injuries, tumors, epilepsy, or senility; indirectly, when damage to, or concentration of blood in, cerebral tissues was secondary to other body conditions, such as stomach and liver disease, consumption, pregnancy, fevers, or unusual labor or exercise, or when forces such as powerful intellectual strain or emotional traumata, known as "moral" agencies, damaged the brain through the medium of the mind.

The latter category of pathological forces included overattention to abstract studies, overworking the memory, or a job characterized by "the frequent and rapid transition of the mind from one subject to another," which, Rush noted, is often a danger to "booksellers [who] have sometimes become deranged from this cause." [8] Dangerous concentration of blood in the brain or pathological lesions could also be caused by sudden shocks or by dwelling on powerful emotions such as fury, grief, disappointment, homesickness, terror, or religious fanaticism, or, as Rush noted, "an exquisite sense of delicacy . . . [which] Dr. Bruton says, produced madness in a school-teacher, who was accidentally discovered upon a close-stool by one of his scholars." [9]

Other forms of derangement were thought to occur from the opposite extreme of causes, when age or lack of adequate stimulation allowed cerebral circulation to slow and brain tissues to fade and atrophy. Forbes Winslow wrote:

To preserve the intellectual powers in a state of health (setting aside altogether the idea of insanity), they must be subjected to regular exercise. If a person be placed in such a position, that he is excluded from all intercourse with his fellowmen, no attempt being made to call the powers of the mind into operation the brain will fall into a state of atrophy and great weakness of mind will result, as the natural physiological consequence.[10]

Believing this, Rush urged that the minds of the old should be properly exercised to avoid senility; several members of the Association of Medical Superintendents warned against the so-called Pennsylvania system of penology, in which all prisoners were kept in solitary confinement, and a concerted attack was made against the idleness of patients in mental hospitals.

The psychosocial aspects of moral treatment thus hinged on a thesis that was basically physiological. The brain's outstanding characteristic was thought to be its extreme sensitivity to environmental and somatic stimuli. Its surface was thought to be highly malleable, and in its convolutions all powerful or habitual experiences, thought, or feelings became etched. What we would now consider psychological forces were then felt to have a direct, physical effect. As Amariah Brigham wrote:

In mental alienation the brain invariably presents appearances of disease which can be distinctly recognized. Exceptions to this, if ever observed, are extremely rare. . . . In simple intellectual derangement, of an acute or recent character, the gray outer substance of the convolutions of the brain is altered in color and consistence; it is red, marbled, and indurated. Sometimes these appearances are confined to the anterior and superior portions of the brain. In chronic cases all these are more marked. The external layer in such may be separated like a membrane from the lower stratum. In the very chronic cases, especially in dementia, there is often wasting or diminution of the gray substance of the convolutions of the brain.[11]

At birth, the brain was thought soft and "almost liquid," in the words of a leading anatomical text of the day.[12] Although it was susceptible to the effects of all subsequent sense impressions and emotions, it also had inherited predilections to weakness or strength, just as the child's frame had an hereditary tendency to a particular build. These inherited traits were discoverable through the science of phrenology, a materialistic theory according to which every mental faculty was governed by a particular structural region of the brain. Although all attributes were, therefore, hereditary, they could be modified by education and habits that might develop certain embryonic facets of the personality while minimizing others, just as the body's natural tendencies might be modified by exercise and diet. Thus education, emotions, and habits of thought, as well as temperamental traits and habits of life, were regarded as stimuli that mold the contours of the brain and thereby determine personality, thought, and behavior. A statement by John Fonerden of the Maryland Hospital for the Insane may further clarify this concept:

Any thoughtful observer of young children may see a thousand illustrations of the principle that a habit affects a child's mind favorably or unfavorably. Notice a child's face-expression in any instance when the child is in the act of indulging a bad habit and you will see a clear indication of a state of mind and brain very far from being as intellectual and beautiful as that always noticeable when the child is in an act proceeding from a good habit. If single acts are thus demonstrably attended with visible manifestations of the influence flowing from the brain into the face, how plain it is that a succession of acts pertaining to a good habit, will give to the brain a permanent habit of order in its progressive formation, in its functions, precisely in the ratio in which there is an absence of all wrong habits.[13]

This malleability of the brain surface was at once its greatest asset and its gravest danger. Proper habits and training and a regular, healthy life could nurture goodness and sanity. On the other hand, an injudicious upbringing, vicious habits, or injuries and shocks could produce a dissolute or unstable character.

The essence of moral treatment was the belief that, because of this great malleability of the brain surface, because of its susceptibility to environmental stimuli, pathological conditions could be erased or modified by corrective experience. Therefore, insanity, whether the result of direct or indirect injury or disease, or of overwrought emotions or strained intellectual faculties, would be cured in almost every case.

Two further concepts contributed to this optimism. First, physicians believed that the mind was divided into a number of compartments, each the seat of a different faculty, such as "understanding, memory, imagination, passions, the principle of faith, will, the moral faculty, conscience, and the sense of Deity." [14] It was held by phrenologists that, although one or several of these might be affected by brain damage, the rest of the cerebral surface would survive unharmed. Thus the older idea of total insanity was replaced by the less grotesque and more manageable one of partial insanity, or monomania.

The second cause for optimism came from the belief that intellect, an attribute of the spiritual mind, would remain unimpaired in spite of a diseased brain. Thus, once the physical damage had been repaired, intelligence was expected to emerge unscathed. As Samuel B. Woodward, Superintendent of the Massachusetts State Lunatic Hospital, wrote:

The mind, in the most deplorable cases, is not obliterated, its integrity is only disturbed; it remains the same, its faculties ready, as soon as the deranged physical structure shall have regained health and soundness, to resume operations and exhibit the manifestations which legitimately belonged to them.[15]

The one reservation in this hopeful picture was the fear that in chronic cases the damage would become so deeply imbedded in the tissues as to be virtually indelible. Woodward therefore added, "It is only when the organic structure of the brain and its appendages have undergone such physical changes as to be apparent and enduring, that insanity is utterly hopeless." [16] Throughout the era of the so-called curability myth, therefore, when insanity was said to be the most curable of all diseases, physicians placed most emphasis upon differentiating recent from chronic cases in tabulating treatment outcome.

The belief that social and physical environments were critical factors in molding the surface of the brain and hence in determining the individual's state of mental health or illness had far-reaching implications for prevention and cure of insanity, because it brought a major area of etiology within reach of possible control and modification. Early nineteenth-century practitioners, therefore, were eager to manipulate facets of both extramural and institutional life in order to encourage optimum conditions for the prevention of mental disorder, for early case finding and rapid treatment, and for averting relapses among discharged patients. They tried to reach these objectives first in programs directed toward the lay community, second in the organization of institutions, and third in the interface between these two milieux.

NOTES

1. Albert Deutsch, *The Mentally Ill in America* (New York: Columbia University Press, 1945), p. 163.

2. Richard Hunter and Ida Macalpine (eds.), *Three Hundred Years of Psychiatry, 1535–1860* (London: Oxford University Press, 1963), p. 960.

3. *Ibid.*

4. Deutsch, *op. cit.*, p. 134.

5. Benjamin Rush, *Medical Inquiries and Observations Upon the Diseases of the Mind* (New York: Hafner Publishing Co., 1962), p. 10.

6. *The American Journal of Insanity*, I (1844–1845), 99.

7. Rush, *op. cit.*, p. 17.

8. *Ibid.*, p. 37.

9. *Ibid.*, p. 39.

10. *The American Journal of Insanity*, VI (1849–1850), 371.

11. Amariah Brigham, *An Inquiry Concerning the Diseases and Functions of the Brain, the Spinal Cord, and the Nerves* (New York: George Ablard, 1840), p. 292.

12. *Ibid.*, p. 282. From Buchat's *General Anatomy*, Vol. I.

13. *The American Journal of Insanity*, VII (1850–1851), 60–61.

14. Isaac Ray, *Mental Hygiene* (Boston: Ticknor and Fields, 1863), p. 5.

15. *The American Journal of Insanity*, VIII (1851–1852), 18.

16. *Ibid.*, p. 19.

Chapter 2

ATTEMPTS TO MOLD THE
COMMUNITY ENVIRONMENT

Nineteenth-century psychiatry has been stereotyped as isolated from the public behind institution walls. Early practitioners of moral treatment, however, remained integral members of their communities. They retained the broad interests in science, literature, foreign travel, and public affairs shared by other members of the intelligentsia; and in spite of clinical duties, their jobs carried them into courts, legislative chambers, and lecture halls.

Among the thirteen founding members of the Association of Medical Superintendents, for instance, Amariah Brigham was noted for his skill in surgery and his interest in chemistry, art, and politics. Pliny Earle, superintendent first of Bloomingdale Asylum in New York and later of Northampton State Hospital in Massachusetts, was a poet and mathematician as well as a noted and innovative physician. Isaac Ray of the Butler Asylum in Rhode Island was an authority on law; Luther V. Bell of McLean Asylum for the Insane in Massachusetts had served as a legislator; and John Galt of the Asylum at Williamsburg, Virginia, was proficient in a number of ancient and modern languages and was reputed by an awed historian of the period even to read Arabic.[1] The major reference group of these men remained the lawyers, doctors, clergymen, and educated merchants who composed upper middle-class society. Such men as Pliny Earle, for example, moved in high social and political circles both in the United States and Europe, attending balls and soirées with the leading legislators, businessmen, and reformers of their day.

Because they participated so actively in community life, it is hardly surprising that practitioners of moral treatment foreshadowed modern psychiatrists in their concern for the mental health of the entire population. Evidence of this may be found in the *American Journal of Insanity*, the publication which gave members of the Association of Medical Superintendents a medium of contact with the lay world. During the years when Amariah Brigham served as editor, the *Journal* was designed not merely for communication among fellow superintendents but as a vehicle for public instruction. As Brigham explained:

The object of this Journal is to popularize the study of insanity—to acquaint the general reader with the nature and varieties of this disease, methods of prevention and cure. We also hope to make it interesting to members of the medical and legal professions, and to all those engaged in the study of the phenomena of the mind.[2]

Members of the Association urged their friends in general medicine, law, and religion to subscribe,[3] and they established reciprocal relations with other scientific and literary groups in order to exchange volumes of their respective journals.[4]

The *Journal* was intended not only to acquaint learned men with the phenomena of insanity but also to remove fears, thus easing mistreatment and stigmatization of the mentally disturbed. It was also meant to serve as an organ for disseminating information both to combat causes of insanity in the community and to promote mental health; and the ardor with which superintendents set about their task gave early volumes of the *Journal* a tone of crusading, and often outraged, citizenry. This zealous passion may be seen in the following excerpt from a description of the murder trial of a patent lunatic, which had apparently been conducted in a manner fitting European stereotypes of American backwoods savagery:

It is with feelings of unspeakable mortification and sorrow, that we find it reserved for the year of our Lord 1845, in the State of Kentucky, to present us, in the administration of the law, with a triumph of passion, revenge, ignorance and political faction over the pleadings of humanity and science, unparalleled, we venture to say in the judicial history of our country. We shall not spend words upon the actors in this affair, for such persons would heed the strongest expressions of public indignation as little as the wind. People who are addicted to such pungent arguments as bowie-knives and pistol-bullets, would scarcely feel the paper pellets of the brain. . . .

A proper pride of country would have induced us to bury in

oblivion, if possible, a case indicative of a state of civilization more like that of the Middle Ages than of the nineteenth century. But an imperative sense of duty impels us to hold up its atrocities to the public view, in the hope that such exposure will convey an impressive and salutary lesson. When a gross outrage is committed on the rights of humanity, we regard it as the duty of every honest man, when seasonable opportunity offers, to proclaim his disapprobation in tones that shall reach the wrong-doer even in his most secret refuge.

In taking leave of this case, we would express the hope that no similar one will ever be permitted again to disgrace our country or the age.[5]

Superintendents were particularly eager to prevent insanity, because "In a malady entailing in its train consequences both remote and immediate, of a nature so deplorable, prophylactic and preventive measures were entitled to the first consideration." [6] Practitioners realized that certain stages of life and certain situations and crises were particularly important in determining the course of an individual's mental health. Thus, they attempted to delimit populations at a special risk because of exposure to individual trials and shocks and to adverse environmental conditions. Benjamin Rush had listed a heterogeneous collection of such groups, including children of insane parents; [7] individuals who are isolated and lonely, such as unmarried persons or women living in frontier settlements; [8] those with dark hair; [9] those between the ages of twenty and fifty; [10] and those rich and idle, who, unlike the toiling, pragmatic poor, had "leisure to look back upon past, and to anticipate future and imaginary evils." [11]

Later practitioners tried to study the ecology of insanity, to compile statistics on the incidence of illness and suicide, and to list the causes of disturbance among populations of asylums. Guided by these findings, members of the Association of Medical Superintendents tried to warn groups whose mental health appeared to be threatened, and to exhort the public and its leaders to modify pathological environmental conditions.

Superintendents felt that the largest and most critical group at risk was that of young children, whose impressionable brains were being molded for the first time by their upbringing and education. These vital offices were thought to be widely mismanaged and consequently to contribute to the seemingly ever rising rate of insanity. Therefore, not for the last time in the history of psychiatry, practitioners saw the education of parents and the modification of childhood experience as primary steps toward eventual eradication of mental illness.

Parent education was already developing in early nineteenth-century America. British and European publications on infant care were circulated; and mothers' groups met regularly to discuss the moral upbringing of children and to pray for their conversion to a godly life.[12] The advice of the superintendents added a milder and more permissive tone to the repressive regimes commonly advocated by many such journals and associations, particularly those that prescribed breaking the child's will in order to subdue man's animal nature and to control the workings of original sin.

Practitioners held that healthy mental development in children depended on maintaining a balance between influences that cultivated the intellectual and moral character and those that acted on the physical medium of the brain. "Defective education" and "injudicious early training"[13] were cited as primary causes of insanity in a number of patients but were listed among contributory factors in hundreds of others. Many authorities believed that damage often resulted from schooling that crammed the intellect while ignoring the needs or limitations of "that material medium through which alone it manifests itself."[14]

An educational system was advocated in which understanding of the needs and limitations of the developing brain would produce an harmonious balance in physical, moral, and intellectual growth.[15] Care of the physical brain was felt to include observance of the general rules of health, the inculcation of regular habits of life, and the avoidance of such pernicious and debilitating practices as masturbation. As John Fonerden noted:

The right growth of the brain in childhood is promoted or hindered by the habits which are formed in the nursery. Happy is that infant whose mother is its nurse; thrice happy, if the mother has faith in useful knowledge and applies it diligently to the gentle training of the bodily functions. The infant is an animal, born with the faculty of becoming rational. He may be so ignorantly managed that this glorious faculty will be almost extinguished; or he may have the blessed advantages of infantile education which will lay the foundation of goodness, intelligence, usefulness and every virtue, the active exercise of which is necessary to make a human being more and more rational in his pilgrimage on earth.[16]

A regimen for mental health might also incorporate the dictates of phrenology, and thus include the principles of eugenics, in order to ensure a healthy, well-formed brain, and a program of education tailored to the idiosyncratic needs of the individual. With the latter plan, weaknesses or dangerous proclivities might be minimized, and inherent, healthy tendencies might be cultivated. In this area, alerting the individual to his own mental capabilities or dangerous tendencies would be an asset

by which means he is forewarned of danger and avoids the circumstances likely to disturb the equilibrium of his powers:—or if perchance, he is occasionally surrounded by adverse influences, from which there can be no escape, he is thereby better prepared to submit to their effects; and if thoroughly imbued with the principles of the science [phrenology], will do so, evincing the calmness of the philosopher and the patience of the Christian. Can anything be conceived as better adapted to prevent insanity, than the habitual exercise of faculties thus trained for action or for Christian submission under trial? [17]

Slavish adherence to old and rigid rules was discouraged, because these were felt to have contributed to many breakdowns.

It is not so necessary that a mother should know what others have to say of rules for the proper discipline of her little pupil, as it is that she should well understand the *end* which is ever to be kept in her mind as a ray of light to guide her, namely,—so to take care of and prepare the corporeal habits of the child as to qualify the body to be a good instrument for the uses of the mind.[18]

Parenthetically, it is interesting to note that although the mother's influence was generally considered dominant, the father's role was not so neglected as it was to be both in some later parent education programs and in the administration of many child guidance clinics:

The father's duties are as important, if not as uninterrupted as the mother's. Besides contributing his best thoughts to the service of the young being, to whom he has transmitted a share of his own mental and bodily qualities, he ought by *his* habits of affection and attention to aim to bend the instinctive and capricious habits of his offspring into harmony and order. . . .[19]

Parents were urged to strengthen the moral training of children. They were particularly warned against leaving their early education to servants, or exposing them to the bad habits that were rife in boarding schools and in the streets.[20] Fathers who were so preoccupied with business concerns that they were strangers to their own families were particular targets of professional disapproval, because they were neglecting one of their most vital responsibilities, the molding of their children's moral fiber.[21]

Members of the Association of Medical Superintendents suggested that education be redesigned not only to avoid damaging the child but also to prepare him to withstand future trials with relative equanimity. It was thought that this might be done in part by instilling a firm sense of reality by exposing him to useful work and the duties of adult life, rather than by allowing the child to feed on a fantasy world gleaned from cheap novels:

Youth must not be passed in idleness, nor in reading romances and reveling in imaginary scenes of future happiness. But a portion of it should be allotted to actual toil, to manual labor, whereby a healthy and vigorous physical system will be secured, which is the best safeguard against the development of that too sensitive and nervous condition which usually precedes and predisposes to mental disorder. Then with moderate and rational notions of life and of its duties, and with a firm resolve to discharge them faithfully and timely there will be good hope that if disappointments and misfortunes come they will not crush the spirit, but on the contrary will purify and strengthen it.[22]

Resistance to the dangers of society could also be cultivated by strict inculcation of self-control and self-discipline rather than by forcing obedience to external coercion.

Every means calculated to strengthen the mind and the body at the same time, and to bring the affections and passions in complete subjugation to the reasoning faculties and the moral sentiments, should be commenced at the earliest period of life, and perseveringly followed up, in order to establish as perfect a balance of the understanding and intellectual powers as possible. . . . A person who has not been duly controlled in childhood is ill able to endure the vicissitudes and reverses to which active life exposes him in the present state of society: his passions being thereby deprived of a salutary curb, and the reason of its surest prop, insanity often follows upon the least adversity. . . . Early training—early mental discipline—self-control—self-denial—mastery over the passions; how much of our future welfare and happiness depends upon the steady cultivation of such habits of mind.[23]

Much of the advice formulated for the guidance of growth in childhood was applicable to the safeguarding of adult health; for the practitioners of moral treatment held that brains and characters continued to change throughout life. Just as a child's brain might be strained by onerous education, so might the mind of a man be unhinged by too much work, by fanciful fears and speculations, and by undue concentration on problems of science or philosophy.

Just as children required a strict upbringing to mold a healthy brain, adults required the discipline, reinforced by self-control or by the surveillance of others, of orderly habits and a balanced regimen of work and recreation. Like children, adults were warned against self-indulgence, idleness, and daydreams; they were advised to ground themselves firmly in the duties of the real world. In 1861, when alienists were speculating about possible effects of the Civil War on national mental health, J. E. Tyler, Superintendent of McLean Asylum in Massachusetts, predicted that rates of insanity would fall, not rise, because army life had therapeutic aspects.

600,000 men have, by the rigid rules of military necessity, learned to *obey*,—a wholesome lesson, and which leads more directly than any other to the all-important end of *self-control*.[24]

In their efforts to prevent insanity, therefore, physicians warned the public against a variety of hazards in the physical and social environment. Some of these were relatively simple. Sudden shocks, for example, were thought dangerous, so people were advised to break bad news gently and to avoid frightening practical jokes.[25] Popular novels, particularly Gothic tales, were denounced for inciting fantasies of lust, cruelty, and terror of the supernatural instead of fulfilling the proper, didactic function of literature.

The public was also warned to rest and refresh the brain, because superintendents believed that lack of sleep was itself a frequent cause of insanity and a contributory factor in breakdowns from grief and other conditions that produce chronic wakefulness.[26] This is particularly interesting to twentieth-century psychiatrists in view of recent research into the pathogenic effects of sleep and dream deprivation. Brigham wrote in 1840:

So rarely do we see a recent case of insanity that is not preceded by want of sleep, that we regard it as almost the sure precursor of mental derangement.

Notwithstanding strong hereditary predisposition, ill health, loss of kindred or property, insanity rarely results unless the exciting causes are such as to occasion loss of sleep. A mother loses her only child, the merchant his fortune—the politician, the scholar, the enthusiast, may have their minds powerfully excited and disturbed, yet if they sleep well they will not become insane.[27]

The public, particularly "those who are predisposed to insanity, or . . . those who have recovered from an attack" [28] was therefore warned to shun the frivolities of contemporary culture, such as dances and theaters, that kept them from their rest. They were further advised to use proper kinds of beds and to sleep in well-ventilated rooms. It was also suggested that the Chinese practice of brushing the teeth before retiring was salutary, because it placed one in a restful mood.[29]

Early nineteenth-century American psychiatry was oriented toward the problems of populations, because it was felt that, whereas personal shocks, exhaustion, poor upbringing, and other crises and components of a pathological environment threatened the mental health of individuals, equivalent stresses on a macrocosmic scale threatened the mental health of societies. As Rudolf Virchow wrote in 1840, "If disease is an expression of individual life under unfavorable conditions then epidemics must be indicative of major disturbances of mass life." [30]

This belief was in part an extension of the pre-Darwinian concept of a homocentric universe in which man, the highest in the chain of created beings, was placed in a world ordered for his welfare. It was felt that prevailing climatic, political, and economic conditions were intimately related to health, so that sudden changes might be accompanied by a heightened incidence of disease; for disruption of divinely ordained harmony would produce chaos. Thus it was thought that man, in order to protect his well-being, must strive to maintain a homeostatic state in nature that is free, simple, traditionally ordered, and least enervating.

Wars, revolutions, and economic upheavals, like the bursting of the South Sea Bubble or the American depression of 1837 to 1844, were expected to produce physical and mental illness on epidemic scale because they subjected a population to unnatural pressures. Virchow, for instance, wrote that all major historical changes are accompanied by outbreaks of insanity, such as the witch hunts that followed the Reformation. George Burrows noted earlier,

Insanity . . . bears always a striking relation to public events. Great political or civil revolutions in states are always productive of great enthusiasms in the people, and correspondent vicissitudes in their moral condition; and as all extremes in society are exciting causes, it will occur, that in proportion as the feelings are acted upon, so will insanity be more or less frequent.[31]

Rush, one of the classic writers on this theme, noted the paradoxical effects of the American Revolution on Patriots and Royalists in his famous *Account of the Influence of the Military and Political Events of the American Revolution upon the Human Body.*

In their attempts to prevent insanity by modifying the environment, asylum superintendents were not afraid to confront large issues. One of the hazards thought to impinge on the mental health of the entire population was the weather. The American climate, particularly that of the Northern states, was thought conducive to insanity of a particularly maniacal or suicidal nature, and cold wet weather appeared to produce moodiness and irritability in the otherwise sane. Although all are affected by atmospheric conditions, some are hypersensitive, and, as the members of the Association warned, the fluctuating disposition of vulnerable individuals is a threat to their own safety and to that of the community:

Upon the minds of some, unpleasant weather, with damp wind, has very serious effects—often changing the entire moral character. We apprehend it often leads to quarrels and crimes, and influences the disposition of jurors and legislators—teachers and scholars—clergymen and their hearers, etc.[32]

Because brains were thought to atrophy because of inaction or monotonous stimuli, superintendents suggested that people be subjected to periodic change, such as movement of settlers from one climatic region to another, or from one trade to another.[33] In his optimistic predictions about the effects of Civil War army life, Tyler cited the stimulation of changing scenes and changing companions:

These men have left home and the restricted circle of home labours, influences, and associations, for novel duties and new scenes, and for the friction with other minds trained under the greatest variety of circumstances. Experiences are interchanged; information of persons, places, and things is gained; opinions concerning government, religion, trade, and labor are discussed; prejudices are softened, and views expanded and liberalized. All this . . . is favorable to vigorous mental health.[34]

Superintendents did not hesitate to indict hazards of societal dimensions, and they pointed to civilization itself as another major environmental cause of mental disorder. A certain distrust of cultivated life was characteristic of many Americans, who felt that they had escaped from the effete ways of Europe to a natural, and hence healthier, way of life.

It was thought that man in his primitive, "natural" state was free of insanity but that, as the level of education rose, so did rates of pathology because the brain was being actively developed and hence was more liable to strain. Civilization suspended the hardening discipline of reality and cultivated tastes, sensibilities, and emotions, which heightened nervous susceptibility and morbid imagination. The frivolities of civilization, such as theaters and dances, robbed individuals of their rest and seduced them into idleness and self-indulgence. The accelerated pace of industrial life added further strain; and superintendents warned against the effects on body and mind of high-speed railway travel.

Among the groups felt to be at immediate and acute risk were the persons—businessmen, community leaders, and clergy—who were most exposed to the exhaustion, competition, and shocks of civilization. It was believed, by such physicians as Brigham, that the stresses of politics and the marketplace contributed to the apparent rising rate of insanity and accounted for the fact that statistics showed higher numbers of insane in the United States than in Europe.[35] This higher rate of pathology appeared to accompany both an uncertain economy that fluctuated during the nineteenth century between booms and depressions and a life in a democracy, where the individual was confronted with unlimited and bewildering freedom of choice. Superintendents, however, were quick to point out that the pressures of uncertainty also served to stimulate brains to achieve their full potential, raising them to a higher level of agility than did monolithic dictatorships and theocracies that produced steady but torpid minds.[36]

The menace to the community leaders from the pressures of modern life was discussed at length in the *Journal*:

The great increase of mental diseases among our merchant and professional men, during the past few years, calls for serious consideration. . . . But to these we must add perhaps, thousands of cases in which premature old age, or permanent ill-health, and mental imbecility have arisen from similar causes. Paralysis, apoplexy, softening of the brain, and spinal affections, with kindred diseases, are striking down our scholars, jurists, physicians, professors, and clergymen with fearful frequency. In our great cities business is pushed to the highest point of human endurance. The weight of public duties, and the extraordinary calls upon our clergy would be enough to crush a race of giants.[37]

A forum was provided to encourage further exploration and public education:

But is not something . . . needed to arouse public attention to the subject? If some of our medical philanthropists would give it special attention, collate facts and exhibit the wasting and fatal physical and mental tendencies of this system of overwork which is consuming the best energies of our national mind, it would be a public boon. Nor do we know on what theme a prize essay might be more profitably proposed than this . . . [we] shall be most happy if those who are competent to the task will take it up, and prosecute it in the columns of this paper.[38]

Pliny Earle summarized the various possible dangers of civilization as follows,

Insanity is . . . part of the price that we pay for civilization. The causes of the one increase with the developments and results of the other. This is not necessarily the case, but it is so now. The increase of knowledge, the improvements in the arts, the multiplication of comforts, the amelioration of manners, the growth of refinement, and the elevation of morals, do not of themselves disturb men's cerebral organs, and create mental disorder. But with them come more opportunities and rewards for great and excessive mental action, more uncertain and hazardous employments, and consequently more dangers of accidents and injuries, more groundless hopes, and more painful struggles to obtain that which is beyond reach, or to effect that which is impossible.[39]

In their attempts to sanitize the environment in order to prevent insanity in present and future generations, superintendents strove to attack other potential causes of mass disturbance. In the early 1840's a major target of concern among practitioners was Millerism, an apocalyptic movement whose revival meetings were thought to be spreading epidemics of insanity throughout the country. The dangers of religious mania had been recognized since the inflammatory sermons of the Great Awakening during the mid-eighteenth century had reduced congregations, including young children, to paroxysms of guilt and terror; and Rush had given detailed instructions in his textbook on how to deal with various forms of this condition.

Advice on how to stem Millerism and similar causes of epidemics was based on an awareness of the phenomena of mass hysteria. Warnings were given to all, but particularly to community leaders, to avoid swelling the crowds at revival meetings. Attendance at such affairs would not only expose individuals to personal danger, but their very presence, however peripheral, would appear to sanction and encourage a pernicious situation:

Do not go to *hear* any new, absurd and exciting doctrine taught, and keep away all those over whom you have influence. This need not and should not hinder you from obtaining a knowledge of all new truths and new doctrines, for such are in this country immediately published. Read about them if you wish, but do not go to *see* and *hear—to swell the throng of gazers and listeners,* for as has been said, such things spread chiefly by *contagion* and *imitation.* . . .

Thousands of printed tracts upon Millerism, scattered through the country, would have done no harm, if there had been no *preaching* of the doctrine,—*no nightly meeting and collecting in crowds to hear and see.*[40]

This *Journal* article continues with an appeal to the churches, to their social conscience, and to their self-interest:

We beg very respectfully, to suggest to all religious denominations, the propriety of lessening the number and frequency of protracted religious meetings, and especially of those held in the evening and night. We are confident, that although some good results from them, that very much evil does also. They prepare many to entertain the delusion referred to, by creating excitement bordering on disease, and unfitting the mind to contemplate important subjects calmly. They also seriously impair the health of the clergy, and unfit them for other duties. . . .[41]

The conclusion of this piece shows the eagerness of early superintendents to extend their influence as specialists into areas of community life in which they had no direct competence, but in which they nevertheless perceived dangers to mental health:

These few hints we have thrown out with all candor, and hope they will be so received. While we would carefully avoid saying anything that might hinder the spread of the truths of the Bible, or the conversion of a single soul, we feel it to be our duty to call attention to methods of attempting to extend religious doctrines which we believe are not unfrequently productive of disease, madness, and death.[42]

It may thus be seen that, in their relations with the lay community, practitioners of moral treatment foreshadowed many concepts and modalities of modern community psychiatry. They noted both the benign and pathogenic effects of certain physical and social environments on mental health, realizing that sudden shocks were dangerous but that change provided necessary stimulation, and that hysteria was contagious but that social pressures could discipline and support the weak. Practitioners sought to prevent mental illness in individuals and populations by delimiting and warning groups at special risk and by educating the public to modify pathogenic situations and forces in their environment. In pursuit of this objective, superintendents were not only willing to communicate with the public, but they also crossed into the domains of other professionals in order to expose hazards to mental health. They assumed this watch-dog role in their capacity not only as experts on insanity but also as concerned citizens.

Members of the Association of Medical Superintendents were also concerned with the positive goal of promoting mental health. They sought to do this by instilling general awareness of the importance of regular and healthy habits of life and the role of early education in producing a robust personality. In connection with the latter point, it is interesting to note the advice of some nineteenth-century practitioners to use what is now called emotional inoculation or anticipatory guidance in order to prepare minds to withstand future stress, thus increasing the internal resources and capabilities of the personality.

NOTES

1. Henry M. Hurd (ed.), *The Institutional Care of the Insane in the United States and Canada* (Baltimore: Johns Hopkins Press, 1916), Vol. I, p. 13.

2. Albert Deutsch, *The Mentally Ill in America* (New York: Columbia University Press, 1945), pp. 198–199.

3. *The American Journal of Insanity*, I (1844–1845), 288.

4. *Ibid.*

5. *The American Journal of Insanity*, III (1846–1847), 27ff.

6. *The American Journal of Insanity*, XI (1854–1855), 264–265.

7. Benjamin Rush, *Medical Inquiries and Observations Upon Diseases of the Mind* (New York: Hafner Publishing Co., 1962), p. 53.

8. *Ibid.*, p. 59.

9. *Ibid.*, p. 54.

10. *Ibid.*, p. 53.

11. *Ibid.*, p. 62.

12. Orville G. Brim, Jr., *Education for Child Rearing* (New York: Russell Sage Foundation, 1959), p. 323.

13. *The American Journal of Insanity*, XI (1854–1855), 264–265.

14. *Ibid.*, 217.

15. *The American Journal of Insanity*, VI (1849–1850), 129.

16. *The American Journal of Insanity*, VII (1850–1851), 59–60.

17. *The American Journal of Insanity*, VI (1849–1850), 129–130.

18. *The American Journal of Insanity*, VII (1850–1851), 60.

19. *Ibid.*

20. *The American Journal of Insanity*, XIV (1857–1858), 378.

21. *The American Journal of Insanity*, XV (1858–1859), 277.

22. *The American Journal of Insanity*, I (1844–1845), 42.

23. *The American Journal of Insanity*, XI (1854–1855), 265.

24. *The American Journal of Insanity*, XIX (1862–1863), 366.

25. *The American Journal of Insanity*, IV (1847–1848), 281.

26. *The American Journal of Insanity*, I (1844–1845), 319.

27. *The American Journal of Insanity*, XIV (1857–1858), 22.

28. *Ibid.*

29. *The American Journal of Insanity*, I (1844–1845), 320.

30. George Rosen, "Social Stress and Mental Disease from the Eighteenth Century to the Present: Some Origins of Social Psychiatry." Public Lecture delivered July 8, 1958, Institute of Psychiatry, Maudsley Hospital, University of London, p. 5.

31. *Ibid.*, p. 8.

32. *The American Journal of Insanity*, I (1844–1845), 340–341.

33. *The American Journal of Insanity*, XIV (1857–1858), 88.

34. *The American Journal of Insanity*, XIX (1862–1863), 368.

35. Rosen, *op. cit.*, p. 8.

36. Richard Hunter and Ida Macalpine (eds.), *Three Hundred Years of Psychiatry* (London: Oxford Press, 1963), pp. 823–824.

37. *The American Journal of Insanity*, XIII (1856–1857), 95.

38. *Ibid.*

39. *The American Journal of Insanity*, VIII (1851–1852), 360.

40. *The American Journal of Insanity*, I (1844–1845), 251.

41. *Ibid.*, p. 252.

42. *Ibid.*

Chapter 3

MOLDING THE HOSPITAL ENVIRONMENT: MORAL MANAGEMENT

Although prevention of insanity in the general population by educating the public to demand modification of the environment was a recurring theme in the early writings of the moral treatment movement, the primary job of its practitioners was the management and cure of those already afflicted. This was to be achieved by *moral management*, a system based upon the theory of corrective experience, and implemented by molding the physical and social environment of the hospital.

The goal of moral management was the reconstruction of damaged brain tissue by resocialization, by influencing the physical organ through the medium of the mind. The pivot of this system was education and the imposition of regular habits of life and work, appropriate mental stimulation, orderly thinking, and correct values on those who were "mental aliens," who suffered from "alienated minds." Thus, in spite of its humane nature, moral management consequently had a highly didactic and authoritarian flavor.

Early nineteenth-century physicians emphasized moral, or psychological, modes of therapy rather than medicinal and surgical remedies. This was, in part, a reaction against the prescriptions of Benjamin Rush to subject the insane to physical shocks and pain in order to jerk them out of their delusions; to force rest with restraining apparatus; and to use depletory measures, such as low diet, purges, and bleeding, to reduce capillary pressure in the brain.

Depletory measures of all kinds, but particularly bloodletting, or venesection, were widely used in the treatment of many diseases. This method had been unknowingly inherited from the Middle Ages, when it was thought that disease was caused by an imbalance of bodily humors. Thus, fevers and other delirious or inflamed conditions from malaria to rheumatism, which were felt to be evidence of an overabundance of blood in the body, were treated by the local use of leeches or by general bleeding. Physicians continued for years to employ similar remedies. For example, they continued to shave and blister the heads of lunatics, a treatment originally devised to allow the escape of vapors trapped in the brain.

In the first half of the nineteenth century, humane physicians began to avoid the general use of shocks and physical abuse. Clinical experience led many to doubt the value of depletory methods. Superintendents were particularly alarmed by the plight of patients admitted to asylums suffering from fatal loss of blood because general practitioners sometimes withdrew up to three or four quarts to relieve "inflammation of the brain." [1]

An early opponent of bloodletting was Eli Todd, first superintendent of the Hartford Retreat. His opposition to drastic physical measures may have been influenced in part by the Tukes, on whose institution the Hartford Retreat had been modeled, and who were themselves laymen, noted for their distrust of traditional medical usage. Later practitioners, like Amariah Brigham and Pliny Earle, had begun their careers with faith in depletory treatment, but becoming alarmed by its effects upon patients, had discontinued its use. In 1840, while still a New England surgeon, Brigham had written,

The greatest error I have seen committed in the medical treatment of the insane, is the neglect of depletion in the early stage, and of narcotics and tonics in the subsequent. At the commencement of a considerable portion of the cases of insanity, there is an inflammatory condition of the brain or of its membranes, . . . and depletion will sometimes arrest the disease.[2]

After a number of years of clinical experience, however, Brigham's views changed. In a *Journal* article, he noted a case of insanity brought to Utica that he felt to have been caused by bloodletting.[3]

For practitioners who had come to doubt the medical resources at their disposal, moral methods of treatment seemed safer and more effective. They still retained much of the older psychiatric armamentarium of purges, diet, baths, and opiates as auxiliary measures and even experimented with new methods such as ether and chloroform, which proved particularly helpful in handling exhausted maniacal patients. But major reliance was placed on social restraints and re-education for a healthier life. As Brigham wrote,

That some cases of insanity require medical treatment we believe, but we also believe that a large majority of the patients in lunatic asylums do not. There is much analogy between many of the patients found in all such institutions, and the passionate, mischievous, and what are called bad boys in a school, and there is about as much propriety in following the example of Mrs. Squeers, and physicking and medicating the latter as the former, in order to cure them or to change their propensities. Rational hopes for the improvement of either should, we believe, be founded on moral management alone.[4]

In the 1841 Report of McLean Asylum for the Insane in Massachusetts, Luther V. Bell wrote in the same vein.

Each year that I have passed in this extensive field, has served to diminish my confidence in an active medical treatment in almost every form of disease of the mind, and to increase my reliance upon moral means. No individual at the head of an institution would now think of combatting any form of insanity with the depletory and reducing means once regarded as indispensable. The practice of bleeding, violent purgatives, emetics, vescatives and derivatives, has passed away before the light of my experience.[5]

Instead of medicinal and surgical techniques, therefore, practitioners turned to moral management, whose basic objective was the resocialization of "mental aliens" in order that they might rejoin society. This goal determined, and was itself determined by, the entire physical and social organization of the patient community. By regulating the milieu in order to impose absorbing tasks and civilized social intercourse, it was hoped that pernicious habits and associations would be broken while correct and socially acceptable patterns of thought and behavior would be fostered. This in turn would lead to the amelioration of the organic lesion in the brain, which was believed to underlie the mental illness.

This idea governed the very removal of the patient to a rural asylum. It has since been thought that the placing of mental hospitals at a distance from centers of population was an act of rejection. In fact, the sites of moral treatment institutions were chosen with a view to the recognized mental health needs of their inmates. It was thought necessary first to remove the lunatic from all the people, objects, and places associated with, and further exacerbating, his delusions, because the longer he ruminated on them, the more deeply they would irritate the damaged brain surface. This idea had apparently been made generally known by Thomas Willis, who insisted that King George III be placed in new rooms with unfamiliar attendants and furnishings in order to distract his mind from unhealthy thoughts. Change of scene became one of the most common treatments for mental disturbance among the enlightened. The usual prescription was travel, but other choices existed. In *The Way of All Flesh*, Samuel Butler's bitter study of English manners and family life in the 1840's, 1850's, and 1860's, there is an episode in which Ernest Pontifex, the young hero, overcome at last by the trials of his life, suffers a mental collapse, and is taken by his guardian to a noted London practitioner. Because the young man was apparently too poor to travel widely, the doctor suggested instead a trip to the Zoological Gardens,

I should prescribe for Mr. Pontifex a course of the larger mammals. Don't let him think he is taking them medicinally, but let him go to their house twice a week for a fortnight, and stay with the hippopotamus, the rhinoceros, the elephants, till they begin to bore him. I find these beasts do my patients more good than any other.[6]

Monkeys, reptiles, and birds would not do; they were frightening or restless; but the larger mammals were both distracting and soothing.

With the elephants and the pig tribe generally he should mix just now as freely as possible.[7]

The larger mammals did indeed help to restore the sanity of the young hero, and they even soothed his guardian, who felt that he

was receiving an influx of new life, or deriving new ways of looking at life . . . by the process.[8]

The ideal method of removing the insane from the environment associated with the onset of illness was institutionalization. Only in an institution could all facets of the patient's existence be regulated in order to provide an optimum chance of recovery; and only in a rural hospital was it possible to furnish enough surrounding land for farms, pleasure grounds, and open vistas to provide work and recreation. Isolation was particularly chosen in order to safeguard the privacy of patients who might otherwise be stigmatized by the gossip of spying neighbors or victimized by sensation seekers out to bait and mock the lunatics. On the other hand, institutions had to be placed on main roads so that supplies could be easily carted and so that patients and their relatives would not be subjected to the hazards and discomforts of long journeys. Superintendents were also advised to remain close enough to towns so that advantage might be taken of local philanthropists and of "the social, scientific relations indispensable to cultivated minds" and the "useful kinds of recreation and amusement." [9] It was also thought advisable to remain close to settled areas so that responsible citizens might visit the asylum, thus showing patients that many were concerned about their welfare.[10]

The internal design of asylums was a highly specialized subject on which many articles were written and for which numerous trips were made around American and European institutions by prospective superintendents planning new hospitals. The effects of spatial arrangement, light, and temperature on emotions were recognized, and although buildings were designed for safety, they were also planned to minimize unpleasant features that might further disturb vulnerable brains. A soothing homelike atmosphere, for instance, was cultivated. James McDonald, the resident physician at Bloomingdale Asylum for the Insane in New York, announced proudly that in his institution,

The interior has been finished and furnished like a private dwelling. Some of the rooms are equal to any found in the best hotels and boarding houses, and the long corridors running the length of the wings, are light, airy, and uncommonly beautiful. It is worthy of remark, that the ceilings are higher, and ventilation better than in most of our public buildings.[11]

To avoid a prison-like appearance designers used specially constructed iron window sashes instead of gratings. Rooms were placed on only one side of the halls, so that windows could be let into the other, giving light, a pleasant view, and a feeling of space and freedom. Great emphasis was placed on clean and comfortable methods of central heating and adequate ventilation, as well as on baths and water closets. There was also an attempt to provide open hearths, because these contributed to a cozy, homelike atmosphere.

The essence of moral treatment can be seen most clearly in the social organization of institutions, and it is here that modern psychiatrists find some of the earliest examples of therapeutic milieux.

Early practitioners had recognized that the classic madhouse environment damaged patients, that restraints produced violence, and that idleness and sensory deprivation produced mental stagnation. Moreover, such alienists as John Conolly, the English crusader against restraints, noted that traditional custodial institutions might create chronic insanity in less disturbed patients who were reinforced in their symptoms by a pathogenic milieu, by idleness, brutality, and the example of bizarre behavior among their peers. As Conolly wrote in 1830,

In an asylum for lunatics the eccentric man makes little or no effort to correct his irritability; and the man of gloom sits in motionless despondency from morning till night, without any salutary disturbance of duty, or necessary exertion, or the visit of a cheerful friend. To all these patients, confinement is the very reverse of beneficial. It fixes and renders permanent what might have passed away, and ripens the eccentricity, or temporary excitement or depression, into actual insanity.[12]

Moral treatment differed from earlier and later custodial cure in its sensitivity to the reciprocal influences of patients and hospital personnel for control or license. It sought, therefore, to manipulate the milieu in order to produce therapeutic rather than pathogenic pressures.

To distract the patient from his delusions, to restore healthy functioning, and to stave off further deterioration of chronically damaged brain tissue, physicians created a closely knit social system to support and control him. They believed that patients would respond to kind and liberal treatment with docility and trustworthiness, particularly if they were provided with examples of correct behavior and with the support of other patients and were treated as much as possible like sane individuals. As Pliny Earle wrote in 1845 of the administration of Bloomingdale Asylum,

The primary object is to treat the patients as far as their condition will possibly admit, as if they were still in the enjoyment of the healthy exercise of their mental faculties. An important desideratum for the attainment of this object is to make their condition as boarders, as comfortable as possible; that they may be the less sensible of the deprivations to which they are subjected by a removal from home. Nor is it less essential to extend them the privilege, or the right, of as much liberty, as much freedom from personal restraint as is compatible with their safety, the safety of others, and the judicious administration of other branches of curative treatment. The courtesies of civilized and social life are not to be forgotten, extending, as they do, to the promotion of the first great object already mentioned, and operating, to no inconsiderable extent, as a means of effecting restoration to mental health.[13]

The ideal institution was intimate enough to cater to individuals; and it was originally suggested by the Association of Medical Superintendents that it contain only two hundred beds. The superintendent and his family lived in the hospital, spent their time with patients on the wards or at their occupations, and joined them at meals and recreation. Charles Dickens, in *The American Notes*, described Boston State Hospital, in which inmates were trusted with the tools of their trade, however dangerous, and with appropriate cutlery at meals,[14] and where the superintendent and his family provided a constant example of appropriate dress, language, and manners to be emulated by the patients.

The superintendents who followed moral treatment were idealists without illusions. They had inherited from the eighteenth century the "Low View of Man." This view of humanity, shared by such eighteenth-century writers as Pope, Swift, Fielding, and other Augustins, held that man is naturally selfish, greedy, and depraved. Unlike theologians who pointed to this as evidence of original sin, eighteenth-century humanists associated no guilt with man's animal nature. Moreover, they saw man as redeemable, not only through correct religious experience but also through education and the restraints of enlightened laws. The passions of the mob, therefore, were deplored but not condemned. The recognition of human frailty did not disillusion these reformers; they planned with it in mind, much as their contemporaries did who drafted the Constitution of the United States and who included in it safeguards against usurpation by both tyrants and mobs. Similarly, superintendents incorporated checks and balances into their administration to forestall degeneration of the social and physical milieu and to safeguard their patients against force, bad language, and ridicule. An adamant stand was taken, for instance, against separate institutions for curable and incurable, for well-to-do and paupers. In an impassioned speech before the New York Assembly, Michael Hoffmann, a legislator, presented the superintendent's view:

To receive . . . only incurable insane paupers, would convert the institution into a mad-house—a mad poor-house—a den of filth and misery, and an object of abhorrence and disgust which nobody would begin to approach. But place those there who have friends of wealth and consequence, and you secure that vigilance, that inducement to look into its entire management, which is necessary to make it a well-ordered institution. Make it a poor mad-house and the poor have no feet to travel after them, and the patients would be left to the cold inhuman care of brute officiality, not to be cured but to be cursed. But admit freely the curable and the rich to the institution, and they have kindred who could and would travel after them, relatives who have eyes, and voices. They would constitute an active committee of vigilance to look into its affairs, and see they were properly managed.[15]

One of the arguments in favor of segregated institutions was that they would be cheaper to run, because therapeutic programs would be omitted. This rationale infuriated the superintendents, and this was to become a bitterly contested issue by the 1860's.

Superintendents opposed all budget cutting, believing it could lead only to lowering the quality of food and facilities for work and recreation, and reducing the number of staff. Not only were legislatures admonished to provide funds, but hospitals were advised by the Association to keep their fees high so that proper services could be given.

One of the most common and realistic fears of the superintendents was that their patients might be molested by attendants. This led to the following recommendations: Teachers and clergymen who had been invited to aid and advise the patients were encouraged to wander around the hospital alert for any signs of neglect or abuse, which they were to report to the physician in charge. Noisy and obstreperous patients were not to be placed in a separate building, because these were the inmates most likely to evoke punitive action from attendants; and if they were placed in a separate house, the superintendent might not inspect as often as he should, particularly at night or in bad weather. Instead, agitated cases were to be placed in a wing of the main building, insulated by corridors, bathrooms, and so forth from those who should not be disturbed.

In the same spirit of human foresight, it was recommended that hospitals remain small and that the superintendent and his family live in the building so that the physician could always be aware of the condition of every patient and be available at once to treat a disturbance before the sick could be molested by an irritable attendant. In order to ensure good treatment, manuals were prepared for selecting and training attendants and hospitals were encouraged to obtain a competent board of trustees, who would make frequent inspections. Finally, the Association itself conducted examinations of American institutions and did not hesitate to pour criticism and scorn on outmoded and ill-conceived hospitals.

Although the regimen for each patient was tailored to fit his special needs, most of the activities in a moral treatment institution were designed for group participation. It was recognized that patients had a salutary effect on each other, providing sympathy, support, and control. The 1838 Report of the Friends' Asylum of Frankfurt, Pennsylvania, noted:

By association of the patients thus together, it was expected (and we have not been disappointed), that they would act as a collective body in every employment or amusement set before them, rather than in their individual capacity as they had previously done; so that the industrious might stimulate the indolent, that the grave might check the boisterous, that the amiable might restrain the vindictive, and that the gay might cheer the sorrowful and divert their minds from any train of reflection likely to produce gloom and despondence.[16]

Because most patients were believed to be suffering from only partial insanity, it was felt that associations among them could be conducted on a rational level stimulating to all. This provided a further objection to building institutions exclusively for chronic cases because it was felt that even advanced forms of mental degeneration left some faculties undamaged that might benefit from lively and rational conversation.[17] It was also thought that therapeutic results might be obtained if patients discussed their disturbance with one another. As Thomas S. Kirkbride wrote,

Patients are often much interested in the delusions of their neighbors, and by their effort to relieve the affliction of others, frequently do much toward getting rid of their own.[18]

Finally, social skills were another requirement of healthy functioning that the patient had to learn in order to take his place once more in society.

Work in farms, greenhouses, workshops, and at household chores was usually done in groups and was regarded as a useful method for focusing a wandering mind on reality and teaching it to perform set tasks in a disciplined way. Dickens, for instance, described a decorous sewing circle at Boston State Hospital that was making clothes for the poor and that was presided over by the wife of the Superintendent and one of her friends.[19]

Moral management also provided for diversions and amusements, such as games, books, rides, and walks. Pliny Earle, in his *Description and Statistics of the Bloomingdale Asylum for the Insane*, wrote that his institution's library had boasted one thousand volumes, five daily and eight weekly papers, two monthly magazines, and four quarterly reviews. Bloomingdale also had facilities for such games as bowling, quoits, bat-ball, football, swings, bagatelle, battle-dore, chess, checkers, backgammon, and cards. It had a piano, viol, violin, bugle, drum, flutes, and fifes. The asylum held parties in the parlor once a week for convalescent patients and held a cotillion dance once a month for all who were able to attend. Dickens described a similar weekly dance at Boston State Hospital which gave great pleasure to the patients and encouraged proper deportment.

Immense politeness and good breeding are observed throughout. They all take their tone from the Doctor; and he moves a very Chesterfield among the company. Like other assemblies, these entertainments afforded a fruitful topic of conversation among the ladies for some days; and the gentlemen are so anxious to shine on these occasions, that they have been sometimes found "practicing their steps" in private, to cut a more distinguished figure in the dance.

It is obvious that one great feature of this system, is the inculcation and encouragement, even among such unhappy persons, of decent self-respect.[20]

Utica State Hospital had a calendar of such activities. There was a celebration on the birthday of Pinel; the meeting of the Association of Medical Superintendents was greeted with a pageant, original poetry, music, and speeches of welcome; and an annual fair was held to which the local community was invited to inspect and buy objects, many of which had been made cooperatively by groups of patients.

Patients were provided with religious services, which were intended to confirm another salutary educational experience as well as to give direct comfort and hope to the downhearted. This was particularly valuable during the early nineteenth century when, as has been mentioned earlier, religious mania developed at revival meetings and when depressions born of theological misgivings were frequently cited causes of insanity. Institutions were encouraged to appoint clergymen to minister to their patients. Occasionally, however, this backfired, when "fire and brimstone" preaching terrified the congregation. Also, on one occasion, a clerical gentleman gave a sermon, "To the Feeble Minded," and dilated at length on "how you got your feeble mind." This caused sufficient agitation among the worshippers for the preacher to resolve to keep to more neutral topics in the future.

Education, the quintessential element of moral treatment, was accomplished not only by training in regular and healthy habits of life and work, not only by instilling social graces and skills, and not only by religious instruction but also by formal schooling. The ideal mental hospital would resemble a boarding school, as may be seen from the following:

Institutions for the care and cure of those affected by mental disorder will be made to resemble those for education, rather than hospitals for the sick, or prisons for criminals, and when one calls to mind that the greater part of those committed to such establishments are . . . suffering from deranged intellect, feelings and passions, it is evident that a judicious course of mental and moral discipline is most essential for their comfort and restoration.[21]

An educational program was intended not only for mental reconstitution but also to stave off further deterioration from intellectual idleness, particularly in chronic cases. It was intended to provide distraction from morbid thoughts; to give, if possible, enough primary instruction to facilitate a better life outside the hospital, and hence perhaps ensure against further breakdown; and it offered another area for the group activities around which the asylum was organized.

The establishment of schools received impetus from the success of Edward Seguin's experiment in France in teaching the mentally retarded. News of this was greeted enthusiastically by the *American Journal of Insanity*:

We rejoice at this attempt of M. Seguin. This class of our fellow creatures has been too long neglected. Because a youth has but little mind, instead of that little being neglected, as it usually is, the greater pains should be taken to improve it. By increased efforts in this respect, we have no doubt many that would otherwise ever remain imbeciles, might be made to hold not a degraded rank among intellectual beings.[22]

A lesson of immediate salience was drawn:

Asylums should be well supplied with books, maps and apparatus illustrative of different sciences, and also collections in natural history, etc. Schools should be established in every institution for the insane, where patients could engage in reading, writing, drawing, music, arithmetic, geography, history, and also study some of the sciences, as chemistry, mineralogy, conchology, physiology, etc.[23]

Institutions were advised to hire teachers to act as resident tutors or governesses,

who should spend all their time with the patients, eat at the same table with them, but have no labor or other duties to attend to, than to interest the patients and contribute all they can by their presence and conversation to their contentment and enjoyment. They should join them in their amusements and walks, and be their constant companions.[24]

Pliny Earle had originated this form of treatment in America by giving evening lectures on topics ranging from descriptions of modern Greece to recitations of poetry to his patients at the Friends' Asylum in Frankfurt, Pennsylvania, and later by establishing formal classes at Bloomingdale State Hospital. Earle was particularly fitted for such work because he had been a schoolmaster before turning to medicine. Other hospitals followed the example of Bloomingdale, such as Utica, where a number of classes were regularly held and were sometimes taught by patients as well as by professional teachers. Classes at Utica began with the singing of a hymn in unison, and every two weeks all assembled in the chapel for a program of choral music and recitation of memorized pieces and original compositions. At the end of the winter term, a grand exhibition was held, which included

The speaking of original pieces, recitations, music and the performance of original plays, and other exercises, which in the opinion of good judges who were present, would not have been discreditable to any literary institution.[25]

The organization of moral treatment hospitals, although based on a different conceptual framework, resembled what is now advocated by community psychiatry. Environmental factors in the causation of mental disorder were recognized and were counteracted by manipulation of the physical and social milieu of the asylum. This was done in large measure by mobilizing staff and patients into small groups to support and control the individual strictly but without undue coercion through encouraging him to perform according to the high expectations of his associates. There were attempts to involve other care-giving groups, such as teachers and clergymen, in the treatment of the insane. And, in spite of geographic isolation, violent dislocation of the patient from the community was perhaps avoided because the undesirability of long-term institutionalization was recognized and because the entire therapeutic program was designed to inculcate normative cultural values and modalities so that the individual could return to society better able to cope with its demands.

NOTES

1. Pliny Earle, *An Explanation of the Practice of Bloodletting in Mental Disorders* (New York: Samuel S. and William Wood, 1854), p. 15.

2. Amariah Brigham, *An Inquiry Concerning the Diseases and Functions of the Brain, the Spinal Cord, and the Nerves* (New York: George Ablard, 1840), p. 294.

3. *The American Journal of Insanity*, I (1844–1845), 50.

4. *The American Journal of Insanity*, IV (1847–1848), 10.

5. Pliny Earle, *op. cit.*, p. 12.

6. Samuel Butler, *The Way of All Flesh* (New York: The Modern Library, 1950), pp. 483–484.

7. *Ibid.*, p. 484.

8. *Ibid.*, p. 485.

9. *The American Journal of Insanity*, XXII (1865–1866), 252–253.

10. *Ibid.*, p. 253.

11. J. S. Bockoven, *Moral Treatment in American Psychiatry* (New York: Springer Publishing Co., 1963), p. 69.

12. Charles E. Goshen (ed.), *Documentary History of Psychiatry* (New York: Philosophical Library, 1967), p. 295.

13. Pliny Earle, *History, Description, and Statistics of the Bloomingdale Asylum for the Insane* (New York: Egbert, Hovey and King, 1848), p. 26.

14. Charles Dickens, *The American Notes* (London: Hazell, Watson and Viney, Ltd., 1927), p. 43.

15. *The American Journal of Insanity*, I (1844–1845), 48.

16. Norman Dain, *Concepts of Insanity in the United States, 1789–1865* (New Brunswick, N.J.: Rutgers University Press, 1964), p. 119.

17. *The American Journal of Insanity*, XI (1854–1855), 142.

18. *Ibid.*, p. 143.

19. Charles Dickens, *op. cit.*, p. 42.

20. *Ibid.*, p. 44.

21. *The American Journal of Insanity*, IV (1847–1848), 15.

22. *The American Journal of Insanity*, I (1844–1845), 82–83.

23. *The American Journal of Insanity*, IV (1847–1848), 12.

24. *Ibid.*

25. *The American Journal of Insanity*, I (1844–1845), 6.

Chapter 4

IMPROVING THE LINK
BETWEEN HOSPITAL
AND COMMUNITY

Early superintendents attempted to lower barriers between the mental hospital and the community by efforts to improve public attitudes toward insanity. It was hoped to ease the treatment of those who were, or had been, mentally ill, thus facilitating their reabsorption into the community as well as alleviating mistreatment of unhospitalized cases, and to encourage early case finding, thus contributing to the highest possible rate of curability.

The Association of Medical Superintendents tried to replace stereotypes of the grotesque and inhuman nature of insanity with the idea that, because mental disorder is a natural, curable disease to which all men are susceptible, the mentally disturbed are not monsters or fiends but rather "our unfortunate fellow beings" of whom there was no reason to feel ashamed or fearful. Thomas S. Kirkbride, for instance, wrote:

Insanity should be classed with other diseases. . . . It should never be forgotten that every individual who has a brain is liable to insanity, precisely as everyone with a stomach runs the risk at some period of being a martyr to dyspepsia. . . . It has been too much the custom to say, without any qualification, that insanity is the greatest infliction that can befall humanity. . . . It must be borne in mind . . . that the symptoms are in almost endless variety; that many cases are attended with very little suffering, require but little restraint of any kind, are not disabled from appreciating books, or the society around them, or from enjoying many intellectual and physical comforts.[1]

Superintendents insisted that prejudice against the insane was a mark of medieval superstition and ignorance, now happily anachronistic in the enlightened nineteenth century:

The treatment of the insane has ever varied with the philosophy and intelligence of the age. That they are treated better in modern times, more kindly and judiciously, is not owing to any increase of benevolence, but to an increase of knowledge. . . .

The burning of Joan of Arc, and the thousands of supposed sorcerers . . . which we now look upon with horror, was caused by the ignorance of the times. In fact, ignorance has ever been the worst of all *diseases,* and as relates to insanity much yet remains, and we should regard it among our highest duties to endeavor to dispel it, and to diffuse such a knowledge of insanity among all classes, as will prevent the recurrence of the enormities we have mentioned.[2]

Vehicles of stigma nevertheless remained to be attacked. *The Prison Journal of Boston,* for instance, listed facilities for the insane next to those for criminals. The superintendents protested that to class the mentally disordered with lawbreakers was unnecessarily cruel.[3] The article in the *Journal of Insanity* drew a sharp letter from a judge who demanded to know why such charitable men, so concerned with one group of unfortunates, were not equally troubled by the fate of prisoners.[4] The following issue replied that indeed the superintendents were concerned with criminals; and the *Journal* cited a list of recommendations from one of the standing committees of the Association concerned with prison administration. Nevertheless, they stood by their original protest, because classing the insane with willful social offenders did not help the latter, but it actively damaged the reputations and self-respect of the former.[5] This kind of outspoken exchange with members of the community was a valuable link with the extramural world, which, unfortunately, was not maintained for long.

In their efforts to ameliorate public attitudes toward the insane, superintendents wrote a series of articles painstakingly describing both their patients and the details of institutional life. They presented the mentally disturbed sympathetically, even admiringly, and occasionally with cloying sentimentality so typical of the nineteenth century, both in the explicit content of writings and through a common imagery in which the insane were compared to children and poets.

The comparison of the insane to children was based not only on superficial similarities or irrational thoughts, emotions, and behavior but also on the inevitable parallels between the educational theories and techniques of moral treatment and the socialization of the young. Like children, patients were mischievous, uncontrolled, innocent, and original, but basically honorable. And like children they had to be protected against their own dangerous willfulness and taught the manners and obligations of the adult world. Such analogies pervade the literature. Pliny Earle, for example, wrote in the Bloomingdale manual for attendants,

The motives, the influences, and, as a general rule, the means necessary for the good government of children, are equally applicable, and equally efficient for the insane.[6]

And an article calling for separate institutions for male and female patients was couched in these terms: "If a school is established, the separation of the sexes is carried out. . . . The insane require much the same care and watchfulness that is necessary for children." [7]

The charming and beguiling nature of the delusions and behavior of patients were recorded in such articles as Earle's "The Poetry of Insanity." Earle was well equipped to deal with this subject because he himself wrote poetry and published in Edgar Allan Poe's literary magazine.[8] The author rebuked lay critics for whom nothing could be more incompatible than the juxtaposition of "poesy" and those whom they considered

a race of beings entirely distinct from themselves, dissociated from human sympathies, alienated from the hallowed affections, the deep wellsprings of love, which rise fresh fountains in the desert of the heart, divested of every attribute of the Godlike image in which man was created, with the exception of bodily form alone, fallen like Lucifer, from all which may be termed their angelic nature, and worthy of no moral associations more exalted than that of fiends, and no mental connection more elevated than that of brutes.[9]

On the contrary, Earle continued, the insane have a divine and immutable soul that enables them still to feel "those emotions which are the attributes of angels," and to retain "the germ of moral beauty." [10] Their actions and emotions are as innocent and pure as those of children:

In their attachments and antipathies, their sources of pleasure and of pain, their feelings, motives, all their secret springs of action, they appear to have returned again into childhood. But childhood and early life are emphatically the poetical age of man, when hope is unclouded

and care is but a name, when affection is disinterested, the heart unsullied, and imagination untrammeled by the serious duties of a
working world.[11]

A number of cases were cited to demonstrate the wit of patients
and the imaginativeness of their delusions, as, for instance, those of
a lady "overflowing with the milk of human kindness," who felt so
sorry for a table on which she kept a large Bible that she was found
one day, the Bible at her feet, holding the table in her lap, where
she was giving it a rest.[12]

A number of articles dwelt on the connection between poetry
and insanity, each of which faithfully quoted Dryden's couplet,

> Great wits to madness closely are allied
> And thin partitions do their realms divide.

As one superintendent remarked, this does not preclude insanity
in fools.[13] These articles carefully examined the lives, works, and
mental diseases of Cowper, Johnson, Elizabeth Lamb, and a number of others.

The connection between poetry and insanity was based not only
on observation of actual cases but also on theory, both aesthetic
and medical. The effectiveness of poetry was felt to depend on the
vividness with which a poet could visualize and present his images
as true. This verisimilitude depended, in turn, on the extent to
which the poet, as well as his readers, could submit to "a willing
suspension of disbelief which constitutes poetic faith." As Earle
pointed out, this gave lunatics a clear advantage, for although a
sane poet always knows that he is only using his imagination, a
lunatic has no disbelief to suspend, his images thus being always
real and enduring.

The second theoretical link between poetry and insanity depended on the contemporary model of the malleable brain surface.
Benjamin Rush pointed out that certain professions are more
susceptible to insanity than others because they dwell too much on
emotions and illusions. He cited Phillippe Pinel's statement that
"Poets, painters, sculptors, and musicians, are most subject to [in-
sanity], and . . . he never knew an instance of it in a chemist, a
naturalist, a mathematician, or a philosopher." [14]

Superintendents tried not only to dispel stereotypes about the insane but also to remove fears of what took place behind institution
walls so that patients and their friends would not hesitate to seek
help in the earliest stages of disease when mental disorder was most

curable. Articles were therefore prepared detailing the histories of certain asylums and explaining the methods and rationale of administration and treatment modalities. The pleasant features of such hospitals were emphasized; and it was suggested that although some cases might be dealt with at home, the greatest chance of cure was to be found in an asylum.[15]

Certain institutions, such as Utica, invited the public to attend hospital functions, a practice that had been developed in England to gain good-will after gross abuses had been exposed by Parliamentary investigations. The annual fair at Utica was apparently well attended, and was described by the sympathetic editor of the *Utica Gazette*:

These glimpses at the occupations and amusements of the Asylum must lead many to regard a residence within its walls, as anything but disagreeable, and dissipate entirely those prejudices which frequently prevent the friends of the afflicted from immediately placing them in the only place where a cure is likely to be effected.[16]

Nevertheless, in spite of cheerful surroundings, the editor noted that the crowd of visitors remained strangely hushed throughout their stay.

Certain institutions further promoted interaction with the outside world by sending their patients into the surrounding community. For instance, Jon Galt of the Eastern Lunatic Asylum, Williamsburg, Virginia, boarded out suitable patients with families, and paroled others to find employment in nearby towns. He felt that the seclusion of the insane was "too monastic," and that alienists should strive for

greater freedom [for] the insane, the removal of the interdiction of association with the public, and the establishment of means whereby the accustomed life of the lunatic shall be less essentially at variance with that pertaining to persons generally of sound mind.[17]

This opinion well summarized the prevailing attitude of practitioners of moral management about the value of reducing distance between the inmates of mental institutions and the extramural community.

NOTES

1. Albert Deutsch, *The Mentally Ill in America* (New York: Columbia University Press, 1945), p. 207.

2. *The American Journal of Insanity*, IV (1847–1848), 2–3.

3. *The American Journal of Insanity*, I (1844–1845), 382.

4. *The American Journal of Insanity*, II (1845–1846), 175.

5. *Ibid.*, p. 177.

6. Pliny Earle, *History, Description, and Statistics of the Bloomingdale Asylum for the Insane* (New York: Egbert, Hovey and King, 1848), p. 37.

7. *The American Journal of Insanity*, VII (1850–1851), 136–137.

8. F. Sanborn (ed.), *Memoirs of Pliny Earle, M.D.* (Boston: Damrell and Upham, 1898), p. 149.

9. *The American Journal of Insanity*, I (1844–1845), 193–194.

10. *Ibid.*, p. 194.

11. *Ibid.*, p. 196.

12. *Ibid.*, pp. 205–206.

13. *Ibid.*, p. 18.

14. Benjamin Rush, *Medical Inquiries and Observations Upon the Diseases of the Mind* (New York: Library of the New York Academy of Medicine, 1962), p. 63.

15. *The American Journal of Insanity*, III (1846–1847), 372.

16. *The American Journal of Insanity*, I (1844–1845), 350.

17. *The American Journal of Insanity*, XIV (1857–1858), 391.

PART TWO

Mid-Nineteenth Century:
The Change from Moral
Treatment to Custodial Care

Chapter 5

FACTORS IN THE CHANGE FROM MORAL TREATMENT TO CUSTODIAL CARE: AN OVERVIEW

Moral treatment introduced a body of progressive practice into nineteenth-century American psychiatry that included a kind of milieu therapy for patients and a deep involvement of practitioners in the affairs of the lay community. The system also developed a number of assumptions that molded, with mixed results, the course of subsequent professional development.

First, the example of the early mental hospital and the pressure of such reformers as Horace Mann and Dorothea Dix from the 1830's to the Civil War made the treatment of the insane virtually synonymous with residence in an asylum. Although this eventually liberated the mentally disordered from inadequate care in jails, almshouses, private homes, and the offices of general practitioners addicted to bloodletting, it also entailed erecting, maintaining and staffing expensive institutions that burdened a nascent economy. Moreover, in frontier regions, where the population was widely scattered, and where roads were rudimentary if they existed at all, such institutions were inaccessible to outlying areas.

Second, moral treatment established a partnership between laymen and professionals in the management of the insane. Public and semiprivate hospitals were erected, financed, and supervised by governmental or charitable groups, thus enabling institutions to survive and maintaining lay concern and involvement. However, it also produced much friction because professional judgment had to contend with nonpsychiatric demands for such attributes as frugal administration, political patronage in staff appointments, an absorption of a massive flow of violent, chronic, and troublesome patients who overburdened institutions. Moreover, because moral management was based on the fostering of a "correct" social atmosphere in wards, it was easily disrupted by an influx of patient-criminals, alcoholics, paupers, and immigrants—who did not share the normative values of middle class, Protestant New England. Alienists were unable to cope with the violent and outlandish ways of these persons, and so began to rely on force, regimentation, and mechanical restraints rather than on trust and persuasion.

Third, moral treatment evoked a large body of legislation governing insanity. Before its advent, the insane had been subsumed under the poor laws if they were helpless and destitute, or under criminal law if they disturbed the peace or public decency. By the efforts of reformers and legislators, however, the insane became a new legal category. Special legislation was enacted to remove the insane from jails, almshouses, and other unsuitable surroundings into hospitals, to regulate the administration and funding of institutions, to determine who would pay how much for the support of the indigent, to regulate commitment procedure, and to establish criminal responsibility and property rights for the mentally disturbed. These laws arose in part as an outcome of a militant reform movement, bent on creating change as fast as possible; in part because laws are the mode of government, which had now become deeply involved in asylum affairs; and in part because of the necessity of defending civil liberties in such areas as the commitment of an individual against his will. These laws, however, surrounded professional functioning with an often constraining welter of regulations that proved difficult to modify once their drawbacks were realized.

Fourth, moral treatment imbued professionals and laymen alike with expectations that insanity could be controlled, that it could be cured, prevented, and eventually eradicated. This optimism attracted eager young practitioners to the field; it reduced public fears and prejudice to some extent; and it mobilized support for erecting more asylums. However, it meant that the system was oversold and hence was liable to be damaged by public disillusionment. It meant that, with disappointing results, alienists abandoned what we might now regard as progressive therapeutic ventures and contact with the community, retiring either to attainable although secondary goals, such as good administration, or to pure research that isolated them further from patients and laymen.

Fifth, the system imposed a medical model on the care of the insane, the concept that mental disorder was a disease requiring the attention of a qualified physician, not a metaphysical visitation to be exorcised by means of religion, magic, or quack remedies. This concept established a more humane and uniform standard of practice than had existed earlier; and a professional guild developed to police its members and to inform them of developments in the field. On the other hand, the profession tended to denigrate the role of nonalienists in the care of the insane at a time when trained manpower of any kind was scarce; it also absorbed current general medical theories and eventually pursued a course of physiological and often post-mortem research into the nature of insanity that reduced communication with patients and helped to exclude the lay community from an understanding of alienists' work by the growing esotericism of procedures and theories.

These five points bear strongly on alterations in professional theories and clinical practice as well as on the relations between practitioners and the lay and patient communities that led to the decline of moral treatment and its replacement by custodial care.

Moral treatment and custodial care were not so antithetical as has often been implied. The prime factor in the growth of the latter system was not the replacement of a humane and progressive regimen of patient management by cruelty, neglect, or a repressive and pathogenic total institution; it was rather the acceptance of the fact that asylums could no longer be devoted almost exclusively to active therapy and cure of recent cases, but had to provide, instead, a sheltered environment for chronic misfits. The custodial era thus was marked not by lowered concern for the unfortunate, but by loss of faith in the concept of easy cure, the cornerstone of earlier moral treatment.

Such pessimism meant, however, that the system was particularly vulnerable to deprivation: deprivation of funds because the public was more likely to deny tax revenues to the "doomed" and "useless" when such money could be spent with benefit elsewhere; and deprivation of social ties with the community because there was less apparent need to maintain contact with those who would never return. The operation of both these forces helped to produce stereotypically isolated, overcrowded, and ill-equipped mental hospitals that contrasted so unfavorably with those of moral treatment.

It should also be stressed that the rate of change in psychiatric practice was uneven during the mid- and late nineteenth century. There was no point dividing the era of moral treatment from that of custodial care. Asylum policy varied from state to state and from asylum to asylum, depending on local laws, on the personality of the superintendent, and on the auspices under which each hospital was founded and administered. In a number of institutions, such as the state hospital at Northampton, Massachusetts, under the superintendency of Pliny Earle, moral management and custodial care coexisted well into the 1880's and 1890's, to be replaced by the most stereotyped custodial system.

Moreover, there was often a time lag between the most clearly stated theories and the realities of practice. Men committed to the modes of one era lived to practice in another, when other ideas were dominant. The architecture of earlier periods similarly molded the organization of later hospitals. For example, some of the repressive paraphernalia of the eighteenth century were carried over into moral treatment institutions and survived to become part of another wave of custodial institutions. Thus, when in 1881 Theodore W. Fisher became superintendent of the Municipal Asylum in Boston, later to become Boston State Hospital, the institution that Dickens had eulogized, he reported the survival of restraining and isolating rooms, the absence of heating, light, and ventilation on one side of the 1839 building, of dark and narrow corridors used as day rooms, of gloomy and scanty furnishings, and of a dining room seating twenty-five built when the hospital housed about three hundred patients.[1] Similarly, the State Asylum at Taunton, Massachusetts, erected in the 1850's at the height of enthusiasm for the curative powers of moral treatment, was designed by a lay planning group for two hundred and fifty patients, and was equipped with *forty-two strong rooms* to house violent and destructive patients. These cells were bare and powerfully constructed with small openings in the doors to admit food without endangering an attendant. In the lower level of cells designed for incontinent patients, brick floors sloped into drains for easy washing; and the bricks could be heated to protect from the cold those who were expected to tear off their clothes. The first superintendent, G. C. S. Choate, however, managed to have these cells demolished and replaced by more constructive facilities; [2] but in other moral treatment institutions, such as McLean Asylum for the Insane, barred windows and other evidences of forcible seclusion survived into the 1880's and 1890's [3] in spite of the doctrines of moral management. It should also be noted that the development of American psychiatry during the mid-nineteenth century has been particularly hard to chronicle, because every facet of shifting hospital organization, community relations, and professional theory was entwined with every other. The practice of superintendents, for example, directly affected lay demands and attitudes toward mental hospitals, which, in turn, affected the relations of alienists to the extramural and patient communities. Moreover, the entire changing system of American mental hospitals was contained in and was affected by the larger kaleidoscope of national growth. Heavy immigration clashed with and changed the dominant culture of the nation and hence of patient populations. Economic trials and the Civil War altered the goals and capabilities of public authorities and hence of superintendents in the administration of asylums. And the idealism, lack of planning, impetuosity and disdain for traditional expertise characteristic of many developing nations in the twentieth century also marked the life of nineteenth-century America, altering in their turn the values and modes of professional practice and the nature of public demands.

NOTES

1. Henry M. Hurd, ed., *The Institutional Care of the Insane in the United States and Canada* (Baltimore: Johns Hopkins Press, 1916), Vol. II, p. 649.

2. *Ibid.*, p. 657.

3. *Ibid.*, p. 609.

Chapter 6

THE CONSTRAINTS
OF INSTITUTIONS

Early practitioners of moral treatment considered institutionalization only one of several possible means of treating insanity. At an early meeting of the Association of Medical Superintendents, a committee was formed to examine the relative merits of private practice for alienists, or asylum work; and one practitioner advised the public,

The patient ought never to be sent to an asylum when the means of treatment are equally accessible and the probabilities of relief great at home; but if the nature of the derangement be such as to require that constant watchfulness and decided control which can only be obtained in an establishment devoted to this purpose, there can be no hesitation in deciding upon his removal.[1]

Home medical care of the insane continued for some time. General practitioners were advised about moral and medical management; and Pliny Earle, for example, went into private practice after resigning the superintendency of Bloomingdale Hospital. However, the propaganda of professionals and lay reformers made treatment of the insane increasingly synonymous with hospitalization. By the mid-nineteenth century, it was expected that if every state erected one or two suitable asylums, insanity would be eliminated. As Edward Jarvis wrote,

We doubt not, that before many years every state will have its asylum for its insane; and several of the states that have now one or more will add others, until all of their diseased in mind shall be provided with the proper means of protection and cure.[2]

The proliferation of such hospitals, however, proved impractical, quite apart from the question of whether or not they were capable of attaining their stated goal. Their most significant drawback was that an institutional approach was singularly unsuited to a frontier society, and the adoption of such a system marked an early and significant stage in the growth of dissonance between alienists and the lay community.

In the first place, mental hospitals proved impractical in a country where the population lived scattered sparsely over hundreds of miles and where there were few roads and only rough vehicles to travel them. The horrors of long journeys to an asylum through the back woods were described in the 1867 Report of Alabama Insane Hospital at Tuskaloosa,

One man was carried over 150 miles tied down to the bottom of a wagon without springs, exposed to the burning rays of the sun in midsummer, neither eating nor drinking during the whole journey! No wonder he died within 10 days after his arrival at the hospital.[3]

Other institutions in early nineteenth-century America confronted the same dilemma. Their response, however, was better adapted to native conditions than was that of alienists tied to European prototypes. Teachers, clergymen, and judges, for example, gave up their traditional link to buildings and became itinerant, traveling circuits to reach dispersed settlers. Alienists, on the other hand, remained in their hospitals, waiting for patients to come to them.

One suggestion on how better to reach the public was offered by Jarvis and was adopted by the Massachusetts legislature and by the Association of Medical Superintendents as theoretically normative. It was in effect a system of catchment areas.

Jarvis conducted a survey of mental hospitals, first in his own state in 1854 and later throughout the country, in which he correlated hospital admissions with place of residence of patients. He discovered that most asylum inmates came from within a circumscribed radius of the hospital. He thus concluded,

An insane hospital is, and must be to a certain extent, a local institution. People will avail themselves of its privileges in some proportion to their nearness to it. No liberality of admission, no excellence of its management, no power of reputation can entirely overcome the obstacle of distance, expense, and of the difficulties of transporting lunatics, or the objections of friends to sending their insane patients far from home, and out of the reach of ready communication.[4]

Jarvis noted that hospital admissions increased when institutions were opened in new areas or when access to existing facilities by such means as canals, railroads, and public conveyances became easily and cheaply available. Not only did the difficulty and expense of travel control patient flow, he felt, but the proximity of hospital to people dispelled fear and prejudice, while distance made mystery:

The ideal of the hospital purposes and its management is familiar to those who live in its vicinity. They know its means, its objects, and its administration; they know the character of its officers and its attendants.

They are frequently witnessing its operations and results in the many who are going to and returning from it, in improved or restored mental health. Whenever they think of the possibility of their becoming insane, the idea of the hospital presents itself to their mind, in the same connection, almost as readily as the idea of their own chambers, their own physician, and the tender nursing of their own family is associated with the thought of having a fever or dysentery. And, when any one of their family or friends becomes deranged, the hospital occurs to them as a means of relief, and they look upon it as a resting place from their troubles.[5]

These findings and opinions influenced the Massachusetts legislature to establish hospitals throughout the state, rather than to continue enlarging such institutions as Worcester Hospital. Jarvis's work was also much talked of in the 1860's, when the State of New York proposed to build Willard State Hospital to receive chronic insane from the whole state. This plan was bitterly opposed by superintendents, and indignant articles appeared in the *American Journal of Insanity* citing Jarvis's work.

Jarvis's concept was perhaps one of the earliest versions of the "catchment area," now one of the central concepts of community psychiatry; and the resolution, proposed in 1866 by Charles H. Nichols of Washington, D.C., and taken by the Association of Medical Superintendents at its annual meeting that year, has a ring familiar to late twentieth-century practitioners:

The large states should be divided into geographical districts so that hospitals could be placed nearly in the center of them and thus be accessible to all persons living within their boundaries and available for treatment . . . all state, county and city hospitals shall receive persons in their vicinity, whatever may be the form or nature of their mental disorder.[6]

Catchment areas, however, implied a large number of small hospitals, an impractical proposal because there was a shortage of trained personnel to operate them. Not only were there few teachers and clergymen who would minister to a tiny population of patients, but there was also a shortage of attendants who, as hospitals became overcrowded, became the only staff members in frequent contact with patients. Finding decent, able-bodied men and women willing to work in asylums was a difficult task. In spite of the protests of the Association of Medical Superintendents, convicts were employed in such hospitals as Blackwell's Island; and practitioners complained that only the very young, whose maturity of judgment was in question, were willing to take such jobs. Disobedience was a constant problem, particularly from a vagrant class of attendants of evil character who drifted from one asylum to another taking temporary work.

The shortage of medical staff was even more acute. Most doctors had little or no training in the diagnosis and treatment of insanity. Until the 1870's few lectures were given on the subject, and none were part of a medical curriculum from the death of Benjamin Rush in 1813 until 1867, when William Hammond, a neurologist, was appointed professor of nervous and mental diseases at Bellevue Hospital Medical College in New York.

Publications and lectures of individual superintendents helped to dispel some of this ignorance. Pliny Earle, for example, gave a lecture on "Psychologic Medicine: Its Importance as a Part of the Medical Curriculum" to the Berkshire Medical Institute of Massachusetts in 1863. General medicine, however, only gradually became interested in psychiatry, thus giving the discipline low status and directly affecting the quality of recruits to the field.

Creating many small institutions was also impractical because such hospitals were expensive to erect and maintain. Unlike European countries like Germany, England, and France, the United States had no great buildings from another era to convert into asylums. Although the monasteries, manor houses, and bedlams of Europe were often inadequate and forbidding, they could be made habitable relatively easily. The founders of nineteenth-century European mental hospitals were thus spared the initial cost of construction that drained public and private philanthropy in America.

In addition, American planners had to cope with the high inflation of a developing country and with a demand equally characteristic of young nations that public buildings be grand, that they

represent the aspirations of the people rather than their present resources, and hence that they be lavishly equipped with pillars,
porticos, domes, and grand stairways as well as with all the approved heating, ventilating, and plumbing systems suggested by
the Association of Medical Superintendents. Some idea of the cost
of equipping a moral treatment establishment may be gained from
the 1854 Annual Report of the Retreat for the Insane at Hartford:

A green-house would be a never-ending and ever-varying source of
delight, especially to our female patients; . . . I would gladly see a
small library in every ward, and pictures and prints upon all our
walls. . . .

Additional musical instruments, and additions to our magic lantern
apparatus of dissolving views, etc., would be of great use to us. In some
asylums a large room is devoted as a museum, where objects of curiosity, specimens in various departments of natural history, etc., are
collected, and which is also made to serve the purpose of a reading-
room, supplied with books, prints, pamphlets, newspapers, games, etc.
We have already some beautiful shells and minerals, which we have
not arranged for want of such a room.[7]

In spite of much emphasis among members of the Association of
Medical Superintendents on maintaining high standards in planning
and constructing asylums, hastily conceived and shoddy structures
sprang up, particularly those erected specifically for paupers, like
the municipal hospitals of Boston and New York City, as well as
many state institutions. It was felt that because the poor were unused to ornamentation or luxury, plain surroundings and plain living would be more "suitable," both in view of their former life and
also their present status as recipients of charity. In 1867, for example, John P. Gray, the second superintendent of Utica, commented
as follows on the "Plans, Descriptions and Estimates of the Boston
Hospital for the Insane, at Winthrop," "We regret to see an item
of $5,000 for mantels and grates in an institution for the city poor
. . . to be heated with steam and hot water." [8]

Locally controlled and supported facilities were themselves
chronically impoverished in part because the local tax base was inadequate for all the demands on community funds. One such institution was Blackwell's Island in New York City, which, during the
1840's and 1850's suffered from politically appointed superintendents, attendants drawn from local prisons, and a pervasive air of
idle hopelessness described by Charles Dickens during his tour of
America,

I cannot say that I derived much comfort from the inspection of this charity. The different wards might have been cleaner and better ordered; I saw nothing of that salutary system which had impressed me so favorably elsewhere [Boston]; and everything had a lounging, listless, madhouse air, which was very painful. The moping idiot, cowering down with long dishevelled hair; the gibbering maniac, with his hideous laugh and pointed finger; the vacant eye, the fierce wild face, the gloomy picking of the hands and lips, and munching of nails: there they were all, without disguise, in naked ugliness and horror. In the dining room, a bare, dull, dreary place, with nothing for the eye to rest on but the empty walls, a woman was locked up alone. She was bent, they told me, on committing suicide. If anything could have strengthened her in her resolution, it would certainly have been the insupportable monotony of such an existence.[9]

Among state hospitals criticized for poor planning and construction was that at Worcester, Massachusetts. It was distinguished by having been erected within the limits of the original appropriation. Isaac Ray, who long fought pinch-penny legislation as not only harmful to patients but also short-sighted and wasteful, wrote of Worcester,

Being intended for the poorer classes, it was unwisely concluded that every subordinate object might be disregarded, provided the principal one—the custody of the patient—were secured. It was the first considerable example of cheap construction, and one, unfortunately, which building committees have been too ready to imitate.[10]

In his report on European asylums, Ray advised his colleagues to emulate the English principle that held that

There is no such thing as a just and proper curative or ameliorating treatment of the insane in cheaply constructed and cheaply managed institutions.[11]

Alienists, trustees, and architects, however, began to equate expensive facilities with good care. This, plus galloping inflation during such major periods of hospital construction as the 1830's and 1840's and the years following the Civil War, plus perhaps inevitable profiteering, drove the cost of hospitals up from about $100,000 in the 1840's to well over $1.5 million by the 1860's and 1870's. Few alienists were sufficiently detached or courageous to object to this trend. An exception was Pliny Earle, who was for a time heartily hated by colleagues for exposing the vain wastefulness of much hospital construction. In 1872, however, the Association of Medical Superintendents was obliged to pass a resolution against "embellishments."

The high initial cost of mental hospitals made legislatures increasingly unreceptive to further requests for new construction, or even for maintenance and expansion of existing plants. This helped to produce a massive overcrowding, which paralyzed the therapeutic programs of moral treatment hospitals.

A major reason for this overcrowding was the fact that the prevalence of insanity in the population was not known, so that all early provisions made for the care of the insane were inadequate. Massachusetts had attempted to assess the number of beds needed in the state before building Worcester State Hospital. In 1830, Horace Mann sent questionnaires to 310 cities and towns in the commonwealth asking for lists of their insane and whatever provisions existed for their care. He received only 114 answers, from which he estimated that the population of insane numbered 300, and Worcester State Hospital was designed accordingly.

The next, and more disastrous, attempt to count the mentally disturbed was the national census of 1840. The census-takers, entering numbers on enormous grids, then copying and recopying the results for various local, state, and national archives, managed to produce some startling statistics, particularly on the number of insane among free Northern Negroes:

In Maine, the town of Limerick is stated to have no colored persons, but four colored lunatics. Scarboro had no colored people, but six colored lunatics. In Massachusetts, Freetown, Leominister, Wilmington, Sterling, and Danvers are all stated to have no colored persons of any age or sex, yet each is stated to have two colored insane. Other towns in the free states, according to this document, have the same wonderful faculty of making bricks without straw, of creating colored insanity without colored subjects for it to rest upon.[12]

These results not only inflicted a grave disservice to the cause of abolition but also hindered planning and legislation for insanity because states acted on them before the figures could be revised. Moreover, they hindered the course of science, because for example, Boudin of Paris, author of a work on medical and geographical statistics, developed an entire theory based on this census. Because the census showed the insanity rate of Negroes to be in the ratio of 1 to 4,310 in Louisiana, 1 to 1,309 in Virginia, 1 to 257 in Pennsylvania, 1 to 44 in Massachusetts, and 1 to 14 in Maine, Boudin discovered that "cold vitiates the mental health of the Negro," until Isaac Ray corrected his figures.[13]

In an effort to gain more figures, a Massachusetts committee led by Edward Jarvis was appointed in 1848 to discover the number and condition of the insane in the state in order to learn whether Worcester should be enlarged or replaced, or whether another asylum should be built. Circulars were sent to selectmen, mayors, and aldermen; and 1,512 lunatics, or 1 in 623 of the population, were discovered, a dramatic increase over previous figures and one that many found very frightening.

The rates of insanity appeared to rise again according to the Census of 1850, in which 1,680 lunatics, or 1 in 590, were found in Massachusetts. In 1851, in the midst of anxious professional discussions, Jarvis noted that

It is impossible to demonstrate, whether lunacy is increasing, stationary, or diminishing, in proportion to the advancement of the population, for want of definite and reliable facts, to show, how many lunatics there are now, and still less to show, how many there have been at any previous period. Wanting these two facts, we cannot mathematically compare the numbers of the insane or their proportions to the whole people at any two periods of time, and thus determine whether lunacy increases or retrogrades.[14]

In 1854, Jarvis was asked to conduct another state inquiry to assess the situation with more accuracy. Realizing that his previous sources of information were not those likely to be most knowledgeable about the private and hidden affairs of local families, he tried another tack.

I therefore got a list of all the physicians, learned and unlearned, quack and regular, man and female, all sorts of doctors, and wrote to every one of them, sending a schedule with thirteen questions to be answered, and asked them to make returns to me. By perseverance and urgency in every kind of way, by using every sort of aid and influence, writing to some a half dozen times, and visiting sixty-five towns, I got returns for every reliable physician in active practice, in Massachusetts, except two regular physicians who refused to answer and two quacks who took no interest in the matter. I got, probably, as complete a survey of insanity as ever was made in the world. 2630 lunatics, or 1 in every 427 was the result.[15]

Meanwhile, in the midst of all these fluctuating figures, Massachusetts, which by the mid- and late nineteenth century had more public and semiprivate asylums than any other state, was still short of beds; and no matter how many more were added, there were never enough.

The drawbacks of institution-based treatment of the insane in the United States soon became apparent. By then, however, so much money had been invested, and the public had become so accustomed to the idea that the insane required hospital care, that alienists were powerless to change the system in any significant way.

By the middle of the century, most alienists could only watch impotently as the mounting backlog of chronic cases in their hospitals disrupted the social organization on which their therapeutic system depended. Institutions were strained even further by pressure from the surrounding community to admit yet more patients, many of whom were apparently "unsuitable" for moral treatment. The degree to which asylums could disregard or to which they were forced to acquiesce to such demands depended in large measure on the nature of the individual hospital and on the auspices under which it operated.

During the first half of the nineteenth century, there were five types of mental institutions, distinguished by the auspices under which they were founded and administered. By 1861, there were forty-eight asylums in the United States. One of these had been erected at the insistence of Dorothea Dix by the Federal Government to serve the District of Columbia; twenty-seven had been erected by the legislatures of twenty-one states and were supported by state funds; five were financed and controlled by cities or counties in four states; ten were corporate institutions which had been founded by private persons, financed by both private endowment and public funds, and managed by boards of trustees; and five were chiefly private, family-run institutions.

The five private institutions charged the highest fees. They provided liberal and individualized care for quiet patients or for those to whom the stigma of insanity was so overwhelming that they could not enter a recognized asylum. Although some superintendents admitted a role for such institutions in the United States (they held a key position in the care of the insane in England), they feared the abuses that might be perpetuated in houses that had no outside control or supervision.

The ten corporate institutions were bastions of moral treatment. Many had been founded in the 1820's by benevolent laymen, particularly Quakers and Unitarians, and they had since received, in addition to handsome bequests and donations, some state aid. Patients had to pay for their services, but because they owned their own buildings, their fees were moderate; and their boards of overseers could guarantee sound standards of care. By the mid- and late nineteenth century, such institutions received a growing number of paupers at the expense of the state.

City and county hospitals like New York City's Blackwell's Island or the Boston Lunatic Asylum, had been designed for paupers, and they continued the pattern of local responsibility for the poor. As state institutions became overcrowded with chronic cases, many were discharged to a growing number of such institutions. These often provided unsuitable accommodations, insufficient food, and no trained staff. The directors had frequently secured their jobs by political patronage, and they had no medical qualifications. The local asylums eventually became targets for reformers anxious to transfer their inmates to more orthodox hospitals.

Finally, there were state institutions built in increasing numbers after the campaign of Dorothea Dix, and after it had become generally apparent that private philanthropy could never cope unaided with so large a burden as insanity. These hospitals were designed for both self-supporting and indigent patients. As time went on, however, many became inundated by pauper, immigrant, and chronic cases, and their facilities showed the ill effects of penny-pinching appropriations.

NOTES

1. *The American Journal of Insanity*, III (1846–1847), 372–373.

2. *The American Journal of Insanity*, XIV (1857–1858), 253.

3. *The American Journal of Insanity*, XXV (1868–1869), 104.

4. *The American Journal of Insanity*, XXII (1865–1866), 361.

5. *Ibid.*, p. 402.

6. Henry M. Hurd (ed.), *The Institutional Care of the Insane in the United States and Canada* (Baltimore: Johns Hopkins Press, 1916), Vol. I, pp. 31–32.

7. *The American Journal of Insanity*, XI (1854–1855), 260.

8. *The American Journal of Insanity*, XXIV (1867–1868), 424.

9. Charles Dickens, *The American Notes* (London: Hazell, Watson and Viney, Ltd., 1927), p. 78.

10. Albert Deutsch, *The Mentally*

Ill in America (New York: Columbia University Press, 1945), p. 143.

11. *The American Journal of Insanity,* II (1845–1846), 17.

12. *The American Journal of Insanity,* XIX (1862–1863), 77.

13. *Ibid.*

14. *The American Journal of Insanity,* XIV (1857–1858), 333.

15. *The American Journal of Insanity,* XIX (1862–1863), 76.

Chapter 7

GOVERNMENT INVOLVEMENT

One of the most important factors in nineteenth-century American psychiatry was the involvement of laymen, and particularly legislators, in the foundation and administration of mental hospitals. Friction was produced, because the goals of laymen, state and local officials, and professionals were often hard to reconcile.

The roots of this controversy were, on the whole, amiable, and they dated back to the establishment of the first formal institutions for the insane, such as the ward for lunatics in the Pennsylvania Hospital. The striking feature of the foundation of these early asylums was that they were initially proposed and financed by concerned laymen, who only later approached a suitable physician, asking him to plan and direct the institution on their behalf. Initiative, financial support, and major decisions governing the management and control of the asylum rested primarily in lay hands. Power was delegated to the superintendent, and its maintenance was conditional on his personal prestige and therapeutic success, rather than on the fact of his professional position.

Among enlightened and generous patrons, and enthusiastic, effective superintendents, this proved a successful partnership; and such practitioners as Isaac Ray pointed to their boards of overseers, visitors, or trustees as their surest guarantee of maintaining high standards of professional practice and ethics. How closely identified such trustees were with their asylums may be seen from the example of the Friends' Asylum at Frankfort, Pennsylvania. Early in the hospital's history, a former patient brought a successful suit for damages; and the $15,000 awarded him was paid by the trustees, not by the asylum.[1]

Professional resentment of lay control, however, soon became acute. Because all facets of hospital organization were felt to impinge on treatment, any nonprofessional intervention was suspect. Friction became particularly noticeable as legislative bodies began to erect public asylums and to support paupers in semiprivate hospitals, for the values and modes of government proved maladaptive to professional practice. This was most acute in the area of admission and discharge of patients, and in the area of financing and supervising institutions.

The major source of difficulty in the relations of superintendents and legislators was the ever growing welter of laws and regulations evolved during the century to govern every aspect of psychiatric practice. Legislation grew piecemeal, with little coordination of one set of laws with another, often leading to paralyzing confusion. In 1891, for example, a superintendent in Kansas reported in disgust that his state had just passed an eight-hour workday law, which hopelessly disrupted his asylum. The law required a full day's wages for every eight hours of work and punished any lowering of the pay scale by employers by imprisonment. The asylum, however, was governed by other laws, which stipulated a line item budget that could not be modified. The superintendent was further forbidden to hire additional staff without legislative permission, again under pain of imprisonment. He thus had to devise a method of providing round-the-clock services on his wards with inadequate personnel and with neither funds nor authority to hire more staff until the state legislature could meet the following year to unscramble the confusion.[2]

Further examples of poor legal drafting may be seen in regulations governing the admission and discharge of patients. Confusion was especially acute here, particularly when individuals were transferred to mental hospitals from the jurisdiction of other social or legal agencies. Omissions and redundancies were common, and superintendents were often confronted with categories of patients whose management on every front was blocked by regulations. The most troublesome of these was that of the criminally insane, a class of patients for whom final responsibility and disposition was ambiguous in many states, in spite of a plethora of laws on the subject.

In the 1880 annual report of the Illinois Southern Hospital for the Insane, for example, Horace Wardner wrote,

I have had much annoyance in caring for the criminal insane. The law regarding them is very defective. It makes no provision for notifying the superintendent, consequently they are thrust in unannounced, whether there is room or not. The law is also silent upon the subject of the expense of returning those who recover, to prison, and makes no provision for expense of clothing. It also makes no provision for the treatment of those who are still insane when the term of their sentence expires. It says they "shall be treated as other patients." Other patients would be retained as long as necessary; but the Attorney General has decided that the hospital has no legal right to keep convict insane beyond the expiration of sentence. The Prison Commissioners have refused to furnish the usual allowance given to convicts at their discharge; the counties cannot be held for the expense of their return, and they naturally try to avoid any responsibility on their account. So it may often happen that the superintendent must choose between turning a dangerous lunatic loose upon the community, and retention in the hospital without due authority, and at his own peril.[3]

The enactment of laws governing insanity, particularly those ordering the removal of the unfortunate from inadequate "receptacles" into hospitals where medical care was available, was a sign of growing public enlightenment. It meant, however, that superintendents lost control over the number and type of patients admitted to their hospitals. This produced overcrowding and an influx of "unsuitable" cases for whom moral treatment was apparently ineffectual. It also led to financial difficulties and friction with town and county officials.

Since the colonial times, there had been laws governing the custody of the insane. As wealthy families confined their own members, only two categories of the mentally ill concerned the community. The first included indigents, who, under the Poor Laws, were the responsibility of local officials, who housed them in the county poorhouse or jail.

The support of dependent classes, however, was an unwelcome burden. Because early villages, especially those agricultural settlements in rocky portions of New England, had little public money, facilities for the confinement of dependent classes were rudimentary, and communities preferred to lighten their own responsibility by making all classes of poor partially self-supporting. Some were placed in workhouses; in many parts of New England, paupers were auctioned off to whoever would keep them for a year at the lowest expense to the community. Because townships were also anxious to avoid responsibility for vagrants, they established residence criteria that limited local liability. Sometimes communities tried further to escape responsibility by smuggling lunatics into another locality during the night in the hope that others would care for them.

The other category of insane recognized by law were, in the words of a 1798 Massachusetts statute, those who were "furiously mad, so as to render it dangerous to the safety or the peace of the good people to be at large." [4] The courts committed such individuals to local authorities to be placed in prisons; and thus the mentally disordered commonly occupied a clause in the criminal statutes of most communities.

None of the early laws recognized any public responsibility toward the insane per se. Rather, they protected the community's property and safety. Another set of laws, governing guardianship and commitment procedures, was equally concerned with the preservation of property rather than with the human aspects of insanity.

The reform movement of the nineteenth century forced enactment of a series of laws, dealing with the welfare of the mentally disturbed. In 1827, for instance, New York prohibited overseers of the poor from imprisoning lunatics with criminals and directed that communities make separate provisions for their confinement.[5] In 1838, county poorhouses and private and public county and city asylums were recognized by law, but the care of the insane was still not recognized as a public duty.[6]

In 1832, after Horace Mann and other reformers had proclaimed, as had John Stuart Mill, that the care of the insane was the responsibility of the state, Massachusetts opened Worcester State Hospital. The legislature directed localities to release insane inmates from jails and poorhouses and to send them instead to the new asylum.[7] Counties and municipalities, however, were still required to pay the fees of indigent residents, or "town-paupers." The state accepted responsibility only for vagrants and newcomers, known as "state-paupers"; richer families could board their patients at Worcester at their own expense.[8] This last was an important advance, because it placed a public facility at the disposal of all the insane, not just of indigents subsumed under the old Poor Laws.

Because the fee at Worcester, $2.50 a patient a week, was more than the cost of supporting paupers in almshouses, communities still refused to hospitalize harmless patients and often tried to gain the release of those committed by the courts. This was not simply a matter of parsimony, as many contemporaries claimed. Many towns, poor to begin with, were becoming depopulated by western migrations, but they still remained liable for the fees of an increasing number of chronic insane. Local governments were unable to pay these costs, and the state was eventually obliged to relieve their burden.

Although the Commonwealth of Massachusetts did not assume full liability for all the insane until 1904, it made a number of concessions much earlier, at least one of which had major repercussions. In 1835, the state allowed all houses of correction to include suitable accommodations for idiots and quiet insane. It also released the localities from paying for nonresident insane and allowed them to recover whatever they might have paid in the past.[9] The state assumed responsibility for state-paupers, immigrants and vagrants, who consequently received care much sooner than either native paupers or the middle class. "Town-paupers," however, remained a local responsibility for many years, partly at the insistence of citizens' reform groups, who felt that parsimonious overseers of the poor should be taught a proper sense of responsibility. For example, the Massachusetts Commission of 1863, inquiring into the conditions of insane residents, wrote,

Shall we never learn the simple lesson that "charity begins at home?" Shall we never realize that we are doing no good service in the holy cause of humanity, by relieving other communities of their rightful burdens, and thus encouraging them in their unchristian repudiation of their duties to God and their brethren? And all this to the discomfort, and perhaps irreparable injury of the sufferers from our own hearthstones, our hearts, and cherished, though absent, in our fondest memories! [10]

This illustrates the manner in which divergent goals created barriers between hospitals and communities. High costs as well as traditions of local autonomy discouraged the state from assuming full support of the insane. At the same time, charitable objectives led to the erection of approved, expensive, centralized institutions to which towns and counties were reluctant to send their patients. Consequently, alienists were obliged to battle local overseers of the poor to prevent their removing patients prematurely in order to save money. Superintendents often hid the progress of patients and tried to avoid inspection by local officials. The patient was thus removed from ready contact with his home community, and he was made a greater and more resented financial burden on his locality.

Because asylums were never large enough to accept all those seeking admission and because a growing number of chronic patients were taking up beds, government-run institutions evolved a scale of priorities. Admission and discharge were regulated by law, on terms that did not always accord with the surest attainment of professional goals. Superintendents and trustees had little control over patient flow. Professionals preferred recent, curable cases that would allow them the greatest possible chance for success and hence the greatest possible public support. Laymen, on the other hand, demanded that the patients who had been confined for years under atrocious conditions be removed to more pleasant surroundings and that the community be protected from dangerous lunatics. In states such as Massachusetts and New York, therefore, priority for admission was given to court referrals.

Laws permitted magistrates to commit troublesome persons to asylums but made no provision for coordinating such dispositions with the availability of beds. Thus, there was an unregulated and inexorable flow from courts to asylums leading to massive overcrowding.

Commitment and discharge laws forced asylums to accept the types of disorder that the community considered particularly troublesome. Alcoholics, the criminally insane, epileptics, and the mentally retarded poured into hospitals and became chronic patients. Superintendents were forbidden to discharge such court-referred cases if they might still menace the community. As a result, asylums like Worcester State Hospital had a built-in escalator clause because courts were not required to wait until a bed became vacant before committing someone who was "violent and furious." One of the most significant indications of the growing gulf between alienists and the community was the increasing powerlessness of superintendents to communicate their plight to the courts and to stem the flow of cases.

At first, practitioners welcomed as a humane reform the fact that chronic patients were remaining in mental hospitals, because laws in states such as New York had required asylums to discharge quiet, uncured cases to their families or to a local poorhouse *thirteen months* after admission.[11] Alienists objected to this rule because it sentenced many to unnecessary deterioration and created a rash of substandard local receptacles, often administered for profit by nonmedical personnel. With beds in high demand, these institutions festered on for years despite efforts to abolish them. In the thirteenth annual report of Utica State Hospital, the superintendent, John Gray, wrote,

It has been the custom of the institution, in accordance with law, to send annually to the poor-house, or to the care of friends, many who had been under treatment two or three years, and in their place receive a corresponding number of new cases. During the past year we had adopted this course in as few instances as duty would permit—first, because the receptacles for this class are filled; and secondly, we believe the provision of the law advising this step originated in a mistaken notion of the disease to be treated and is at variance with justice and humanity. Insanity is a grave disease, requiring the most careful investigation, the most patient observation, and the skillful application of means—all of which must often extend over a period of many years. The idea of consigning the unfortunate victims of such a malady to poor-houses—places, with few exceptions, not only destitute of medical and moral means of treatment, but even without the ordinary physical comforts of life—is a species of cruelty which should excite universal disapprobation.[12]

Alienists and laymen alike saw that the overcrowding of mental hospitals reduced the efficacy of treatment. It was felt, first, that overcrowding produced greater violence in the wards, particularly at night, and that

In a colossal refuge for the insane, a patient may be said to lose his individuality, and to become a member of a machine so put together as to move with precise regularity and invariable routine;—a triumph of skill adapted to show how such unpromising materials as crazy men and women may be drilled into order and guided by rule—but not an apparatus calculated to restore their pristine conditions and their independent self-governing existence.[13]

The vital individualized regimen of care given by the superintendent to each patient was jeopardized. As the 1854 trustees' report of Worcester State Hospital warned,

To attend to 200 patients faithfully and efficiently is good work for a good man; to attend to 250 will tax the energies of the best one to the uttermost. More than this one man cannot do, and do well; and let not Massachusetts require him to make the vain attempt [enlarging the hospital].[14]

The burden of superintendents was extreme because they were not only obliged to spend all their time with patients, but they also had to administer the hospital and the hospital farms, supervise attendants, manage the budget, keep the hospital records, deal with visitors, and serve as public-relations men in the community. They did this work with at best two or three assistant physicians; and at first they had no vacations other than special leaves of absence granted by trustees. There was, apparently, a high breakdown rate among alienists.[15]

Not only did overcrowding tax the strength of superintendents, but it also contributed to greater distance between doctor and patient. This negated a key factor in moral treatment and a primary goal of the mental hospital, the provision of medical services to the insane. Patients fell more and more into the exclusive care of attendants, most of whom were untrained and themselves overworked. Restraints, therefore, came into frequent use as a substitute for moral control.

The overburdening of superintendents also helped to break their ties with the community, because a variety of authorities agreed that extramural work should be avoided. J. Parigot of New York noted that it was no wonder superintendents failed to do their paper work, because they spent most of their time outside their asylums. The 1863 Massachusetts Report on Insanity recommended that

Superintendents should not, in the opinion of the Commission, engage in anything that has an exacting claim on their time and attention, or which can conflict with the claims of their patients.

They should engage in nothing that will engross their attention from the varying and capricious wants of the insane, and more especially, they should at no time be engaged in permanent duties, of a public or private nature, unconnected with, or outside of, those pertaining to their hospital.[16]

The 1872 Annual Meeting of the Association of Medical Superintendents discussed the problem of overcrowding. One member suggested that superintendents might refuse to accept more patients than they could house, thus forcing the public to erect more institutions. Arthur Earl Walker, of the Boston Lunatic Asylum, wondered whether such refusals could work, whether they could even be conveyed to the magistrates who sent a steady stream of patients. This was a commentary on the extent of contact between practitioners and community leaders. Many alienists said that they felt morally obliged to receive all recent, and hence curable, cases; others called for the freedom of superintendents to regulate admissions or for laws to limit hospital capacity. Various suggestions were made for modifying hospital architecture to avoid over-crowding, such as replacing, by single and double rooms, long dormitories that, once crowded, bred violence. One alienist playfully suggested eliminating corridors which would be filled with beds too easily.[17]

Despite the variety of suggestions, the major solution was always the same deceptively easy one: to build more institutions and to enlarge existing facilities. This solution was not only impractical in itself, but it also failed to reach the root of the difficulty, the inability of the various lay and professional groups to specify their goals. This left them eternally frustrated, fighting about means because they never realized that they were all pursuing different ends.

NOTES

1. Henry M. Hurd (ed.), *The Institutional Care of the Insane in the United States and Canada* (Baltimore: Johns Hopkins Press, 1916), Vol. I, p. 179.

2. *The American Journal of Insanity*, XLVIII (1891–1892), 145.

3. *The American Journal of Insanity*, XXXVIII (1881–1882), 101.

4. Hurd, *op. cit.*, p. 82.

5. *Ibid.*, p. 86.

6. *Ibid.*

7. Gerald N. Grob, *The State and the Mentally Ill* (Chapel Hill, N.C.: University of North Carolina Press, 1965), p. 38.

8. *Ibid.*, p. 84.

9. *Ibid.*, p. 91.

10. *Ibid.*, p. 177.

11. Hurd, *op. cit.*, p. 147.

12. *The American Journal of Insanity*, XIII (1856–1857), 46.

13. Richard Hunter and Ida Macalpine, *Three Hundred Years of Psychiatry, 1535–1860* (London: Oxford University Press, 1963), 1029.

14. Grob, *op. cit.*, p. 132.

15. *The American Journal of Insanity*, XXII (1865–1866), 201.

16. *The American Journal of Insanity*, XXI (1864–1865), 263.

17. *The American Journal of Insanity*, XXIX (1872–1873), 187.

Chapter 8

IMMIGRANTS AND PAUPERS—
OVERCROWDING AND
CULTURAL DISSONANCE

One result of laws allocating state funds to maintain paupers in
public institutions was that asylums became filled with those whom
the community considered pariahs. Vagrants, criminals, and immigrants were hospitalized more promptly than town-paupers and
self-supporting patients because government paid their fees. Protest
rose from many groups against "undesirables" who, it was claimed,
not only occupied much-needed beds but also lowered the social
level of hospitals, making them objectionable to anyone who did
not share the uncouth ways of the very poor. In 1863, for example,
the Massachusetts Commission investigating lunacy reported,

The wealthy can seclude their afflicted relatives, amid the luxuries of
a private asylum, from all that can disgust their taste or shock their
better instincts. Must the great middling interest of Massachusetts,
the farmer, trader, and mechanic—must the larger class of the respect-
able and the deserving poor be deprived of the privileges they are
taxed to pay for and subjected to associations and influences which
necessity itself could hardly excuse, simply to gratify a sentiment of
morbid sympathy of a class of would-be philanthropists? [1]

The same year, the *American Journal of Insanity* published the following complaint from a Worcester State Hospital report:

It is not necessary to go abroad to find the connection between the
terms of admission and support, and the readiness with which people
avail themselves of hospital privileges for the care and custody of their

friends. We have proof of this in our own daily experience. Our Irish patients go free and stay without cost, and they are sent early and have the best opportunities of restoration. The Americans go at their own cost, and pay all and more than all of the expense of their support, and consequently a large proportion are kept away, some for months and years, as long as their friends can endure or take care of them, and many for life, because their friends lack courage or money to take due advantage of the means of restoration so largely provided in the state. In 1859, 97.5% of all the foreign and only 58% of the native lunatics then living in the state had been sent to some hospitals.

If from the beginning, our public hospitals had, by favoring legislation, been made as accessible and available, and offered on as easy terms, to the American as to the Irish insane, and if the popular sentiment and general custom had induced the native families to send their lunatics to these institutions in as large proportion as the foreign families send theirs, then these 731, or that proportion of the people annually attacked, would have left but a small number to be permanently deranged, and Massachusetts would not have the great insane population which, in 1854, was 2436, and probably is not less now.[2]

The largest class of unwelcome state-paupers flooding institutions were immigrants. Nearly 80,000 newcomers a year arrived in the United States between 1839 and 1844, increasing the population at an abnormal rate, and further straining already inadequate facilities. Most of the new cases of pauper insane were Irish and German peasants. Weakened by the transatlantic journey and by city slums, they were unusually prone to febrile diseases, birth defects, nutritional deficiencies, and alcoholism.[3] As they flooded the state hospitals, displacing native patients, they created problems even more acute than overcrowding, for, unwittingly, moral treatment had become tied to a particular culture.

Moral treatment had been created to serve an elite group of patients, well-mannered, clean, self-supporting Protestant artisans and farmers who shared their superintendent's adherence to the gospel of work and to the value of worship and education. Now, however, it was treating persons who did not fit these cultural patterns. The bewilderment of superintendents trying to cope with illiterate, poverty-stricken patients was summed up by Isaac Ray in 1863:

In endeavoring to restore the disordered mind of the clodhopper, who has scarcely an idea beyond that of his manual employment, the great difficulty is to find some available point from which conservative influences may be projected. He dislikes reading, he never learned amusements, he feels no interest in the affairs of the world, and unless the circumstances allow of some kind of bodily labor, his mind must remain in a state of solitary isolation, brooding over its morbid fancies, and utterly incompetent to initiate any recuperative movement.[4]

Alienists had suspected that their system was not universally applicable, and they wondered, in particular, whether moral treatment was suitable for immigrants. In 1850, Mark Ranney, the resident physician at New York City Lunatic Asylum, Blackwell's Island, presented a paper to the Association, "On Insane Foreigners," a topic that had been assigned by the group and was hence felt to be of immediate importance. This was a subject, moreover, on which Ranney was well qualified to speak, because in the year ending 1849 he had received 1,229 foreigners, twice the number of native-born admissions. Ranney presented a sympathetic picture of the overwhelming burden of "moral and physical causes" that had led to the insanity of so many immigrants; and he noted the particular benefits of moral treatment on these patients:

Insane foreigners are more susceptible to the influence of kind treatment than any other class. Previous to their admission they feel they are friendless, and from having associated with those who have refused to assist, or aided in robbing them, draw the conclusion that everyone is an enemy, and even after being admitted to any asylum, look with suspicion at first upon the kind efforts made for their welfare. But if these efforts be persisted in, their complete confidence will be gained, and the great change from a hopeless and forlorn condition gives an influence of the strongest character.[5]

Most institutions, however, were far less optimistic or sympathetic. Immigrant insane were thought to have unusually maniacal symptoms that disrupted wards. Furthermore, they were thought to endanger the social organization of asylums in which group activities had been central, because it was feared that uncouth foreigners would corrupt "civilized" patients.

The influx of immigrant paupers was bewailed by many institutions. The annual reports of Worcester State Hospital in Massachusetts, for instance, contain a series of petitions to be relieved of this unwelcome burden, and their tone became progressively more racist. The 1853 Report, for instance, states:

A very large and still increasing proportion of the admissions is of foreigners. . . . Unless something is done to avert it, the benefits of this institution will soon be denied to our native population, except to such as may be paupers or criminals. It is fast filling up with a class of incurable foreign paupers, which circumstance is already seriously impairing its usefulness as a curative institution.[6]

The following year came a yet more pointed statement:

The Hospital at Worcester is fast becoming a hospital for foreigners and its doors are becoming practically closed against that class of persons who for many years enjoyed its advantages . . . the intelligent yeomanry of Massachusetts, who can afford to pay the cost of their board, and will not ask for charity. . . . [In health, native patients] would have shrunk most sensitively from living next door to a wretched hovel, and from intimate association with those who are accustomed to and satisfied with filthy habitations and filthier habits.[7]

Practitioners were revolted by the "filthy habits" of immigrants, especially the Irish, by their refusal to work, and by their apparently lower levels of intelligence and susceptibility to cure. Superintendents even wondered whether the Irish were more prone to disorder than other "races." Physicians from the Northeast tended to think so, but those, like Kirkbride and Butler, who came from parts of the country where mental hospitals had not been similarly flooded, were more optimistic.[8]

The difficulty of treating foreigners was the result partly of ethnic prejudice and partly of an inability to communicate with patients who spoke other languages and had other customs. Some superintendents, such as Luther V. Bell, found that using attendants of the same nationality as patients was helpful and suggested that separate institutions be erected for the care of foreign groups.[9] This, however, was widely denounced. In 1848, for instance, a committee reviewing the conditions of insanity in the Commonwealth of Massachusetts wrote that to separate immigrant and native patients

would tend to an invidious distinction; a distinction not reconcilable with the humane and tolerant spirit of our country and age; and not in accordance with that lofty design of our institutions, to make all who occupy American soil American citizens.[10]

Nevertheless, alienists, concerned about their institutions and the comfort of their native-born patients, circumvented this prohibition. In his 1859 Annual Report, Merrick Bemis, superintendent of Worcester State Hospital, issued an ingenious prescription for dealing with immigrant patients with bad habits: create "separate but equal facilities."

During the last year, a complete separation has been maintained between the foreign and native patients, much to their mutual satisfaction and benefit. The foreign patients have the same comforts and accommodations, the same grade of attendants, and receive the same care and attention that native patients do. But looking at the welfare of the patients, there seemed to be good and sufficient reasons for a separation. When in health they separate themselves. They do not occupy the same house or live in the same neighborhood, except in widely different capacities. They have but few feelings in common with each other. Opposite in religion and all the notions of social life, it would not be well to class the two races in the same worlds, where each must bear from the other what was considered troublesome and offensive while in health.

But while an effort has constantly been made to keep up a style of life in the hospital which should not so widely differ from that to which our patients have been accustomed in their homes as to disturb their natural feelings or offend their tastes, the result has been greatly to elevate the condition of the foreign patients while in the hospital, so that the separation has not been brought about by any considerations of economy, such as plainer and cheaper accommodations, or a smaller allowance for the daily sustenance and care of the poor, insane immigrant.[11]

Nevertheless, the quality of care, and particularly the relationship of staff to patients, did in fact decline, creating the deprivations and neglect we now associate with custodial care. Not only did foreigners disrupt hospital management, but they were so generally despised that their presence hindered the efforts of alienists to improve public attitudes toward the insane and to encourage philanthropic support of institutions.

Meanwhile, the public cried out against the influx of pauper immigrants. The *Boston Medical and Surgical Journal,* for instance, wrote in 1851,

This is only the beginning of trouble . . . for the new hospital that is to be reared will soon be in their possession also. Never was a sovereign state so grievously burdened. The people bear the growing evil without a murmur, and it is therefore taken for granted that taxation for the support of the cast-off humanity of Europe is an agreeable exercise of their charity.[12]

The toll of welfare costs, particularly at a time when the Eastern states were losing productive citizens to western migration, led to attempts to limit the immigration of sick persons and to return those who became public charges to their native country. In 1848, for example, Massachusetts appointed superintendents of alien travellers to inspect incoming boats for lunatics, idiots, the maimed, aged, and infirm. Such persons were denied entry unless bond were posted to ensure that they would not become public charges.[13]

NOTES

1. *The American Journal of Insanity*, XXI (1864–1865), 48.

2. *The American Journal of Insanity*, XX (1863–1864), 480–481.

3. *The American Journal of Insanity*, VII (1850–1851), 45.

4. Isaac Ray, *Mental Hygiene* (Boston: Ticknor and Fields, 1863), p. 149.

5. *The American Journal of Insanity*, VII (1850–1851), 45.

6. *The American Journal of Insanity*, XI (1854–1855), 193.

7. Milton Greenblatt, "Beyond the Therapeutic Community," Israel Strauss Lecture, Hillside Hospital, Glen Oaks, New York, April 29, 1962, pp. 2–3.

8. *The American Journal of Insanity*, XIV (1857–1858), 102–103.

9. Gerald N. Grob, *The State and the Mentally Ill* (Chapel Hill, N.C.: University of North Carolina Press, 1965), p. 145.

10. *Ibid.*, p. 151.

11. *The American Journal of Insanity*, XVI (1859–1860), 106.

12. Grob, *op. cit.*, p. 138.

13. *Ibid.*, p. 175.

Chapter 9

FINANCIAL DIFFICULTIES

OF ASYLUMS

The earliest American institutions for the insane had been erected and maintained by private philanthropy. By the 1830's, however, it was evident that continuing and enlarging the asylum system was impossible without governmental support. As Samuel B. Woodward wrote in the early days of Worcester State Hospital,

The day has gone . . . when individual munificence will establish institutions for the insane to any considerable extent; it will aid and foster them, but the states must establish and sustain them. They are no longer subjects of private enterprise, but will be built and supported by the public purse. Almost every state in the union is moving in this matter.[1]

At the height of the moral treatment era, state governments were enthusiastic supporters of mental hospitals, in part because such institutions provided an outlet for religious feelings. This may be seen from the following speech by the governor of Iowa, delivered at the State Asylum for the Insane:

One important method of displaying a just regard for the principles of Christianity is to give due attention to the benevolent institutions of the day. The hand of charity should be extended to all the varieties of human want; multiplying its forms of action in proportion to the forms of suffering; in the erection of hospitals, lunatic, and deaf and dumb asylums; in establishing dispensaries and poor-houses; in opening receptacles for the reformation and punishment of the vicious and wicked; founding institutions for learning of a high order, with charity scholarships, and perfecting our common school system.[2]

Similarly, in 1839, the Unitarian *Christian Examiner* of Massachusetts took a position on the expensive question of the future fate of the overcrowded Worcester State Hospital.

These public Charities should rather we think, be termed public duties. They are, rightly considered, the fulfilling of obligations; not the mere indulgence of benevolent sympathies. We like the doctrine that the state is the parent of the people. It is a genuine part of republicanism . . . that the people, so that the poorest brother of them all shall not want, for the reason that he *is* a brother, an equal, a man, the rest will take care of him. If this is so, and so we believe it to be, then this Worcester Asylum is but an expression of the care which the people feel it to be their duty to take of their suffering members; and while any are still suffering for the want of the necessary care, which they are so abundantly able to impart, they must feel that their duty is not done. This is our feeling as one of the people. And we say: let the Hospital be enlarged to the requisite dimensions, or, if that be better, let another be erected at the other extremity of the state, at Pittsfield or Williamstown. The question of money, in such a case, is surely not to be considered.[3]

Increasingly, however, the question of money was very carefully considered, and public asylums began to complain of inadequate funds. In part, straitened means were caused by a steady rise in the costs of hospital construction and maintenance, while the visible benefits to the public from mental hospitals appeared to decline. In spite of expensive buildings and professional promises, for example, hospitals actually treated only a fraction of the insane. John P. Gray, the second superintendent of Utica State Hospital and editor of the *American Journal of Insanity*, estimated that, in 1840, 2,000 patients were under treatment, whereas, in 1860, with a population of more than 27 million, only 8,500 cases were being treated in 50 overcrowded asylums throughout the country.[4] Alienists appeared powerless to eliminate the growing backlog of chronicity in their wards; nor did their efforts stem the apparently ever-rising tide of insanity.

Meanwhile, the public became suspicious of high rates of hospital construction, because it felt that this enabled staff to live in luxury at community expense in "hospital palaces."[5] There were complaints about the rising cost of maintaining the insane. The Massachusetts Welfare expenses, for example, totaled $60,000 in 1832, when Worcester State Hospital was opened; by 1854 they exceeded $300,000. This issue became more sensitive as institutions became the haven of the pariahs of frontier America, vagrants, criminals, alcoholics, but particularly immigrant paupers.

The crowding of immigrants into asylums drove out Yankee, middle-class, fee-paying patients. This created grave economic difficulties because the fees of state-paupers were fixed by law and failed to keep pace with inflation. Thus, many asylums lost money and were forced to raise the rates of any remaining wealthier patients in order to compensate. However, as courts sent more cases than asylums could house, superintendents were forced to discharge these self-supporting patients prematurely in order to make room for others. Annual reports were consequently filled with notes begging legislatures to raise per capita rates, such as the following from Worcester State Hospital:

The law requires the hospitals to receive, support and treat these alien paupers, but limits the payment from the state treasury to $2.62 per week, which is less than the actual cost. The hospitals have no property of their own, no income, nor resources except the payments made for the board and care of patients. They have no other alternative but to charge upon the other patients the deficiency in the payments of the state paupers, or the excess of the cost of supporting and treating these over the allowance made by the law.[6]

A series of articles appeared in the *American Journal of Insanity* on such subjects as the "Comparative Cost of Support of the Insane and the Sane." The author of the latter recalled the appeal of Worcester State Hospital to the Massachusetts legislature to raise the rates from $2.75 a week to $3.77 and noted that the price of the cheapest boardinghouses was $3.87 a week, or about 40 per cent more than the state was allocating for the insane. The insane, the article continued, required unusual care that cost more than the living expenses of the healthy; they needed special housing, much supervision, and a rich diet to compensate for overactivity and depletion of vital forces. In obedience to a request of the legislature in 1863, the superintendent of Worcester had attempted to give pauper patients a poorer diet; but the experiment was abandoned after several months because it produced greater irritability and a slower rate of recovery.[7]

These arguments produced scanty results, however, because dependent classes were resented as parasites on society to whom only grudging charity was due. Unwilling or unable to live by the Protestant ethic of work and productivity, they carried the signs of divine displeasure both in their worldly failures and in their infirmities.

Alienists at first tried to unlink such prejudice from the mentally disturbed. In an article, "Mental and Physical Characteristics of Pauperism," it was suggested that there were two classes of dependent poor. The first class was "that which may be considered unavoidable," included the "deserving poor," victims of "idiocy, lunacy, blindness, lameness, sickness, decrepitude, deaf-mutism, and old age." In their case,

society does not question the obligation it owes to its citizens thus unfortunately circumstanced. They are afflicted by a providence beyond their control: in many instances possessing the intellectual and moral strength essential to independence, they are debarred from this by reason of their infirmities.[8]

These unfortunates, the article continues, are never to be confused with a second class, "destitute of the desire for self-support or independence" and marked by

Indifference to self and to physical comfort: desire for self-support is wanting: there is a lack of capacity for self-preservation, which is evinced in the low grade of vitality that exists, and in the circumstance that this class suffer largely during the prevalence of epidemics, from their inability to resist disease. The persons composing this class are unable to govern themselves, or direct their energies. They feel entirely indifferent to society, and seek to hold no relation to it, other than dependence upon it. . . . They possess but one quality in common with their more fortunate fellow citizens, in that their appetite is as strong, their digestion as good, their muscles as vigorous, and their love of life as dear.[9]

Appropriations to asylums, however, remained low; and, particularly after the 1840's, requests for new building, upkeep, and salaries were given little attention. This was in part the result of a belated lesson of thrift learned by legislators after a number of states went bankrupt during the late 1830's and early 1840's. A highly inflated economy had collapsed after massive public works, such as vastly overambitious canal and railroad networks, had been constructed on overextended credit. When suspicious foreign banks began to foreclose, a panic developed; the entire structure, built on worthless paper money, disintegrated.

Inadequate funding created grave hardships for mental hospitals. In 1859, for example, the year following one of the financial panics characteristic of the era, the New Hampshire legislature "forgot" to appropriate funds for the New Hampshire Asylum for the Insane. All the state-supported patients were removed to the poorhouse until the oversight was remedied.[10]

Other state hospitals had similar difficulties. Kentucky Western Asylum, for example, had been constructed at a cost of $200,000. It burned down in December, 1859, a few months after the following report had been issued by the superintendent, Francis G. Montgomery,

The roof of the whole building will, before the next meeting of the Legislature, after the coming one, need repair badly; and, should a shingle roof be used like the present, there should be some plan of spark-arresters used in the chimneys, as there have already been a number of holes burned in the shingles by sparks. The risk is great, and with no provision for extinguishing fires, there would be no chance of saving the building, should a conflagration take place; and in such an institution it would be a dreadful calamity.[11]

In even more acute need were Southern hospitals after the Civil War. In the 1873 Report of the Lunatic Asylum of the State of South Carolina, the Superintendent, J. F. Enson, wrote,

For many years past the inadequate provision made for the support of the institution has been a source of the most awkward and disagreeable embarrassment to those charged with its management. For the past four years, at least, the institution has been run entirely upon credit.

Since I have been in charge, we have never had a dollar to pay the cash for anything. Even postage stamps have had to be bought on time. No one can, or ever will know the embarrassments to which I have been subjected since the beginning of my administration here. As the disbursing officer of the institution, I have not only not been able to pay the liabilities of the institution as they fall due, but as an individual, I have not been able to pay my personal liabilities, from the fact that all my efforts, all my means, all my credit, and that of my friends, have been absorbed in maintaining the institution.

No amount of money would induce me to endure for another year the embarrassment, mortification and mental anxiety which I have endured for the past three years on account of this institution.[12]

Enson noted further that he was now unable to supply fuel and food to maintain his 309 patients. Shortages were aggravated both by small appropriations and by a peculiarity of his state, that money was supplied the year *after* it had been voted, not immediately, as in other places.

As legislators were apt to be forgetful, capricious, or even powerless to help asylums, a search was made for other sources of income, preferably guaranteed and extending over several years, so that alienists would not be burdened by the suspense of annual legislative debates over their budgets. In his 1864 report, the superintendent of the Insane Asylum of California, William P. Tilden, suggested, for example, that the state establish a fund for the care of the insane instead of making annual appropriations. Tilden's interest in this matter was profound, because the state of California was considering lowering the salaries of the superintendent and his assistant physicians.[13]

A more ambitious plan for subsidizing the care of the insane was that of Dorothea Dix, who, during the era of land grants of education, urged the Federal Government to reserve 12,225,000 acres of wilderness land for the support of the insane. After years of struggle, the bill passed both Houses of Congress but was vetoed by President Franklin Pierce on the following grounds:

If Congress have power . . . to make provision for the indigent insane, *without the limits of this district* [of Columbia], it has the same power to provide for the indigent who are not insane, and thus to transfer to the Federal Government the charge of *all the poor in all the states.*[14]

This was a most ironic comment in view of present-day simultaneous Federal legislation on both mental health and the War on Poverty. Other nineteenth-century reactions to Dorothea Dix's scheme were equally noteworthy. A number of general medical groups initially opposed the plan because they interpreted it as a call for one "mammoth hospital" into which the states might send their incurable insane, an extrapolation from contemporary developments within the states, which were recognized to have serious drawbacks.

Asylums that depended on public support resorted to a number of stratagems in order to attract funds. Some of these became traditional but bore seeds of trouble. One favorite argument sought to prove that large expenditures for the care and cure of the insane were in fact saving public money, because the state would be spared the burden of perpetual support of chronic debility. This argument was specious, of course, because outlays to support the insane would continue indefinitely and thus be far more costly than inadequate care. One of the most intriguing of such claims appeared in the 1863 report of the Worcester State Hospital, in which there was the following review of records since 1832:

The hospital has received into its wards, and taken care of 6663 insane persons. Of these, it has given 3131 back to their homes and the world, to usefulness and the common enjoyments of their families, society, and to the usual responsibilities of citizenship.

Of the 3532 who were not restored to health, 1200 have been improved, their violence has been subdued, their excitability calmed, their pains assuaged, and their delusions controlled in such a measure that they could live at their homes, be comfortable in their families and neighborhoods, and partake of some, or even many of the blessings of society. . . .

According to the life tables, these 3131 men and women lived or will live an aggregate of 84,886 years after they regain their health, and 82,090 of these were working and self-sustaining years, before they arrived at the period of dependence in old age, making, however, some deductions for those that could have recovered by other means if the hospital had not existed, and also for the periodical cases whose years of health were cut off by every succeeding attack, yet both these deductions will not very materially diminish the total sum of 84,886 years of usefulness and enjoyment and the 82,090 years of labor and self-sustenance, that have been given back to these patients, and through them to society and to the Commonwealth by the labors and influence of the hospital.[15]

The report continues by noting that according to the life tables of Le Cappelain of London, in which he calculated the length of life of those who become permanently insane at various ages, it was proved that the hospital had given the state 50 per cent more "labor and aid" than it would have had if these individuals had not been cured, and, thus, it had greatly reduced potential expense to the community.

Alienists became obsessed by their financial worries and the administrative burdens they entailed; and the style of their treatment came to mirror this stress. Superintendents, for instance, strove desperately to reduce their expenditures, and those who succeeded were lauded by their colleagues. The *Journal*, for example, praised Charles E. Van Arden, superintendent of the Asylum for Criminal Insane in Auburn, New York, for reducing his operating costs in spite of rising prices; in 1864, patient costs were reduced to $2.89 a week, a saving of 21 cents over the previous year, producing an overall saving of approximately $600.[16] Leaders of the Association of Medical Superintendents also began to criticize apparently extravagant ideas of their colleagues. The same Van Arden was thus advised to abandon his suggestion that, because his asylum was overcrowded, it might be wiser to decentralize the system of detaining the criminally insane, placing them instead in small, local establishments.

The relative disadvantages of state and local control were summarized by the editor of the *Journal* as follows,

On the one hand, where the state assumes in theory the entire charge of the pauper insane, the institutions as they become crowded with incurables lose their hold upon the popular interest, and easily fall under the control of political jobbers and placement. On the other, when the matter is left nearly discretionary with local boards in counties and towns, the burden of support falls too directly upon the latter, and a narrow and parsimonious policy is the result. Perhaps the system most generally adopted, a middle one between that of entire state support and wholly local charge, is attended with the fewest evils in its operation.[17]

To some extent corporate, or semiprivate, hospitals filled such an intermediate category. They were spared many of these financial agonies, because they received self-supporting as well as state cases, and they were governed by private boards. They received most of their money from public subscriptions and from bequests. In 1865, for example, the Pennsylvania Hospital for the Insane raised over $300,000 by subscription to erect a building for 250 male patients.[18] McLean Asylum for the Insane, the psychiatric branch of the Massachusetts General Hospital, similarly raised $45,000 for a new cottage in four weeks in the middle of the Civil War.[19] The same institution reported $100,000 in donations for the previous year.[20] As McLean began to receive a larger number of wealthy patients, after many pauper cases were rerouted to Worcester State Hospital and other public establishments, its facilities were made more luxurious: "Carpets, wall paper, mirrors, mantels and better furniture were introduced." [21] In 1853, two cottages were opened, each accommodating eight persons "and providing a suite of sitting room, bedroom, and bath for each." [22] And in 1863, the superintendent, Tyler, reported,

The completion of the edifice, for the accommodation of the most demonstrative forms of mental disorder, marks an era in the history not only of this institution, but also of asylum construction and architecture. The means afforded for its erection were ample; the time and careful attention given to all the details of its arrangements, were without stint, and the result in the present admirable structure is more than satisfactory. Spacious and cheerful apartments, commodiously furnished, free admission of sunlight, thorough ventilation and comfortable temperature, architectural beauty within, and pleasant surroundings without, access at will to the grounds, all are attained in consistency with the entire safety of the occupants.[23]

Even private munificence, however, had limits. By the mid-century, fortunes were made by people preoccupied with personal magnificence and display. Unlike the thrifty old Puritan families with their sense of "stewardship," the new rich felt no similar obligation to use their property to help the unfortunate. In 1868, therefore, the superintendent of the Butler Hospital for the Insane wrote in his annual report,

The great majority of rich men die without devising a dollar to any public purpose. Educated perhaps, at the public expense, protected and prospered in their enterprises by the enlightenment that springs from free institutions, and experiencing, at every moment, in some way or another, the benefit of those noble endowments made by benevolent men of past times, they never think of repaying the slightest moiety of their indebtedness, by turning a portion of their superfluous wealth into the stream of public benefice.[24]

The financial difficulties of asylums strained relationships between doctors and patients and between practitioners and community. In the former case, superintendents were obliged to subordinate therapeutics to administration, to spend a large amount of time on hospital accounts, on plotting economies, and in lobbying for more funds. The liberality of earlier, smaller, well-endowed institutions was necessarily curtailed. In the community, meanwhile, alienists and laymen had contact more and more on money matters rather than on other issues. The legislator was the source of public monies, the private citizen of donations and bequests. This inevitably affected relations between the hospital and the extramural world, in which professionals were suppliants for their own salaries, as well as for hospital funds. Their writings show discomfort and awkwardness with this role.

NOTES

1. Gerald N. Grob, *The State and the Mentally Ill* (Chapel Hill, N.C.: University of North Carolina Press, 1965), pp. 117-118.

2. *The American Journal of Insanity*, XIV (1857-1858), 308.

3. Grob, *op. cit.*, p. 101.

4. *The American Journal of Insanity*, XVIII (1861-1862), 1-2.

5. F.B. Sanborn (ed.), *Memoirs of Pliny Earle, M.D.* (Boston: Damrell and Upham, 1898), p. xii.

6. *The American Journal of Insanity*, XX (1863-1864), 480.

7. *The American Journal of Insanity*, XXII (1865-1866), 257.

8. *The American Journal of Insanity*, XIII (1856-1857), 310.

9. *Ibid.*, p. 311.

10. *The American Journal of Insanity*, XVI (1859-1860), 100.

11. *The American Journal of Insanity*, XVII (1860-1861), 305.

12. *The American Journal of Insanity*, XXXI (1874-1875), 104-105.

13. *The American Journal of Insanity*, XXI (1864-1865), 436-437.

14. Albert Deutsch, *The Mentally Ill in America* (New York: Columbia University Press, 1945), p. 177.

15. *The American Journal of Insanity*, XX (1863-1864), 478-479.

16. *The American Journal of Insanity*, XXI (1864-1865), 252.

17. *The American Journal of Insanity*, XVI (1859-1860), 238.

18. *The American Journal of Insanity*, XX (1863-1864), 454.

19. Henry M. Hurd (ed.), *The Institutional Care of the Insane in the United States and Canada* (Baltimore: Johns Hopkins Press, 1916), Vol. II, p. 604.

20. *The American Journal of Insanity*, XVI (1859-1860), 108.

21. Hurd, *op. cit.*, p. 604.

22. *Ibid.*

23. *The American Journal of Insanity*, XX (1863-1864), 483.

24. *The American Journal of Insanity*, XXIV (1867-1868), 434.

Chapter 10

THE CURABILITY MYTH
AND ITS AFTERMATH

A major weakness of moral treatment was that it had been oversold to the public; whatever success it had was ultimately overshadowed by disappointment in its failure to perform miracles. Overenthusiastic promotion was in part an error of youth, because, of the thirteen founding members of the Association, seven were under the age of thirty-five, and only three were over forty in 1844, and most had had little formal preparation or previous clinical experience to curb their idealism.

Inflated propaganda was also the mode of early nineteenth-century America. It was used successfully by purveyors of quack nostrums and water cures, promoters of wilderness land, and others touting miracle drugs and dubious get-rich-quick schemes. Many farsighted alienists realized the dangers to the public and to the profession of similar styles of propaganda in favor of mental hospitals. Brigham, for example, criticized hyperbole in annual reports of asylums as follows:

We are of the opinion that some of them are too laudatory of the institutions they describe, of their conveniences, improvements and advantages. There is too much *coleur de rose*, and we fear the impression they make upon some minds is something akin to that made by the puffs of mineral springs and Water Cure establishments; as if the various Lunatic Asylums were rival institutions endeavoring to attract customers. They are sometimes too glowingly described as places of great and general happiness and enjoyment, where every taste can be gratified and every want supplied. Some we fear mislead the public, especially as to the number of cures, not however by actual misstatements, but by annual percentages of recoveries deduced from a small number of cures and these the most favorable and recent.

We say these things to guard against the extension of an impression that has already become too general, that nearly all the insane can be cured at Lunatic Asylums, and that such institutions are places where such persons are quite sure to be happy and to enjoy much.[1]

Nevertheless, he later acknowledged that without such claims on public credulity "several of the best establishments for the insane in the country" would not have been built.[2]

Extravagant claims were also made by lay reformers, friends of the insane who sought to counteract the inertia of frugal legislatures and the resistance of a prejudiced public. They therefore stated their cause in the manner of all agitators, by overstatements, by showing contrasts and ignoring shading. As was said of Dorothea Dix,

Her method of agitation, as was intended, produced a state of excited, almost violent, opposition against long existing conditions which most citizens, however kindly disposed, regarded as irremediable, though they knew them to be wrong.[3]

Furthermore, among the well-intentioned promoters of mental hospitals, there was enough unscrupulous manipulation of statistics and enough self-serving claims made by certain alienists ambitious for personal aggrandizement, for the eventual wave of public disillusionment to be both bitter and destructive.

Great claims were made for the comfort of asylums and the pleasantness of treatment, but the most dangerous and exciting were those made for the so-called curability myth, the belief that recent cases of insanity were unusually susceptible to rapid cure, provided that early and appropriate treatment was found. This was not only an article of faith for most early practitioners, but it roused public support and enthusiasm. A greater number of patients were brought to asylums instead of being imprisoned by humiliated relatives or by local legal and charitable agencies. And public munificence was stimulated by the winsome appeals of alienists, arguing that comparatively heavy expenditures for appropriate institutions were more economical in the long run than perpetual custody of incurable patients in local poorhouses, however low the rates of the latter might be. The curability myth also molded the psychiatric profession, for it attracted active, idealistic men, confident of their eventual mastery of insanity. Their personalities and programs hence differed significantly from those of later practitioners who would be recruited to a more hopeless and static profession.

The public was made aware of "curability" in the 1820's by the writings of Captain Basil Hall, an English tourist. Like many other nineteenth-century European visitors, Hall published highly uncomplimentary impressions of frontier America, and gravely insulted his former hosts. He had found, however, one institution to praise, the Hartford Retreat, which he had visited in 1827, and of which he wrote,

Dr. Todd, the eminent and kind physician of the Retreat, showed us over every part of this noble establishment,—a model, I venture to say, from which any country might take instruction. During the last year there have been admitted here 23 recent cases, of which 21 recovered, equivalent to 91.3 per cent. The whole number of recent cases during the year was 28, of which 25 have recovered, equal to 89.2 per cent.[4]

Whether as a contrast to the scathing criticism of the rest of his book, or whether as tribute to the feat of curing the insane, public enthusiasm was aroused by Hall's comment. Pliny Earle, Superintendent of Northampton, Massachusetts, in his exposé of the fallacies of the myth of curability published half a century later, wrote,

Thus recognized and indorsed . . . the report of the Hartford visiting physicians, otherwise comparatively unknown, was sent by the newspapers through the length and breadth of the land; and the people received their first impression that insanity is largely curable. By a few strokes of his magic pen Captain Hall did what, were it not for him, would have required the labor of years.[5]

In subsequent years, asylums put forth extravagant records of cures. Seventy, 80, 90 per cent success was claimed. John Galt, of the Williamsburg Asylum in Virginia, at twenty-two the youngest member of the Association of Medical Superintendents, announced in 1842 that he had cured 100 per cent of recent cases. He claimed to believe "there is no insane institution, either in Europe or America, in which such success is met with as in our own." [6]

Such high figures were obtained in a number of tendentious ways later exposed by more sober members of the profession. High rates of cure were possible in early asylums that had the power to select their own cases. They could thus avoid epileptics, mentally retarded, and other illness categories felt to be incurable, which would spoil their records of success, and hence their reputations with the public. Many asylums discharged "incurable" cases to other institutions, such as poorhouses; thus, by definition, all their patients were cured.

The new science of statistics was little understood and hence easily misused. Alienists treated only a small number of cases, so that percentages sounded unduly impressive. Galt, for example, claimed 100 per cent success for thirteen patients.[7] The percentage of cures was often computed from the number *discharged* from the institution, not from the number *admitted*. There was also a practice, relied on by Galt and many others, of including the number of deaths as part of the figures for recovery, which, as Pliny Earle archly remarked years later, "mathematically demonstrated the curability of *all* the insane." [8]

Another method for obtaining high figures of success was the practice of counting "cases" not persons. Thus the same individual might have multiple commitments and discharges, and each time he would appear as another case and another cure. The latter practice, coupled with uncertainty about criteria of recovery, contributed to apparently impressive success with alcoholics, who were discharged as cured each time their symptoms of delirium tremens abated.

The most flagrant loophole in high figures of success was the division of cases into "recent" and "chronic" categories. Because it was thought that insanity was easily curable only within the first year, it could be claimed that an unusually stubborn case was really chronic, and that relatives, insensitive to the subtler signs that had marked the actual onset of illness, had inadvertently misled doctors about the duration of pathology. It was also possible to hedge, as Luther V. Bell of McLean Asylum for the Insane in Massachusetts did in his report for 1840:

Our records justify the declaration that *all cases, certainly recent,*— that is, whose origin does not, either directly or obscurely, run back more than a year,—recover under a fair trial. This is the general law. The occasional instances to the contrary are the exceptions.[9]

Craftier men juggled figures; and Isaac Ray, then superintendent of the Main Hospital in Augusta, wrote in 1842, "Nothing can be made more deceptive than statistics, and I have yet to learn that those of insanity form any exception." [10]

Many of those who would later denounce the excessive credulity of earlier years, such as Pliny Earle, were, in their youth, devout believers themselves. Earle, in his first report from Bloomingdale Asylum, in 1844, had predicted 80 per cent of those treated, "in which there is no eccentricity or constitutional weakness of intellect," [11] would be cured.

The curability myth, and, by association, much of moral treatment was really discredited in the 1870's when Pliny Earle's book on the subject appeared. By then, disillusioned laymen referred to its earlier adherents as "deluded and deluding alienists," whose claims had been the outcome of "a mistaken opinion which flattered professional pride." [12] Doubts, however, had been felt much earlier. Clinical experience was demonstrating that earlier hopes had been vain, particularly when such uncontrollable conditions as general paresis and nutritional deficiencies began to flood asylums in the 1840's.

During the 1850's and 1860's, as wards became overcrowded with chronic patients, and as more and more discharged cases relapsed, alienists began to worry about the welfare of their patients, about their own reputation among laymen, and about their liability to legal sanctions should former patients cause damage in the community. The dangers of premature discharge were stressed by such leading writers as Isaac Ray, who attempted to change the expectations of the public and the procedures of professionals. To the former he wrote in 1863,

Comparatively few are aware that insanity is very variable, and, at best, not very short in its duration. People are apt to imagine that it runs its course as rapidly as a fever; or, at any rate, that the magical influences of a hospital will cut it short. They expect that amendment will soon follow, and become impatient if it is long delayed. The fact is, that weeks, months, and oftentimes years, may elapse, without recovery or even improvements.[13]

To his colleagues, assembled for an annual meeting of the Association, Ray addressed a cautionary paper, "Doubtful Recoveries." He first noted the well-known and much-bemoaned fact that psychological medicine was sadly deficient in those attributes which gave solidity and certainty to general medicine, such as recognized symptomatologies, nosologies that allowed prognostication, and definite criteria of cure.

He therefore advised a protracted period of convalescence, because, he said, it is easier to cure than to know when to discharge a patient. The former can be learned, but for the latter,

We must depend solely on our own resources, and if these consist of only a little knowledge of routine, we shall seldom avoid mistake, except by accident. . . .

A beginner in our specialty hails every improvement as the commencement of convalescence, and is apt to regard the appearance of a few healthy traits of character as the unquestionable presage of recovery. It is not until a later period that he becomes acquainted with that peculiar oscillation which marks the movements of mental disease, and fully comprehends the fact that serious disorder may exist in connection with many sound, healthy manifestations of character.[14]

Evidence of recovery was thus a subjective judgment of the practitioner, who must know the history of his patient's character sufficiently well to realize when ideas and actions were returning to an idiosyncratic level of normality. The physician must also wait for the patient to realize and admit the fact of his former insanity.

Ray even found it necessary to caution fellow professionals against nearly forty years of propaganda that had held that insanity was a transitory disease.

I do not say it is never very transitory, for there are cases enough on record to put this fact beyond a doubt, but with this unfrequent exception, its duration is marked rather by weeks and months, than by hours or days. . . .

I take the opportunity to remark, in passing, that if these views are correct we are forced to believe that too many are discharged from our hospitals as recovered, within three months of their admission. While admitting that recovery may not unfrequently be completed in that period, I apprehend that this large class of cases which, in our hospital reports are placed in the front ranks of successful results, must embrace many that relapse so soon after their discharge as to render it quite certain that their recovery was never complete.[15]

Ray blamed premature discharges not only on lapses in professional judgment, but also on the blandishments of laymen, relatives, and government officials, who demanded the release of apparently cured individuals from costly institutions. He advised colleagues to distrust and parry lay incursion into asylums. There was thus a development among reputable alienists away from short-term institutionalization and rapid return of individuals to their community toward longer confinement, even in apparently rapid recoveries. As Ray wrote,

It becomes . . . a question worthy of our most serious consideration, whether this practice (early discharges) does not multiply the risks of

relapse, and even when not followed by actual relapse, lays the foundation of a morbid irritability which, sooner or later, is converted into
overt disease. There is much reason to believe that the frequency of
secondary attacks, greater in this country, I apprehend, than in any
other, may be attributed, in a great degree, to the shortness of the
probationary period which prevails among us. If this is so, the éclat of
a rapid cure is but a small compensation for the risk incurred by the
patient.[16]

Ray's paper was met with general enthusiasm among colleagues.
Edward Jarvis of Massachusetts noted also that many patients appeared quite recovered in hospital, where the burdens of life were
suspended, but were still not strong enough to tolerate ordinary
life.[17]

Perhaps surprisingly, there was little speculation at this time
about possible environmental causes for relapse in discharged patients and almost none about after-care. There was, however, an
article from Germany on "The Frequency of Relapse in Insanity:
Whence Does It Arise?" in the *American Journal of Insanity* of
1862, which noted that treatment is often nullified by the fact
that the patient will return to the setting that originally contributed to his illness,

Thus it happens that the restored lunatic is ever forced to encounter
more dangerous rocks after quitting his place of cure than any sailor
that faces the storm after repairing his shipwrecked craft in a quiet
haven.[18]

The public, disillusioned by unkept promises of rapid cure,
began to grumble about supporting an increasing number of insane
and about the poor showing of alienists. A memorandum of the
Boston Sanitary Association in 1861, for example, noted that the
state was "maintaining insanity" at a cost of $372,357 a year, a sum
that was supporting 1,361 patients in five public hospitals, and
1,271 lunatics in homes, poorhouses, and jails.

Seven hundred [a year] of our men and women, in the responsible and
self-sustaining age, are taken from the sphere of action and usefulness,
and cause so much loss of productive power, to their families and the
state, and so much addition to the public and private burden in their
support, and the extraordinary care and watchfulness needed for them.
This is a matter of terrible interest to the people and government, to see
whether . . . this burden upon the sympathies and the comforts of
home, upon private property and the general treasury, this mill-stone

hanging on the neck of the body politic may not be lessened, and a better inheritance of a more general health of mind, as well as of body transmitted to our children.[19]

The Sanitary Commission was calling for prevention; as increasingly did alienists; many of whom came to share the pessimism of Bell, who wrote in 1857, "I have come to the conclusion that, when once a man becomes insane, he is about used up for this world"; [20] or of Pliny Earle, who, on becoming superintendent of Northampton, wrote, "Of the 334 patients remaining in the hospital, not one in ten presents any reasonable probability of recovery." [21]

Suggestions for prevention now became global and visionary. They arose out of despair with treatment, and thus were evidence of growing distance between the public and the superintendents and between the community and the insane. Mental illness was increasingly seen as an ineradicable part of the personality of the sufferer. Hence preventive measures were directed less toward eliminating potential hazards, as had been the case in earlier years, than toward forestalling the appearance of diseased individuals. In 1859, for instance, the *American Journal of Insanity* published a review of a book by an Englishman, George Robinson, *On the Prevention and Treatment of Mental Disorders*, which summarized lay and professional concerns. The author held that insanity is less amenable to treatment than once thought, because even the cured are liable to relapse into chronicity, and because the rate of insanity is rising with civilization. The cost of supporting the insane would thus overwhelm the nation; and the task of erecting asylums for their care would be that of Sisyphus. The only hope, Robinson felt, lay in prevention.[22]

The American reviewer noted that although Robinson set forth the problem with unimpeachable clarity, his suggestions for controlling insanity were disappointing. He enumerated vague areas of possible exploration so vast that they surpassed the tools of the nineteenth century, including research into the causation of mental disorders, and into the physiology and pathology of the nervous system as well as the effects of narcotic and sedative drugs, the admonition of the public in healthy ways of living, and the treatment of insanity in its earliest stages.[23]

The American reviewer preferred the more concrete. He suggested the dissemination from the press, pulpit, and legislative chamber of warnings against hazards to mental health, such as the marriage of cousins, "demented and imbecile persons," "permanent paupers," deaf-mutes, and the congenitally blind, all of whom "are now made too much the subjects of show charities, appealing to a sickly sentimentality but little allied to a system of true philanthropy." [24]

Another practical preventive means to be attained, is the more general isolation and discipline of that large class of the vicious feeble-minded, regarding whom there is a question as to their moral responsibility, and who, falling between law and the gospel, are neglected on every hand. The moral contagion of persons of this class in communities cannot be easily estimated. Confirmed drunkards, the madly passionate, the wantonly vicious, and other "morally insane" are among these; and here the necessity of linking together in one system our charitable and penal institutions, and of considering together crime and disease in their study and treatment, is most manifest.[25]

Thus, disillusionment with highly inflated claims of curability produced a double alienation. The public was questioning the wisdom and necessity of large expenditures on the insane, and professionals were questioning the efficacy of their role as therapists and mentors of their patients. The efficacy of moral treatment itself was being questioned by both, as was the professional competence and integrity of alienists.

The failure of the "myth of curability" illustrates the way in which vicious circles altered the theory and practice of nineteenth-century American psychiatry. The inability of practitioners to cure many of their patients, coupled with a relentless flow of new cases, filled hospitals to overflowing, thus disrupting the physical and social environment upon which the efficacy of moral treatment may have hinged. A lower rate of cures than anticipated helped to increase the overcrowding, which in turn lowered professional effectiveness, which in turn may have created a greater backlog of chronicity.

To this another factor in the evolution of American psychiatry must be added, the role of the layman in professional practice. This produced another vicious circle, because hopes of high cure and notice of atrocious conditions in jails and poorhouses led to greater public expectations from moral treatment and greater insistence that the insane be admitted to approved asylums. This aggravated overcrowding; and as the number of chronic and pauper cases in hospitals rose, public support waned, while pressures on asylums continued to mount.

NOTES

1. *The American Journal of Insanity*, V (1848–1849), 57–58.

2. *The American Journal of Insanity*, VI (1849–1850), 142–143.

3. Henry M. Hurd (ed.), *The Institutional Care of the Insane in the United States and Canada* (Baltimore: Johns Hopkins Press, 1916), Vol. I, p. 108.

4. F. B. Sanborn (ed.), *The Memoirs of Pliny Earle, M.D.* (Boston: Damrell and Upham, 1898), p. 271.

5. *Ibid.*
6. *Ibid.*
7. *Ibid.*
8. *Ibid.*
9. *Ibid.*
10. *Ibid.*, p. 272.
11. *Ibid.*
12. *Ibid.*, p. 267.

13. Isaac Ray, *Mental Hygiene* (Boston: Ticknor and Fields, 1863), p. 331.

14. *The American Journal of Insanity*, XX (1863–1864), 30.

15. *Ibid.*, pp. 34–36.
16. *Ibid.*, p. 37.
17. *Ibid.*, p. 111.

18. *The American Journal of Insanity*, XIX (1862–1863), 122.

19. *The American Journal of Insanity*, XVIII (1861–1862), 94–95.

20. Sanborn, *op. cit.*, p. 273.

21. *The American Journal of Insanity*, XXI (1864–1865), 557.

22. *The American Journal of Insanity*, XVI (1859–1860), 116.

23. *Ibid.*, p. 119.
24. *Ibid.*, p. 120.
25. *Ibid.*, p. 121.

Chapter 11

CHANGING MEMBERSHIP
OF THE PROFESSION

A major factor in the evolution of American psychiatry during the second half of the century was the changing membership of the profession. By the twenty-fifth anniversary of the Association of Medical Superintendents in 1869, only six of the thirteen founding members were still alive, and only four of these were still practicing, while nearly fifty younger men were administering asylums throughout the country.

Early moral treatment had borne the distinctive stamp of the original practitioners, whose catholicity of concerns and proximity to the community were seldom shared by their juniors. Like many of their contemporaries engaged in humanitarian ventures, early practitioners sought to help *all* unfortunates. Neither they nor their partners in the succor of the insane, such as S. G. Howe and Horace Mann of Massachusetts, confined their efforts to a single category of the needy. Superintendents, for instance, were prominent in efforts for prison reform, abolition of slavery, and the relief of the alcoholics. Men like Pliny Earle, who were members of the Society of Friends, shared the concerns of coreligionists for such issues as antivivisectionism.

Alienists also encouraged the use of their humane methods in situations outside their mental hospitals as, for example, in the care of the retarded, the blind, the deaf and dumb. They even suggested its use in general medicine, for as Woodward wrote,

Moral influence is nearly as important in the treatment of any physical disease as in insanity. The mind must be managed, hope inspired, and confidence secured, to insure success in the treatment of any important disease.[1]

Many of the early members of the Association, unlike their European contemporaries, and unlike such notable exceptions as Earle, were not formally trained in medicine; and most had had little previous experience in the care of the insane. Samuel B. Woodward, for instance, had served an apprenticeship to a senior physician. Amariah Brigham, after a career in surgery and medical education, had been exposed to the work of alienists on brief visits to European asylums. He had subsequently become interested in phrenology and neurophysiology, and had written books attacking infant schools and religious enthusiasm, and a treatise entitled "An Inquiry Concerning the Diseases and Functions of the Brain, the Spinal Cord, and the Nerves." This informal background was deplored by later writers, such as F. B. Sanborn, a chairman of the Board of State Charities of Massachusetts and Inspector of Charities, who recalled, in 1893, his impressions of early alienists.

Few of these men had what would now be thought a sufficient medical and philosophical training for one of the most difficult and perplexing branches of the medical and psychological art. The German psychiatrists, as Dr. Earle discovered in 1844, had far exceeded them in preliminary studies and systematic thought. But most of them were sensible, practical men, who had learned much as assistant physicians or superintendents of asylums and hospitals. Several of them were good administrative heads of what were, in one aspect, great hotels. A few were good organizers, and still fewer were good writers.[2]

In spite of the condescension of Sanborn's generation, which had suffered the brunt of disillusionment with the myth of curability and hence with moral treatment and its practitioners, the very inexperience of these early alienists had been an asset. Their approach was pragmatic and flexible, unfettered by theoretical concerns and preconceptions. Although they made none of the original discoveries of the Europeans, they functioned comfortably in the innovative climate of early institutions, where they could experiment at will with individual regimens to suit each patient. Their successes were consequently personal, and their unsystematic and changing approach hard to transmit to juniors. Treatment often depended on intuition, and administration on a tolerable business sense and a personal charisma that enabled them, "without wounding the pride or sensibilities of any, [and] equally securing the confidence and respect of all,"[3] to control raving patients or undisciplined attendants by their presence alone.

These early alienists were masters of the grand, charismatic gesture. It is recounted of Samuel Woodward of Worcester Hospital, for example, that when patients arrived at his institution, manacled and caged, he would greet them and personally free them from their restraints. He would then escort them into the dining-room and seat them beside his family at the head table, as a symbol of the patient's expected return to normal social functioning.

Among the successors of the early alienists were men of a different ilk. Many, like George Chandler, Woodward's successor at Worcester, had been assistant physicians who had risen through the ranks of the asylum. They therefore lacked much of the broad experience in general medical practice as well as the community interest of their mentors. In 1872, Isaac Ray wrote an article on "Ideal Characters of the Officers of a Hospital for the Insane," in which he made some revealing comments about the role of an assistant physician:

To him the hospital is father and mother, brother and sister, sweetheart and wife. . . . He hath no ambition to be independent of his superior in any matters of management, and it is no cross for him to recognize the fact of his subordination.[4]

The assistant was instructed to spend most of his time with patients and to leave all other matters to his superior. Should he meet the relatives of a patient, for example, he was instructed to say nothing of which his superintendent would disapprove.

It is hardly surprising, therefore, that the focus of such men was narrowed to the problems of their own role and institution. Without encouragement to improvise or question, many proved unimaginative. Without a clear corpus of professional procedures, they clung to little orthodoxies of clinical and administrative routine. Chandler, for instance, continued Woodward's practice of compiling statistical charts on patients. He did this mechanically, without his predecessor's goal of using such information to study the nature of insanity. Thus his charts and tables, like those of other institutions, became meaningless collections of random information, the despair of those attempting to compile nationwide figures on the incidence and characteristics of insanity. John Gray once wrote of this passion of his colleagues for collecting meaningless data,

It is too often found in asylum reports that their professional value is inversely as the length and variety of the statistical tables presented.[5]

Similarly, case records became useless as entries for patients were made at longer intervals and in less detail. They were entered consecutively in large ledgers, and no attempt was made to keep information about the same individual in one section. Thus successive notations about a patient might be separated by pages or volumes, obstructing anyone who wanted to review a case over time.

Overcrowded wards and economic worries distracted many younger alienists from clinical work. And as the ideals of moral treatment, individualized care, and effective cure became harder to attain, practitioners concentrated on secondary but more easily attainable goals, such as administering an economical, clean, and efficient establishment. Because there were not enough trained attendants, this kind of management required the frequent use of mechanical restraints, seclusion, and drugs. It also meant imposing a uniform routine on all patients and curtailing liberal and adventurous programs.

Excursions of patients into the community, for instance, or visits by relatives to the asylum, were increasingly discouraged. In 1859, T. Kendrick of the Northern Ohio Asylum announced the end of home visits because they caused administrative complications and public misunderstandings:

It is customary for some institutions to keep what is termed a "Probation List," on which the names of temporary absentees are entered, while no corresponding deduction is made on the daily register. . . . The practice leads to unpleasant results in many respects; the records are complicated, room must be kept for those on the list, and consequently many applicants be excluded from the benefits of treatment, or, by their admission, a false impression be made upon the public mind as to the capacity of the house. Friends, under the influence of a false sympathy, often avail themselves of the custom to seize upon the first evidence of returning reason, as a warrant for removal, and offer their own responsibility as ample surety for the risk incurred and the precious time lost by such interruptions to judicious restraint and systematic treatment. The precedent also becomes known to the inmates, and proves a prolific source of discontent and annoyance.

In view of these facts it was thought best to discontinue the practice here.[6]

The changing style of treatment was due also to the declining caliber of those attracted to asylum management. As the network of state institutions grew, positions in mental hospitals became increasingly lucrative and accessible to those who, although having no outstanding background or abilities, did have influential friends. Sanborn wrote of the veniality of many aspiring superintendents as follows:

Though the real nature of insanity had been but little studied, young physicians perceived that the specialty gave an opening for them in a profession where it was not easy to get a bread-winning position for general practice at the outset of their career. This led to ambition and intrigue for places in the new hospitals and asylums, personal favor and political interest came in to promote the claims of the inexperienced and self-seeking, and a class of physicians was gradually introduced in important positions who had neither the mental endowment nor the high moral purpose of the pioneers in the American specialty.[7]

Because most asylums were established and controlled by state and local government, superintendencies were awarded according to the spoils system to minions of the party in power. Superintendents suffered as acutely as their patients from a system that was liable to oust a qualified practitioner from his asylum with no warning or redress as political currents changed. This meant that many superintendents were totally unqualified for their positions. It meant that there was little job security and that new programs might be aborted at any stage. It meant that young practitioners, passed over for less-qualified outsiders, lost hope of gaining promotion by the quality of their work; and thus research and treatment stagnated.

The spoils system had appeared early in the century, during the presidency of Andrew Jackson, and it implied a profound disrespect for professionalism. The American ideal had become the simple frontiersman, full of natural wisdom, represented in Congress by Davy Crockett or in the White House by Andrew Jackson. Of the latter, George Bancroft, a contemporary historian, had written,

Behold, then, the unlettered man of the West, the nursling of the wilds, the farmer of the hermitage, little versed in books, unconnected by science with the traditions of the past, raised by the will of the people to the highest pinnacle of honour to the central post in the civilization of republican freedom. . . . What policy will he pursue? What wisdom will he bring with him from the forest? What rules of duty will he evolve from the oracles of his own mind? [8]

It was believed that every public position in the nation should be simple enough to be performed by anyone. As an article in *Scrib-*

ner for April, 1881, noted, this meant that the "work of the country has been and still is incompetently done" [9] and that the public official

is always to feel that he cannot keep his place by any excellence of work, or any superlative fitness for it, but only by intriguing, and showing himself ready to do the dirty work of the party on whose good will he depends.[10]

Unfortunately for superintendents, this described their position, their insecurity, and the nonprofessional qualifications on which their jobs depended.

Over the years, political appointments produced many scandals, particularly after the Civil War, when political machines and corruption among public officials became commonplace. A case may be cited at random. In 1889, the *American Journal of Insanity* reported the fate of the mental hospital at Anna, Illinois, where there was a movement under way to oust the superintendent, Horace Wardner. Wardner's opponents petitioned the governor as follows,

We, the undersigned, Republicans of Union County, desire a change in the management of the Illinois State Hospital for the Insane, and would ask your Excellency to grant this request for several reasons, among which are:
(1) This institution is largely controlled by Democratic influence.
(2) Many Democrats have received employment in preference to worthy Republicans and even deserving old soldiers.
(3) The institution has been managed in the interests of political aspirants and favorites, nepotism being largely practiced.
(4) It is to the interest of the Republican party of southern Illinois that an entire change be made in the board of management of said institution.[11]

It was learned further from local newspapers that

Dr. Wardner does not contribute with sufficient liberality to campaign funds, and does not use his efforts to advance party interests as he should; that he does not inquire into the politics of employees, but appoints them regardless of their political affiliation and antecedents; that he, a Republican, buys supplies of Democratic dealers; that relatives of the officials are favored in making appointments to positions; that the employees are induced to support favorite candidates for nomination to office, etc.[12]

The spoils system led to such insecurity that many able alienists left the profession. Some others were corrupted and either became party hacks or tried to pocket as much money as possible before the next election could deprive them of their job.

The issue of political jobbery waxed particularly hot in New York State, where a system of county asylums flourished, with exceedingly poor conditions, but where the machine-appointed management resisted all reform. The resulting conditions disgusted Charles Dickens in the 1840's:

I have no doubt that the gentleman who presided over this establishment at the time I write of, was competent to manage it, and had done all in his power to promote its usefulness: but will it be believed that the miserable strife of Party feeling is carried even into this sad refuge of afflicted and degraded humanity? Will it be believed that the eyes which are to watch over and control the wanderings of minds on which the most dreadful visitation to which our nature is exposed has fallen, must wear the glasses of some wretched side in Politics? Will it be believed that the governor of such a house as this, is appointed, and deposed, and changed perpetually, as Parties fluctuate and vary, and as their despicable weathercocks are blown this way or that? A hundred times a week, some new most paltry exhibition of that narrow-minded and injurious Party spirit, which is the simoom of America, sickening and blighting everything of wholesome life within its reach, was forced upon my notice, but I never turned my back upon it with feelings of such deep disgust and measureless contempt, as when I crossed the threshold of this madhouse.[13]

In a similar vein, the Massachusetts commission appointed in 1862 to inspect the condition of insanity in the Commonwealth regretfully announced that several state-appointed superintendents had been unwisely chosen.[14]

All these factors conspired to bring into the practice of psychiatry a heterogeneous collection of individuals, many of whom lacked the originality, charisma, enthusiasm, and dedication of the founders of the profession. It was these men who influenced the further development of American psychiatry during the second half of the century.

NOTES

1. *The American Journal of Insanity,* VII (1850–1851), 1.

2. F.B. Sanborn (ed.), *Memoirs of Pliny Earle, M.D.* (Boston: Damrell and Upham, 1898), p. 10.

3. *The American Journal of Insanity,* XIV (1857–1858), 18.

4. *The American Journal of Insanity,* XXX (1873–1874), 71.

5. *The American Journal of Insanity,* XVIII (1861–1862), 13.

6. *The American Journal of Insanity,* XVII (1860–1861), 88–89.

7. Sanborn, *op. cit.,* p. xii.

8. Richard Hofstadter, *Anti-Intellectualism in American Life* (New York: Vintage Books, 1966), p. 159.

9. *The American Journal of Insanity,* XXXVIII (1881–1882), 9. Quote from *Scribner* (April 1881), 948.

10. *Ibid.*

11. *The American Journal of Insanity,* XLV (1888–1889), 576–577.

12. *Ibid.,* p. 577.

13. Charles Dickens, *The American Notes* (London: Hazell, Watson and Viney, Ltd., 1927), p. 79.

14. *The American Journal of Insanity,* XXI (1864–1865), 263.

Chapter 12

THE DEVELOPMENT
OF THE GUILD

What began in 1844 as a learned society, when the American Association of Medical Superintendents was founded, developed during the next twenty years into a professional guild. This was a response to the needs of an increasing number of alienists, many of whom were isolated in frontier areas and lacked psychiatric experience, for the educational and standardized procedures that would create professional identity. The Association defended its members against external pressures by creating a body that, it was hoped, would be sufficiently powerful and prestigious to withstand legislative fiat and lay incursions into asylums. It created a reference group to support individual members with burdensome problems, to test the utility of innovations, and to assess the qualifications of prospective members and the standards of institutions.

By serving as a barrier against, and a refuge from, external threats, however, the guild removed alienists from intimate contact with the extramural world. It substituted the supports and sanctions of colleagues for earlier partnership with lay leaders and reformers, thus replacing constant exposure to community concerns by the oblivion of an often self-justifying reference group. It helped to increase distance between physicians and their patients by substituting the dicta of the Association for improvisation and for the mingling with and observation of their charges so characteristic of practitioners of earlier moral treatment. It also began to shift professional focus from therapy as a prime objective to trade-oriented goals like administration of hospital farms or methods of sustaining the dignity of the profession.

Early attempts to impose uniform standards of practice and ethical behavior on members of the Association may be seen during the mid-1840's in critiques of heating, ventilating, and plumbing systems of various asylums. There was an attempt to raise the level of annual reports; and Amariah Brigham took a number of his colleagues to task for their turgid prose. The Association met for annual meetings in different cities, and members inspected and criticized local facilities. At an early meeting in New York, for example, alienists visited the municipal hospital at Blackwell's Island and expressed their displeasure at its conditions.[1] The guild also tried to protect the public against exaggerated claims of successful cures and luxurious facilities made by various superintendents and thus tried to protect the profession against a possible wave of revulsion if the public should become disillusioned with their promises.

John Gray, Brigham's successor as superintendent of Utica and editor of the *American Journal of Insanity*, took a leading role in the development of the guild and maintained surveillance over American psychiatry and attacked its detractors. He has been pictured as a major formative influence on custodial care in America and as dictating the opinions of the guild and creating the so-called Utica School because of his control of the *Journal*. It appears, however, that, although Gray had a definite part in molding and standardizing the views and practices of his colleagues, he was by no means omnipotent.

Gray's power came from his progressive administration of Utica State Hospital and from his adherence to the most modern contemporary theories of psychological medicine, as well as from his editorial policy. He did indeed emphasize his personal prejudices in the *Journal*. He reviewed current books, giving strong views on each; he excluded articles whose writers held opinions divergent from his own; and he commented on the annual reports and speeches of colleagues with often brutal sarcasm. In 1868, for example, he wrote a stinging critique of the Annual Report of Worcester State Hospital, the author of which was the innovative superintendent, Merrick Bemis, a constant target for Gray's wit.[2] Gray quoted an excerpt from his colleague's report that, he warned, would make many smile. Bemis had suggested that middle-aged women be used as nurses and companions on wards for old men, because he felt that young male attendants were brusque and unsympathetic, while older women were more gentle, bringing "Christian sympathy" to their patients. The use of women on male wards would be hotly debated well into the twentieth century. In the 1860's, however, Gray rudely dismissed Bemis' suggestion,

This project of women in the "male wards" we think the brethren will be entirely satisfied to leave to Dr. Bemis' own experiment. The Utopian optimism of the day seems likely to manifest the perfection of science by alienating the sane people in some respects, as by curing the insane in others.[3]

Gray's judgment, in this case, however, did not prevail. Bemis continued to try outrageous ideas, some of which were copied by his colleagues; and at times Gray's editorial style itself was challenged. During the 1860's, lengthy accounts of annual meetings were printed in the *Journal*, after the secretary had sent copies to participants for their approval and minor corrections. In 1868, Gray told members not to add to the minutes, because transcripts of proceedings were of value only if they recorded what had actually occurred. When, however, a colleague attacked Gray at an annual gathering in the latter's absence, the editor, ignoring his own edict, replied tartly and at length in the account of the meeting. The following year the Association condemned editorial liberties and resolved that Gray should print the secretary's report unaltered, a ruling which Gray accepted in good part.[4]

It was the Association itself that molded opinion, rather than the *Journal*. The guild became the major authority for members on issues of practice, and its name was invoked in the community to influence lay decisions. At the 1868 meeting, for example, a newcomer to the guild from Texas reported that his trustees opposed the erection of a chapel for his patients, and he asked the Association to pass a resolution favoring religious services in mental hospitals that could be used to pressure the community. Others also relied on the guild. Charles H. Hughes of the State Lunatic Asylum, Fulton, Missouri, for example, said:

We are accustomed, each of us, to quote the American Association of Superintendents as an authority; and when we have the Association at our back, we can generally succeed in inducing our management to comply with our wishes.[5]

The guild's prestige made it a powerful lobby, able to influence governmental policies when individual alienists would have been overruled. The Association therefore passed resolutions dealing with such issues as the proper size and construction of asylums, opposing separate chronic stay institutions, and drawing up ideal laws to cover such matters as commitment. The latter resolution on commitment was adopted at the 1868 annual meeting; and in 1869 Thomas S. Kirkbride reported that the legislature of Pennsylvania had passed a law that, in places, accepted the exact wording of the guild's resolution.[6]

The mutual support of guild members led to close ties between colleagues who had shared, and sympathized with, each other's difficulties. For example, at the 1866 annual meeting, W. H. Stokes of Mount Hope Institution told of his hospital's legal difficulties after six insane women had charged the staff with conspiracy. During the ensuing discussion, J. E. Tyler, superintendent of McLean Asylum, summed up the sense of the group:

All of us sympathize most deeply with him [Stokes] in the great troubles and annoyances to which he has been subjected almost constantly for many months. . . . I presume as long as the world lasts we shall have this class of experience to go through with, and the only comfort we can derive from it is that others have gone through the same experience.[7]

Fraternal feelings in time developed to such a pitch that at the annual meeting of 1877 in St. Louis, Andrew McFarland, a former president of the Association, got married in the presence of his colleagues. His commitment to the guild was perhaps the result of another agonizing court battle in Illinois in the 1860's, the notorious Elizabeth Packard case. The superintendent had then been subjected to legislative investigations in which the rules of evidence had apparently been suspended but in which he had been strongly supported by the Association.

One of the ambitions of the guild was to exclude nonmembers from the care of the insane. Association membership was at that time confined to *medical* superintendents, excluding the laymen who controlled many county and municipal institutions. According to the membership rules established at the first meeting in 1844, only medical superintendents, medical officers, or their respective representatives, from each legally established institution were eligible to join the Association.

Guild members continued to limit the role of nonmedical personnel, such as attendants, in spite of the overcrowding of hospitals and the low manpower resources of psychiatry, because alienists were anxious to protect their status as medical practitioners and to emphasize that the care of the insane required rigorous training and experience. They tried to make psychiatry a recognized, distinct specialty within medicine, with an exclusive domain by insisting on the delicacy of judgment necessary to accomplish their task. McFarland, for example, presented a paper on "Minor Mental Maladies" before the Illinois State Medical Society, in which he stressed the esotericism of his profession:

Everyone realizes how few of the delusions of the insane mind are ever revealed, and how readily they are revealed under one set of circumstances and concealed under others. All insane asylums abound in cases of unquestionable mental disease, where its palpable manifestations are so obscure that the unskilled observer would doubt its existence. A certain suspicious reserve, a mysterious shyness of manner, some haughtiness of bearing, or something marked and singular in tone of voice and manner of utterance, some strange attachment to some particular position or seat, or special stress applied to the doing of some act, may be all that distinguishes the individual from other men. Yet one guided by experience, has no hesitation in declaring such cases to be instances of a latent delusion, and is prepared for the sudden exhibition of extreme or violent acts, of which any of these almost unobserved antecedent peculiarities furnishes the explanatory key.[8]

McFarland told his medical audience that many of their eccentric and hypochondriacal patients were really insane. He warned that in such cases a physician's inexperience might precipitate a crisis or contribute to chronicity because "the unthinking practitioner" might inadvertently,

by a professional opinion, give a local habitation and a name to what was before an airy nothing of the imagination, [doing] a fellow-being a lasting, and maybe a fatal injury.[9]

In the eyes of the outside world, the exclusiveness of the guild was an affront. F. B. Sanborn described the Association as a self-justifying club,

excluding from their guild persons of high attainments and earnest purpose, who might have raised the tone of their meetings and improved the quality of the *Journal of Insanity*.[10]

Weir Mitchell, the neurologist, addressing the Association in 1894 on its fiftieth anniversary, said that the lack of progress achieved by his audience in curing the insane was in part due to

the tendency to isolation from the mass of the active profession. . . . You were the first of the specialists and you have never come back into line. It is easy to see how this came about. You soon began to live apart, and you still do so. Your hospitals are not our hospitals; your ways are not our ways. You live out of range of critical shot; you are not preceded and followed in your ward work by clever rivals, or watched by able residents fresh from the learning of the school.[11]

Distance between the Association of Medical Superintendents and the American Medical Association developed gradually during the second half of the century. The American Medical Association became interested in insanity and even spoke of inserting psychiatric materials in medical curricula. This idea was influenced by the constant demands of alienists and by the fact that in certain European medical schools, men like Wilhelm Griesinger had become professors of psychological studies which were clearly allied with medicine. The American Medical Association from 1868 on, therefore, sent delegates to annual meetings of the Association of Medical Superintendents to formally invite a merger.

This proposal met with a mixed reception from the Association of Medical Superintendents. On one side was John Gray, who was already preoccupied by what would come to be called by the end of the century "scientific psychiatry." In 1868 he addressed an impassioned plea for union to the New York Medical Society, claiming that psychiatry was a "department inseparable from general medical science." [12] Great advances in the care of the insane, he insisted, took place only at times when its practitioners moved away from metaphysics toward medicine. The condition in which the insane were kept was proportional to the level of contemporary knowledge of cerebral pathology; the greatest practitioners in the history of general medicine had always studied insanity; and, added Gray, apparently forgetting the older Tukes, even moral treatment was never properly implemented except by doctors.

Gray appealed to such medical specialists as pathologists to enter the field of psychological medicine; and he later appointed the first asylum pathologist at Utica State Hospital as well as invited other specialists such as ophthalmologists to practice in his hospital and to teach him and his assistants about their specialties. Gray held that the closeness of general and psychological medicine precluded mutual neglect and isolated specialization:

It seems to me, that every possible consideration urges to the complete union of the profession, and against any further tendency to specialize in study or treatment, in a strict sense of the term. There always have been, and probably always will be, professional men who, after the thorough study and survey of the whole field of medical science, choose to devote themselves to the practice of some one branch—but they are not necessarily specialists. In fact can we admit specialists? [13]

So-called specialists, Gray maintained, were early explorers in the field who concentrated their full efforts in order to open new vistas.

But this practice . . . of expediency should not be carried too far. . . . We should adhere to unity. All are members of one body, with one aim and one glory. Psychological medicine especially, is too intimately allied with general medicine to admit of specialization in any true sense of the word.[14]

Other members of the Association of Medical Superintendents, however, felt otherwise; and once again Gray's influence, though great, was overruled. The subject came up at the annual meetings of 1869 and 1870. Each time attempts were made to shelve discussion with the excuse that the issue was in the hands of a committee headed by Tyler of McLean Asylum, which had failed to report to the gathering because Tyler was ill and thus absent from both sessions.

In spite of this evasion, some pregnant remarks were made. Kirkbride, the president of the Association, said at the 1869 meeting,

I am sure the whole medical profession must sympathize deeply with the great and laudable purposes of the American Medical Association, and I am confident none more so than the members of this body. Yet for various reasons—good and sufficient as we believe them—we think now, as we have always thought, that it is best for us, and the cause we represent, that we should retain our distinct and separate organization.[15]

Kirkbride justified this on the grounds that the two Associations had taken opposite stands on issues such as separate institutions for the chronic insane, which the alienists opposed and the general medical profession approved. Union, therefore, might cause confusion, leading "those not familiar with our own proceedings to wrong conclusions, in regard to the views that we have adopted, after mature deliberation." [16]

The following year, the issue of merger was raised again after the superintendents had sentimentally commemorated the twenty-sixth anniversary of their Association. Kirkbride, the outgoing president, had spoken of the "Original Thirteen," and had attributed great progress in the care of the insane and growth of institutions to the influence of the Association they had founded. It was, therefore, hardly a propitious time to suggest a radical change in the identity of the group. The representative of the American Medical Association, J. Atlee, did not renew the offer:

You want all the time of the three or four days of the meeting for the discussion of insanity and its collateral subjects alone; and I do not see how it is possible to do justice to yourselves, to the community, and to the specialty you represent, by having direct connection with us. You do more good as you are now, and I hope you will remain so. . . . I shall feel it my duty at San Francisco next year [the meeting of the American Medical Association], if I am permitted to be there, to make a report of this kind.[17]

Thus, Atlee, like many others, was so impressed by the magnitude of the superintendents' tasks that he further confirmed their isolation. Members of the Association of Medical Superintendents were relieved by Atlee's speech; and Charles H. Nichols, of the Government Hospital for the Insane in Washington, D.C., the newly elected vice-president of the Association, answered,

It is exceedingly gratifying to me, and I doubt not it is so to all my associates, to find that his [Atlee's] views, evidently well considered in respect to the inexpediency of merging this body with that which he represents, accord entirely with the position the Association occupies on this question, with entire unanimity, I believe, and from a sense of duty to the great cause it aims to serve.[18]

Kirkbride, one of the grand old men of the Association of Medical Superintendents, added the final words, bringing all the opposition of the alienists to the merger into the open.

Most of us know that for several years past there has, now and then, been great surprise expressed, in certain quarters, that we were not willing to be merged into the American Medical Association. While we have endeavored to show that we feel the deepest interest in everything connected with that body, and the highest appreciation of its character and usefulness, we have never entertained a doubt but that it was to our interest and to the best interests of the insane, that we should maintain our separate and independent organization. We have never had any doubts on this point, and when, through the courtesy of the American Medical Association, it has on several occasions sent delegates to us, my impression is, that generally they have felt much inclined to believe we were right, after attending one of our meetings, and seeing how difficult it would otherwise be for us to pursue the course we have always believed to be important.[19]

By the late 1870's, members of the guild became complacent and self-laudatory about their Association, the benefits which society had accrued from its work, and the philanthropic nature of their own endeavors. In 1876, the president of the Association, Charles H. Nichols, opened the twenty-ninth annual meeting by saying,

I congratulate you brethren . . . upon the privilege of belonging to an Association which now possesses an age, it having entered upon the fourth decade of its existence, and a body of valuable doctrine relating to the wants and claims of the insane, a history of usefulness to the most helpless and needy of our fellow-men, a position of responsibility before the American community which confers honor upon every name inscribed upon its roll of membership; I also congratulate you upon that steady increase, in the public mind, of a more correct knowledge of our science, and of a more just and general appreciation of the practical value of our art which underlies the earnest and effective efforts that are being so generally made, in the United States of America, and in the United Provinces of the Dominion of Canada, to provide for the most humane and enlightened care and treatment of all classes of the insane.[20]

The next stage was canonization, of the Association and of its founding members, most of whom were dead and were remembered by only a few colleagues. In 1877, Andrew McFarland wrote "Association Reminiscences and Reflections," in which he noted,

An existence of well nigh the third of a century well entitles this Association to the term venerable. We have seen go from it, generally after lives fully and well spent in this one great department of science and philanthropy, the great majority of those who laid its foundation, and have seen enter it much the larger proportion of those now in the privilege of membership. While we doubt not that the new blood and the new brain entering with each year in a constantly increasing stream will preserve all the vigor of the original stock, we may still be pardoned if we look back with something akin to veneration on those who so well laid the foundation on which we build.[21]

McFarland recounted the incident that had preceded the founding of the Association, the meeting between Samuel B. Woodward of Massachusetts and Francis T. Stribling of Virginia, which was found to have a fortuitous parallel in national history.

This pleasing incident reminds us that it is not the first time Massachusetts and Virginia have been united in council for the promotion of designs of the utmost national importance.[22]

There were florid descriptions of the founding members who had died. Woodward of Worcester State Hospital was said to bear a strong resemblance to George Washington in face and person; Amariah Brigham was remembered for "the spotless purity of his life" and for "a voice like music itself, and a smile singularly winning, there was everything in him requisite in a man born to be loved." Bell was remembered for "a thick growth of raven black hair literally swept across a brow of almost marble whiteness, beneath which were features which a Phidias might have left as his abiding model of the human face divine, if a native nobility of sentiment and a mind's full culture had been the ideas to be expressed." [23]

McFarland listed the benefits of the Association. Among these was the fact that ideas could be readily exchanged between practitioners from coast to coast, so that every advance became common usage. The Association, moreover, maintained professional identity and objectives,

Who does not return from a session of this body with a higher sense of obligation to duty, with a spirit of determination to carry into effect all possible of the harvest of thought with which every meeting is more or less fruitful? It is this annual rekindling of the fire of professional zeal that has placed our institutions for the insane in the first rank of all Christendom.[24]

McFarland concluded with the following lofty praise:

Finally this Association has steadily pursued the object of its formation, and its ends have been abundantly reached. It has presented the noblest incentives under which men can act. It has stimulated the loftiest ambitions, it has kept pure and unsullied the most philanthropic purposes. It is the furthest possible from a "guild" to promote selfish ends. . . . As it has been, so it now is, and so we trust it will ever continue to be.[25]

It may be noted in extenuation of this style of oratory that the guild was at that time under constant attack from many quarters—medical, lay, and legislative—for its isolation and for the poor quality of mental hospital care.

NOTES

1. Henry M. Hurd (ed.), *The In-stitutional Care of the Insane in the United States and Canada* (Baltimore: Johns Hopkins Press, 1916), Vol. I, p. 18.

2. J.S. Bockoven, *Moral Treatment in American Psychiatry* (New York: Springer Publishing Co., 1963), p. 47.

3. *The American Journal of Insan-ity*, XXIV (1867–1868), 430–431.

4. *The American Journal of Insan-nity*, XXVI (1869–1870), 149.

5. *Ibid.*, pp. 151–152.

6. *Ibid.*, p. 139.

7. *The American Journal of Insan-ity*, XXIII (1866–1867), 83.

8. *The American Journal of Insan-ity*, XX (1863–1864), 21.

9. *Ibid.*, p. 15.

10. F.B. Sanborn, *Memoirs of Pliny Earle, M.D.* (Boston: Damrell and Up-ham, 1898), p. xii.

11. Albert Deutsch, *The Mentally Ill in America* (New York: Columbia Uni-versity Press, 1945), p. 265.

12. *The American Journal of Insan-ity*, XXV (1868–1869), 145.

13. *Ibid.*, p. 169.

14. *Ibid.*, pp. 169–170.

15. *The American Journal of Insan-ity*, XXVI (1869–1870), 200.

16. *Ibid.*

17. *The American Journal of Insan-ity*, XXVII (1870–1871), 203–204.

18. *Ibid.*, p. 204.

19. *Ibid.*, p. 205.

20. *The American Journal of Insan-ity*, XXXII (1875–1876), 267.

21. *The American Journal of Insan-ity*, XXXIV (1877–1878), 342.

22. *Ibid.*, p. 343.

23. *Ibid.*, p. 350.

24. *Ibid.*, p. 357.

25. *Ibid.*, p. 359.

Chapter 13

THE GUILD AND
THE COURTS

One example of the guild acting as a pressure group for reform, as an educational service for its members, as creator of professional norms, as an upholder of ethical standards, and as defender of its own honor may be seen in the area of insanity and criminal responsibility. During much of the nineteenth century, court cases provided the main publicly visible contact between alienists and laymen. Much popular hostility against superintendents and their patients crystallized during trials, since these exacerbated both public prejudice and fear of raving lunatics destroying people and property, and public suspicion of any formula by which criminals might elude retribution.

A frequent cause of embarrassment to alienists was their own lack of training and traditions in courtroom behavior. The prosecution usually managed to make fools of expert witnesses unused to cross-examination, and this resulted in loss of face for alienists and doubts being raised about their honesty. Few, after all, were capable of comporting themselves in court with the poise and certainty of Amariah Brigham. It was recorded that while once appearing as an expert witness, he explained to the prosecuting counsel that he could always detect madmen by their eyes. The attorney challenged him to look round the courtroom to see whether there was a lunatic in the audience. Brigham agreed. After casting his "penetrating glance" over the hushed crowd, he pointed to a man at the back of the room. The man leaped shouting and cursing to his feet, his eyes flashing. He was led struggling furiously from the room, thus proving beyond any doubt, as the awed recounter wrote, that he was a raving maniac.[1]

The Association became highly sensitive to the problems of the expert witness. A number of books and articles were written on how to avoid *"breaking down* on the witness-stand," [2] such as Isaac Ray's "Hints to the Medical Witness in Questions of Insanity." Ray warned colleagues that giving testimony is a skilled job that must be specially learned. He advised alienists to study healthy minds, otherwise their daily practice with lunatics might make them see insanity everywhere. He warned against the use of jargon in testimony, against taking sides in the case, and against giving rash and unsupportable opinions in the heat of cross-examination. He concluded,

He [the witness] must bear up his mind to have his sentiments travestied and sneered at, his motives impugned, and pit-falls dug in his path, with the same kind of indifference which he would hear the maledictions of an excited patient.[3]

Alienists remained highly sensitive, however, to a situation in which their reputation and professional standing were felt to be at stake, particularly when public opinion was represented by such statements as the following from the *Saturday Review* of 1857:

Experts are free to hold what opinions they think proper, so long as we decline to allow to the "morally insane" freedom to commit unpunished murder, rape, or robbery.[4]

In order to protect themselves against public sneers, the Association attacked the use of quasi-expert witnesses, both lay and medical, such as the professor of obstetrics who, in 1857, testified for the defense at the trial of Charles Huntington for forgery.[5] They insisted that an assessment of insanity was a highly specialized and subtle task, arrived at after years of study and clinical experience, not a judgment to be made by the common man. As Gray wrote,

Expertness means something more than general skill, or the reputation of it; it means the result of great observation and experience, applied, in a somewhat exclusive way, to a particular subject.[6]

The Association also tried from its beginning to establish precedents for acquitting the insane of criminal charges, and to persuade the public to accept humane judicial reforms. Butler, for instance, urged the New York legislature to remove the death sentence, arguing that because insanity in criminals is often hard to assess, if a mistake were made and a diseased man were convicted, the state might inadvertently be guilty of murder.[7]

Early alienists tried, in particular, to broaden the McNaughton Rules that defined the criminally insane as those unable to distinguish right from wrong. Those concerned with the guardianship of the mentally ill sought to include the concept of *moral insanity* within the statutes, as a category in which an individual, otherwise acting normally, surrenders to an irresistible criminal impulse. This condition had first been described in 1837, by James Pritchard, an English alienist, as a

form of mental derangement . . . consisting in a morbid perversion of the feelings, affections, and active powers, without any illusion or erroneous conviction impressed upon the understanding; it sometimes co-exists with an apparently unimpaired state of the intellectual faculties.[8]

Such forms of insanity, Pritchard continued, are often characterized by "malevolence rages, impulses to evil acts, and a variety of eccentricities."

Pritchard's term, derived from Phillippe Pinel's "manie sans délire," and Jean Esquirol's "impulsive homicidal mania" soon became the focus of a mammoth controversy between superintendents and the public, and, more important for the fate of moral treatment, among alienists themselves. The validity of the whole concept of moral causes and partial insanity was questioned, thus weakening the theoretical structure on which the treatment scheme rested.

Within the guild two camps appeared, one led by Isaac Ray, who believed in both moral causes and moral insanity, and the other led by John Gray, who did not. The argument gradually became vicious as Gray and his followers excluded articles by Ray's group from the *American Journal of Insanity*, thus censoring an entire wing of professional opinion. Gray's attacks on one of the most respected members of the Association were at times so venomous that some of his colleagues were outraged. In a letter to Thomas Kirkbride, John Curwen wrote that he had considered cancelling his subscription to the *Journal* rather than lend his tacit approval to such "criminal foolery." [9]

In the course of this controversy, the meaning of the word "moral" became confused. In "moral causes" or "moral treatment," "moral" meant "psychological," but in "moral insanity," it was closer to our own usage and referred to matters of conscience, and conformity to social norms. Because the same word appeared in all three categories, these were linked and the distinctions between them were confused. Thus, an attack on one became an attack on all. There was a further link among these terms because each of the rival camps was consistent in its support of, or opposition to, all three. Thus Gray came to doubt the existence of moral causes and moral insanity and the efficacy of moral treatment and attacked the believers in Ray's groups on all counts.

The validity of moral insanity was at first attacked because phrenology, one of its theoretical supports, became suspect, in part because it bore the taint of charlatanry, and in part because experience failed to substantiate the existence of a multitude of cerebral organs. There was, for example, the case of a Mexican child, shot through the head, who sustained gross injuries in portions of the brain designated by phrenology as governing particular faculties, and who nevertheless continued to have unimpaired use of those very powers.[10]

The major opposition to phrenology, however, was religious and ethical, and involved the whole problem of detecting the borderline between the physical and the spiritual. The concepts of phrenology were materialistic, stating that the character traits, intelligence, and virtues that were commonly felt to be spiritual and religious attributes were instead determined by the organic configuration of the brain. This was not only a denial of the immortal soul, but it also questioned the accountability of man for his actions, because it implied that urges, even antisocial ones, were inherent and therefore beyond the individual's control and beyond society's right to exact retribution.

Gray confused an already muddied terminology further by using "phrenology" as a smear word to label those who believed in moral insanity, or who, like Merrick Bemis, the third superintendent of Worcester State Hospital, persisted in listing moral causes in their statistical tables. There was a logical connection here, because phrenology had provided a link between psychological and somatic factors, showing that education and environment develop otherwise latent functions of the brain, thus supporting the theory of moral causes. It had also provided a basis for the concept of partial insanity in which only some cerebral areas were diseased, leaving the rest undamaged. This validated the concept of moral insanity and much of the strategy of moral treatment. Thus, an attack on phrenology weakened all three ideas. Furthermore, in Gray's usage, "phrenology" came to mean both "unscientific" and "immoral," "irreligious," or "materialistic"; and, by implication, "moral causes," "moral insanity," and "moral treatment" became similarly tarred. It is interesting to note that alienists judged their work on many levels—scientific, societal, and religious—aware that they were dealing with an ill-defined region, encompassing an individual's body, soul, and social functioning.

Those, like Isaac Ray, who in fact did defend a modified phrenology, did so on rationalistic grounds. In *Mental Hygiene*, a book for laymen published in 1863, Ray held that it was necessary to suspend one's fear of materialism and to admit that the "manifestations of the mind and the organic condition of the brain are more or less affected by each other." [11]

The position labeled "phrenology" by Gray held that many criminal acts were due to insanity and that such acts arose from the same inborn weaknesses that, under pathogenic circumstances, produced other, more readily recognized forms of mental aberration. As Ray had written,

The frequency of insanity among convicts in prison is, probably, not so much owing to the immediate circumstances of their position [as those objecting to solitary confinement, etc. had insisted], as to this latent element of mischief in their mental constitution, which, no doubt, is rendered more active by confinement.[12]

Moreover, he questioned the efficacy of traditional methods of moral persuasion and sanction to modify such innate behavior.

Without discussing the question whether a person whose heritage of infirmity consists of a defective brain should be held to a rigid responsibility for the consequences of his misfortune, rather than regarded with the same emotions, I apprehend there can be no diversity of opinion as to the importance of the facts in connection with the subject of social morality. For the moral and intellectual elevation of the race, we are to look, not exclusively to education, but to whatever tends to improve the bodily constitution and especially the qualities of the brain. In our scheme of philanthropy, we are apt to deal with men as if they could be molded to any desirable purpose, provided only the right instrumentalities are used; ignoring altogether the fact that there is a physical organ in the case, whose original endowments must limit very strictly the range of our moral appliances. But while we are bringing to bear upon them all the kindly influences of learning and religion, let us not overlook these physical agencies which determine the efficiency of the brain as the material instrument of the mind.[13]

Gray's opposing and eventually dominant view was set forth in articles, and at the trials in which the editor of the *Journal* appeared as an expert witness. He maintained that the so-called phrenological concept of "moral insanity" was ethically, legally, and medically suspect. From the pages of the *Journal*, he berated those who would invoke in criminal proceedings a "brood of monomanias which darken the atmosphere of science." [14]

Gray, concerned with tightening and clarifying the standards of his profession, objected to the promiscuous use of a medical classification whose existence was still in doubt among reputable practitioners, as a

plausible pretext for shielding common wickedness from merited punishment, and [forming] a substantial defense against all the crimes in the calendar.[15]

This charge had a certain merit, because the plea of insanity was in fact being liberally used by many lawyers, who called "expert" witnesses with dubious credentials to defend petty crooks. Thus Gray's opposition to "phrenology" was in part an act of professional purism, an attempt to establish the good faith and scientific objectivity of alienists rather than to allow himself and his colleagues to give way to sentimentality.

The philanthropy which of necessity attaches itself to the performance of the sacred duties of our profession, inclines its members on all occasions to take the charitable view of criminal cases, whenever it is tolerably well supported. But it is not impossible that we may err equally in this direction as in the opposite, and, by rendering the establishment of the plea of insanity too easy, may be fully as derelict in our duty to humanity as by being too cautious in the reception of testimony.[16]

Gray distrusted the vague mushrooming list of monomanias, such as pyromania, kleptomania, and oinomania (alcoholism), which, he felt, had not been rigorously and scientifically tested. He doubted whether, in fact, such disease entities could exist, because he considered insanity to be a general brain disorder, not a localized condition as earlier moral treatment had suggested. The issues of criminal justice and protection of the public were, Gray maintained, too important to rest on loose professional conjecture or on impressive nomenclature, because

The effect of punishment, in controlling vicious men and preventing crime, depends so much upon the certainty of its execution that he who opens another loophole for escape, through mistaken views of charity and kindness, is doing a wrong to society and mankind.[17]

Gray maintained that most crimes had a mundane basis, even when motives were hard to fathom. In this he was supported by such European authorities as J. C. Bucknill of England, who wrote an article on kleptomania for the *Journal of Mental Science* of 1862, a subject that, he reported, had become one for jest and cartoons in the popular press. Bucknill did not believe that insanity was a factor in the shoplifting activities of a number of "so-called ladies" in London. Rather, he attributed their behavior to unscrupulous advertising and to their scramble to keep up with the Joneses:

The struggle for existence in the middle and even in the upper classes of our complex social system, combined with the prevailing fashion of an emulative and showy expenditure, make the sense of what felt keenly in many an English home, where no traces of vulgar poverty are discernible. The really poor steal because they want bread; the relatively poor are tempted to steal because they desire the possession of that which seems, to a mind trained in a bad school, as essential as bread itself.[18]

Gray and Bucknill distinguished between accepted legal insanity, in which society admitted the nonresponsibility of criminals, and infirmity of will:

That a man may have a clear perception and consciousness of right and wrong, and the full use of his reason, and yet be so infirm of will that sometimes he cannot refrain from doing what he knows to be wrong, or persist in doing what he knows to be right, is so true that the doctrine of moral insanity can derive no aid from the position. It is the usual condition of those, who, in plain speaking times, were called *bad men.*[19]

Gray believed that the concept of moral insanity weakened the moral fiber of the community. It dignified and excused crime with the name of insanity, and it removed restraints from antisocial action. By teaching that criminality and bad habits were innate and hence beyond the control of the individual, it implied that one prone to destructive and self-indulgent acts could cease to struggle for self-control and could discount moral teachings and restraints, because, in effect, society had sanctioned its deviance.

The general tendency of the doctrine of moral insanity is bad, whatever show or real feeling of humanity there may be in it. It is bad, in a religious view, because it tempts men to indulge their strongest passions, under the false impression that God has so constituted them that their passions or impulses are not generally governable by their will or their reason, and that, therefore, there is no punishable guilt in indulging them. This is fatalism. It is bad in a legal view, because it protects from due punishment offenses which, with the self-denial and self-control that men rightly trained and rightly disposed are quite capable of exercising, might be avoided. It tends to give to bad education, loose habits, vicious indulgence, neglected parental control, and disobedience to God, an immunity from the prescribed penalties of crime, that is not warranted by scriptures, the law of reason, or any code of human law that assumes to be founded on the law of reason or the law of God.[20]

Thus the Association, under the leadership of Gray, Ray, and their respective supporters, attempted to purify and regulate professional conduct in the highly sensitive and visible arena of the courtroom. In subsequent years, the Association became a forum for discussion of such issues as whether or not expert witnesses should accept fees, or whether their impartiality might be better guaranteed if they were agents of the court rather than advocates for one party or the other. Although many such questions remained academic in the nineteenth century, the role of expert witness was being defined and professionalized. And beneath the surface of these, as of other discussions, basic theoretical and moral struggles were going on, which affected the course of professional development more significantly than the nature of the original issue might suggest.

NOTES

1. *The American Journal of Insanity*, VIII (1851–1852), 373.
2. *Ibid.*, p. 51.
3. *Ibid.*, p. 62.
4. *The American Journal of Insanity*, XXII (1865–1866), 135–137.
5. *The American Journal of Insanity*, XIV (1857–1858), 110.
6. *Ibid.*, p. 113.
7. *The American Journal of Insanity*, IV (1847–1848), 31.
8. Charles E. Goshen (ed.), *Docu-*

mentary History of Psychiatry (New York: Philosophical Library, 1967), p. 133.

9. Norman Dain, *Concept of Insanity in the United States, 1789–1865* (New Brunswick, N.J.: Rutgers University Press, 1964), p. 225.

10. *The American Journal of Insanity*, I (1844–1885), 353–355.

11. Isaac Ray, *Mental Hygiene* (Boston: Ticknor and Fields, 1863), p. 2.

12. *Ibid.*, p. 22.

13. *Ibid.*, pp. 22–23.

14. *The American Journal of Insanity*, XXI (1864–1865), 232.

15. *The American Journal of Insanity*, XIV (1857–1858), 115.

16. *The American Journal of Insanity*, XVI (1859–1860), 384.

17. *Ibid.*

18. *The American Journal of Insanity*, XIX (1862–1863), 150.

19. *The American Journal of Insanity*, XIV (1857–1858), 319–320.

20. *Ibid.*, p. 321.

Chapter 14

CHANGING PSYCHIATRIC
THEORY

During this period, psychiatric theory on the nature and management of insanity was reoriented and standardized. In the words of a review in the 1864 *American Journal of Insanity*, psychiatry, like contemporary general medicine, religion, and law was in a phase of conscious revolution, in which the "strife of words and creeds may be replaced by critical and rational inquiry."[1] There was a reconsideration of the role of environment in creating and curing mental disorder; and leading practitioners increasingly gave primacy to purely physical causality and methods of cure. This was due in part to the power of the psychiatric guild to mold the opinions of its members; to general intellectual and scientific trends of the day in which natural philosophy was giving way to natural science; and to clinical experiences that cast doubt on the universal applicability of moral treatment theory.

Insanity was increasingly defined as a condition caused purely by physical factors. The leading American exponent of this view was John Gray, who noted in the 1863 Report of Utica State Hospital,

Each year demonstrates, more and more conclusively, that the true pathology of mental disorder is to be sought in physical enfeeblement. That the disease is dependent on conditions of more or less exhaustion of the vital forces.[2]

Such depletion of vital forces produced, Gray said, observable brain damage, which in turn caused insanity. Although Gray did not discount the indirect power of moral causes, he did question former views about their primacy, seeing moral factors instead as a precipitant of physical deterioration,

There are cases where the general ill health and the insanity are due to an overworked brain, or the anxiety and prolonged tension and sleeplessness which are often the result of grief and pecuniary losses. Even here, however, the cause is physical, because insanity comes on only as a result of defective nutrition of the tissues, those of the brain included; the sleeplessness and deprivation of rest acting powerfully, not only against appetite and the simple ingestion of food, but also by wearing the nerve-tissues, and preventing ultimate cell nutrition.[3]

Of moral management he wrote,

Undue prominence is given to moral means in the treatment of mental disorder. Now, while we would be the last to deprecate moral therapeutics in maladies of the mind, we are forced to regard them as of secondary importance, and to view them rather in the light of necessary conditions to the success of medical therapeutics.[4]

Far as Gray may appear to have moved from the original dicta of moral treatment, he was in fact closer to its basic tenets than were many of his opponents. One of these was H. B. Wilbur, superintendent of the New York Asylum of Idiots, who wrote, in 1872, on "Materialism in its Relation to the Causes, Conditions and Treatment of Insanity," and specifically attacked the theories of John Gray. Wilbur claimed that insanity was a disease of the immaterial mind and that discrete psychic disturbances, caused by moral forces, might themselves produce structural brain damage. He felt that such physiological change was not invariably present and that insanity was in fact a "functional disorder." [5] This view was quite contrary to orthodox moral treatment, which denied the violability of the mind; it was as alien to earlier American psychiatric theory, as was the opposite extreme of materialism which held that mind did not exist, that brains secreted thought as glands secreted bodily fluids.

Gray's position was a logical extension of certain facets of American psychiatric thought. It will be remembered that early moral treatment had itself been a physical system because it had posited the inevitable presence of diseased cerebral tissue in all cases of insanity. It differed from later theory by stressing the role of moral agents in a multifactorial causality which combined both physical and psychological pressures. It had emphasized the primary efficacy of moral programs of therapy in the treatment of all recent cases of insanity, whether the major etiological factors were psychological or physical or a combination of the two.

In 1854, Pliny Earle published *An Examination of the Practice of Bloodletting in Mental Disorders*, a survey of conflicting views of past and present authorities which sought to establish normative practice. Whereas a number of contemporary Europeans advised cupping and leeches in such conditions as insanity due to suppression of the menses, Earle found that by the early 1850's the overwhelming body of American opinion was against Rush's prescription of depletion in most cases. He reported that in 1853, the year before his book had been published, no bloodletting had taken place in the insane hospitals of New York.

In the 1850's, Earle represented normative opinion among liberal alienists when he concluded his treatise by advising against depletion. He also reflected contemporary concerns about the utility of physical treatment in insanity by the very fact of writing the book. He was characteristic of progressive elements in American psychiatry when he cautioned against bloodletting on the grounds that the red globules in the blood were necessary to prevent anemia, itself now considered a major cause of insanity; and he advised those whose patients needed medical measures to use a hearty, fortifying diet, much as in contemporary treatment of tuberculosis.

Earle concluded his analysis by commenting on the theories of Benjamin Rush; and in so doing, he showed the diplomatic way in which the latter had still to be questioned, because, in the absence of any subsequent American theoretician, he continued to be venerated by many as the principal authority:

It is not impossible that during the period in which Dr. Rush was in active life, disease in all its forms, in this country, not only involved the nervous system less than at the present time, but more seriously implicated the circulation, and hence required a more heroic method of attack for its subjugation. It is certainly easier to believe that this was the fact, than to conceive that an acute and sagacious observer, a learned and profound medical philosopher should have formed and promulgated opinions in regard to the treatment of insanity, diametrically opposed to those of many of the most experienced physicians of the present day, and so extreme in their character that but few can now approach them, to any point of near proximity.[6]

It thus came as a shock to some superintendents when in 1857, at an Annual Meeting of the American Association of Superintendents, M. H. Ranney, resident physician at New York City Lunatic Asylum at Blackwell's Island, New York, suggested a return to old ways. In "The Medical Treatment of Insanity," he wrote,

In thus presenting my views it must not be understood that I advocate entire reliance on medical agents in the treatment of insanity. The adoption of proper hygienic rules is essential, as in physical disease generally. Moral treatment, including employment, amusements, the establishment of regular habits, etc., is also a most important auxiliary to recovery. This is particularly true where derangement of mind has existed for years. But while admitting the importance of moral treatment, I would avoid an over-estimate of its mechanical part, and carefully investigate not only the laws of physical action, but the influences of medicine on the manifestations of the mind, that our noble profession may not become simply an art.[7]

In the ensuing discussion, many superintendents were surprised that they should be advised to return to the venesections and tartarized antimony of their apparently discredited predecessors. Some, however, reported good results from experiments with preparations of ether, chloroform, opiates, and even the controversial tartarized antimony, while others said that they would be willing to try these "new" ideas. No one at that time rose to defend the primacy of moral methods of treatment, a situation that had a complicated set of causes.

By the mid-1850's and early 1860's, the theoretical concepts of moral causation and moral treatment had lost much luster, not only because of the decline of the curability myth. Another reason, noted in a review in the *American Journal of Insanity* of 1865, was the tendency of moral treatment to polarize easily toward superstition and quackery,

The great difficulty has been, and is, so to systematize and apply medicine as not to encourage superstition and imposture.[8]

Among such extremists were the Spiritualists, some of whom distrusted all pharmaceutical or surgical methods. They resorted instead to what was frequently religiously-tinged exhortation, thus removing their treatment from the recognized realm of medicine. More moderate practitioners felt that their own reputations as doctors and the scientific standing as well as the efficacy of their practice were threatened by this type of cultism, which foreclosed on possibly beneficial avenues of treatment.

The methods of this so-called system . . . really forbid the use of any medicinal agents, and could they be generally accepted would surely put an end to all true science. Valuable as moral impressions are in the hands of the wise and honest physician, he cannot yet afford to discard other remedies, or to blot out all the noble conquests of science that bring tribute to his art.[9]

An even less attractive group of Spiritualists so subordinated body to mind that they categorically rejected all physical causes, yet resorted to the most drastic somatic treatment measures, heedless of consequences, in order to affect the moral sense. Such, for instance, was the practice of Johann Christian Heinroth and his followers in Germany, products of the anti-intellectualism and pietism of the German eighteenth and early nineteenth centuries, who held that insanity, a lack of moral liberty, was caused by sin, which they sought to treat by physical punishment.

A similar school existed in France, where, after Lauret, they resorted to cold streams of water dropped on a lunatic's head from great heights. Pliny Earle reported his observations of such treatment in Le Bicêtre, where it was apparently used as a form of negative reinforcement whenever a patient persisted in his delusions. Earle disapproved strongly, feeling that this only terrorized lunatics, making them disguise delusions, rather than helping them to gain insight into their own insanity and hence voluntarily abandon false ideas.[10]

There was a sharp reaction among alienists against such extremists, who offended against both the humanitarian and scientific ideas of the day. J. C. Bucknill of England, and such of his American followers as John Gray, held that insanity was caused not by vague and irrational pressures, but by molecular changes in the brain. These were in turn the result of chemical action when blood diseases, such as uraemia or anemia, brought toxins to the cerebral tissues or failed to supply sufficient nutrients to brain cells. Damage might also occur when injuries to peripheral portions of the nervous system transmitted overpowering stimuli that short-circuited brain functioning. As Bucknill wrote,

Not a thrill of sensation can occur—not a flashing thought or a passing feeling can take place without changes in the living organism; much less can diseased sensation, thought, or feeling occur without such changes—changes which we are not able to detect—changes which we may never be able to demonstrate, but which we are, nevertheless, certain of. For whether we adopt the theory that the states and things which we call heat, electricity, vitality, etc., are distinct entities, or what is called imponderable matter; or the more probable theory that they are only phenomena belonging to ordinary ponderable matter; an atom or a cell charged with electricity or heat, or in a state of chemical activity, is essentially in a different condition to a cell or an atom in chemical or electrical equilibrium with surrounding substances. On the lowest view of organic action, therefore, alterations of what are called dynamic force can not exist without corresponding changes in material condition.[11]

To those who claimed that examination of cerebral tissue of the insane revealed no chronic lesions, Bucknill and his followers advised deeper study and finer instruments.

Heightened interest in the interdependence of body and mind produced studies of "psychosomatic medicine" in America; and it was felt that in future research, general medicine and psychiatry would of necessity be partners. Practitioners such as Theodore H. Kellogg in Canada and a number of French and German authorities, explored the reciprocity of physical disease and mental states that appeared to exist in the outbreak of such conditions as hepatitis. They noted that simple exposure to unhealthy physical influences did not cause pathology until coupled with depression and fatigue, mental states that were in turn aggravated by liver disease.[12]

One of the corollaries of the physiological view of insanity was the derogation of environment as a source of pathology and cure. Insanity was regarded as the product of deep-seated physical weakness, to which stress in the social or physical environment was merely an incidental episode in almost inevitable degeneration,

Pathologists have admitted a certain class of diseases, in which are included gout, scrofula, tuberculosis, cancer, insanity and others, which make their appearance at certain periods of life and which depend for their production, not on external conditions, but on certain innate peculiarities of constitution. If we would look for their cause, we must go back to the germ at the moment of fecundation, or even to conditions existing in the parents. This cause is of the same nature as that which determines the conformation of the body, the color of the hair, or the characteristic, intellectual, or moral peculiarities. . . .

Yet, from the common tendency to look for direct and palpable causes, the appearance of these diseases is commonly ascribed to accidental causes. A paroxysm of gout is ascribed to luxurious living, tubercular phthisis to exposure to cold, cancer to the inflammation following some bruise. In one sense these are real causes; but it ought to be understood that they would not produce the disease if the internal conditions were not previously present, and that the presence of these internal conditions would in many instances have produced the disease without the concurrence of those external causes.[13]

It was thought that supposed moral causes of insanity, such as anxiety or proclivity to overwork, might in fact be symptoms of a pre-existing disturbance. The existence of "religious mania," for example was now questioned.

Doubt was cast on religious excitement as a cause of insanity when the revivals of the late 1850's failed to create the expected epidemic; and John Gray, whose devoutness is apparent in many articles, wrote, in 1864,

We, indeed, think it is safe to infer that religious anxiety is rarely, if ever, a cause of insanity. The sublime faith of Christianity is rather a safeguard against it, and is unquestionably a support under its scourging.[14]

Those who did succumb to the frenzy of revivals were "just ready to become insane." [15] If another source of excitement had been available, such as a political revolution, the same individuals would have been stricken with somewhat different symptoms. Thus it was felt that moral agents were accidental rather than substantive causes, and that the primary concern of practitioners was to be with the latter.

Although prevention was advocated with ever greater enthusiasm, its programs were seen as progressively less likely to affect particular individuals, who to a greater or lesser degree were already predisposed. Nevertheless, correct life habits were still advocated to avoid unnecessary risks that might tip the balance toward pathology.

The physiological school discounted the primacy of moral treatment as well as moral causes. It held that although such management was an integral part of any medical procedure, in which hope must be inspired and irritations minimized,

The importance of moral treatment lies in avoiding what is hurtful, but it is of little influence as a direct cure agent. How vain is the attempt to reason with the insane on the subject of their delusions, or to remove the gloom and despondency of melancholics by cheerful or diverting conversation is well understood.[16]

Instead, the depressed vital forces of the patient were to be restored by a fortifying diet and often by enforced rest with the help of physical or chemical restraints, rather than by the earlier social organization of the hospital.

The theories of the physiologists gained only gradually in the United States. In the 1870's a group remained passionately committed to moral causality. At the Association meeting in 1872, members revealed their perplexity and ambivalence. Shaw of the General Hospital for the Insane, Middletown, Connecticut, commented on a speech by Gray and on the views of his opponents,

I acknowledge freely that the more I study this branch of the subject, the more I am inclined to approach the point which Dr. Gray has already reached, and yet I can not bring my mind to acknowledge that all the causes of insanity depend directly upon physical changes of the brain. No, perhaps I ought not to say that; I believe that all cases of insanity are the result of certain changes of the brain; but at the same time those changes may be produced by moral causes, just as directly as by physical causes. Perhaps there is a small proportion of cases of insanity where we can trace a direct moral cause. It seems to me we should be denying to the intellectual, the higher power of man, the influence which it certainly has upon the physical organization. I think you will all acknowledge the great and powerful influence which the mind has upon digestion, respiration, and some of the other functions. Why may it not also be a cause in producing physical derangement of the brain and nervous system? [17]

Similarly, Clement A. Walker of the Lunatic Hospital in Boston added,

I know that in our post-mortem examinations there are more evidences at the present day than ever before, pointing out changes of the brain as not only oftentime the result, but the cause of mental disturbance; and yet I am old fogyish and conservative enough to feel that there is great danger of overlooking the moral entirely, in our surprise and perhaps gratitude at seeing laid out so plainly before us that which formerly was all darkness and conjecture. While I believe, sir, in the very great prevalence of physical causes in the production and continuance of insanity, I can not yet shut my eyes to the very material agency that moral causes have had, and always will have, in the production of insanity.[18]

Nevertheless, as these speakers themselves acknowledged, they were standing against the major contemporary trends in medicine and psychiatry. One of these trends came from the availability of, and interest in, the works of German psychiatrists. These books and articles crossed the Atlantic as Heinroth and his Spiritualist colleagues were being discredited; and in their reaction against the denial of all physical causality of insanity by the older school, young practitioners, somatists and psychosomatists, laid heavy emphasis on physiological explorations.

Because few American practitioners spoke German, these works were hardly known until Earle published his book on asylums in German-speaking countries, and until J. Workman and other alienists translated and reviewed them for the *Journal*. Once available, however, they aroused considerable interest, for the Germans, unlike their American colleagues, were trained and universally recognized specialists, whose work, it was hoped, would both raise the scientific status of the guild and solve some of the perplexing problems of insanity. The allure of their publications was explained by John Gray:

From the eminence of Germans in all matters literary, moral and scientific, from the peculiar constitution of the German mind—their plodding, patient research into the most abstruse subjects—we are naturally led to expect that the subject of psychology has received due attention, and such is undoubtedly the fact. . . .

The German fixes upon some subject or branch of a subject and proceeds at once to an exhaustive investigation of it; vast erudition is brought to bear upon it, every phase of it is carefully considered, and when all the knowledge gathered from an extensive range has been brought to the elucidation of it, and the writer has given his neatly printed paper covered, unpretentious looking book to the world, we feel, on perusal, that in the present state of our scientific knowledge little more can be said upon the subject.[19]

Although some of these German works contained social and environmental theories of etiology and cure, most were clear, well-organized, and authoritative descriptions of brain and nerve pathology, and statistical studies of such issues as suicide.

In 1864, the *Journal* reprinted a speech by Wilhelm Griesinger, on "German Psychiatrie," in which this authority on psychopathology stressed the medical rather than the metaphysical aspects of his field. He discussed the need for categorization of diseases, for including within the diagnosis "not merely the character of the mental aberration, but, as far as possible, the nature of the lesion of the brain and nerves," and he defined "psychiatrie" as an area closely allied with that of cerebral and nerve pathology.[20]

Except, however, for a few leading alienists, like Gray and Earle, absorption of German thought was superficial and passive. Ideas and categories were accepted, but little original research was carried out. German terminology, however, became fashionable and was considered more precise than English equivalents. By 1880, *psychiatry* and *psychiatrist* were in relatively common use; and R. M. Bucke, Superintendent of the Asylum at London, Ontario, wrote in an article "The Growth of the Intellect," that the process of building concepts into compound images has no proper name in English, "we sometimes call this act imagination— the Germans have a better name for it, they call it Vorstellung." [21] The major implications of German thought, however, were seized not by the superintendents but by neurologists, pathologists, and psychologists, whose research and discoveries at times threatened to make members of the older profession aliens in their own field.

The interest of leading American alienists in cerebral pathology was stimulated by technological advances in science. Post-mortem examination of diseased brains was not new. Benjamin Rush had based his contention that insanity was a physical disease, rather than an affliction of the mind, in part on the fact that he had found brain damage in almost every case; [22] and Pliny Earle had contributed articles on cerebral pathology to the second and third volumes of the *Journal*. Crude observations had limited interest; but the importance of this field was established when microscopy, chemical analysis, and the developing fields of histology and pathology allowed greater depth to examinations of the structure of diseased brains. John Gray was a pioneer in this area, instituting the first pathology department in an American asylum at Utica; and others, such as Earle and Workman, attempted to isolate the physical mechanisms of diseases.

These scientific techniques gave alienists new pride in their calling. They were now able to claim that they, like practitioners of general medicine, saw tangible, measurable traces of disease. Such advances, however, minimized interest in the observation of living patients, and also helped to form a barrier between alienists and lay community leaders. They no longer shared the common language of natural philosophy and humanism. Instead, practitioners were developing their own esoteric terminology and methodology, which was becoming increasingly incomprehensible to outsiders.

Another contemporary scientific tool that worked against the proponents of moral treatment was statistics. One of the great deficiencies of psychiatry frequently bemoaned by superintendents was the lack of any usable figures on the incidence and nature of insanity in the past against which contemporaries might measure their own hospital admission rates and assess their degree of treatment success. Attempts made to supply this want were hindered by the difficulty of defining and standardizing "moral causes" for use as an etiological category. Their enumeration was subjective, depending on vague reports of relatives and friends; and the records of each superintendent reflected idiosyncratic terminology and nosology. As John Gray wrote in a characteristic attack on those who used "moral causes" as an etiological category,

In the case of a patient who first exhibits what, in the judgment of the observer, is an insane manifestation during a thunder-storm, is the cause to be given as lightning, or thunder, or tempest, or flood?, or, is it a moral cause, as anxiety or alarm? Accidents of this sort are constantly stated as causes, and such an instance as the above is by no means an exaggerated one.[23]

Gray, Edward Jarvis, and others called for standardized, objective categorization by means of which they might expose factors contributing to the high incidence of mental disorder, and thus facilitate the organization of programs of prevention by making manifest the "laws of insanity."

In general, we study ecology in order to find preventive means. It is needless to say that no one seriously supposes meteorological phenomena to contain the elements of a prevention of cerebral symptoms any more than he does that planetary aspects control the virtues of medicinal herbs. Neither does he intend to urge the necessity of abating thunder-storms, or any of their incidents. We hope to be excused for seeming to trifle here, but we are at a loss how else to comment upon the grave burden of burlesques of scientific forms which the subject calls before us.[24]

He suggested that the classification by causes which Morel put forward in *Traite des Maladies Mentales* be adopted, in which patients were divided into the three categories of hereditary insanity: insanity the effect of toxic agents, such as narcotics, alcohol, food poisoning, puerperal insanity, and so on; and insanity caused by the transformation of certain nervous disorders.[25] In the late 1860's, various standard statistical forms were developed, and it was hoped that they would be adopted by all alienists so that figures could be collated across the United States and in a number of foreign countries.

Ironically, the new emphasis of psychological medicine on the scientific method contained a high degree of irrationality, for science was becoming the new cult, filled with infinite promise and mystery. Advances and discoveries in the physical sciences made nothing appear impossible. Thus, even while professing the most rigorous adherence to concrete facts and repudiating subjective notions, alienists were eager to accept almost anything, so long as it carried the labels of science. For example, alienists insisted that even when microscopic and chemical investigation failed to expose any lesion or other disturbance in brain tissue, the existence of physiological damage should nevertheless be accepted on the faith that perfected instruments would, in the future, make the invisible manifest. Similarly, in 1874, Charles H. Hughes of St. Louis published an article in the *Journal* entitled "Psychical or Physical," in which he discussed the possible existence of "thought molecules":

The conjecture is as plausible as the undulation, or the emanation theory of light, or the undulation theory of sound, or other theories in physics or chemistry. We have in this world to accept many such unreasonable but irrefutable truths.[26]

Natural science was regarded as a new panacea. It was hoped that in psychiatry, as in all other areas of life and letters, there were strict and knowable laws, which once discovered, would yield the key to prognostication. In a review of the second volume of the *History of Civilization in England* by Henry Thomas Buckle in the *American Journal of Insanity*, it was noted that

The universe is governed by inexorable ordinances; there are no breaks or blanks where law is intermitted. Science is such an exact acquaintance with this order of nature as will enable us to foretell occurrences; such a familiar knowledge of her regularities as will enable us to see beforehand, and predict in what time, places and conditions effects will take place. The test of science is the *prevision*.[27]

Isaac Ray carried this idea to its pregnant conclusion for mental health when he noted that

Disease, whether of body or mind, is governed by laws as inflexible as those of health, and that there is an invariable relation between them, whereby, within certain limits, we are able to infer with no less certainty, than to observe.[28]

A later article noted the role of epidemiological studies in this quest.

The "medicine of the future," in many of its departments likely to become almost wholly preventive, and thus of a public and general character, must owe more of its progress to statistical science.[29]

Categorization became the passion of late nineteenth-century American psychiatry, as patients were divided into separate wards according to disease entities. Nosological studies became the over-riding concern in an effort to bring order into the chaos of cases and symptomatologies flowing through asylums, and in an attempt to equip psychiatry with the same tools as general medicine. A number of recognizable and distinct disease entities was sought, of which the prognosis and treatment would be known, and knowl-edge of which could be transmitted systematically to younger men. So powerful did the dictates of classification become, that when Charles Guiteau, the assassin of President Garfield, was examined by such authorities as John Gray, there was widespread feeling among both European and American psychiatrists that despite a lifelong history of marked irrationality, the defendant could not possibly be judged insane. His symptoms were so bizarre and varied that they did not conform to those of any clinical cate-gory! [30]

This new psychiatric technology, however, had a poor effect on the patient community. Individual care was subordinated to mass treatment of categories. The flexibility of the earlier system, in which different methods of cure might be tried in turn, was lost in a general uniformity. Practitioners no longer noted idiosyncratic symptoms of a patient, but dealt with the label that he had once been given. John Galt, superintendent of the Eastern Lunatic Asylum, Williamsburg, Virginia, complained that patients were being treated as "senseless atoms," and subjected to a "daily routine proceeding with the inexorable monotonous motion of a ma-chine." [31]

Gray once commented that an undue emphasis on moral treat-ment and cures is nourished in libraries, not on wards; and indeed, while the organic orientation of mid-nineteenth-century American psychiatry was both a reaction against past excesses and a concord-ance with contemporary movements in medical science and gen-eral intellectual trends, clinical experience also had a major influ-ence in changing theory and practice.

The lesson of daily association with the mentally disturbed re-vealed the limitations of moral methods in treating a majority of the insane at a time when public law and clamor prevented practi-tioners from selecting their own patient population. Many of the cases admitted to hospitals in the 1850's and 1860's seem, in fact, to have been organically caused conditions, such as epilepsy, retardation, febrile conditions such as malaria, and tertiary syphilis. Of the latter perplexing condition, for instance, Workman noted,

After much reflection on the phenomena of insanity accompanied by paralysis, I am almost tempted to the belief, that it should be excluded from the general subject of mental alienation, and ranked in our nosology as a distinct and essential disease of the brain.[32]

Workman expressed the further confusion of his colleagues in an article "On Latent Phthisis in the Insane," in which he raised the issue that would be discussed for decades, whether the frequent co-existence of tuberculosis and mental disorder was coincidental, or whether it was an important factor in the course of insanity. As Workman noted,

Of all the morbid complications of incurable insanity, none is perhaps more extensively present, or more certainly fatal, than pulmonary tuberculosis phthisis. Esquirol estimated that in one out of every four persons becoming insane, thoracic disease exists.[33]

Asylums were also filled with a variety of nutritional deficiencies, such as pellagra; chronic alcoholism, which Jarvis estimated to account for 10 per cent of insanity;[34] as well as various toxic states and accidental brain injuries. The latter were particularly frequent in an early period of industrialization. As Jarvis wrote,

Almost the whole class of accidents, injuries, and exposures has increased. With the new improvements in the mechanic arts, the multiplication of machinery, the new and sometimes uncontrolled, if not uncontrollable, motive powers, and with the new modes of travel, more accidents happen, more injuries are inflicted, and in their way they multiply the causes and the cases of insanity.

In the course of the same progress of improvement, there are more chemical agents discovered, and numberless new applications of this science, and its discoveries to practical use, in the common arts and business of life. Men are, therefore, more exposed to minerals, acids, gases, paints, dye-stuffs, and combustibles, and explosive elements and mixtures, which are sometimes more or less injurious to health, or cause accidents dangerous to those who are connected with them, and consequently multiply the causes and cases of lunacy.[35]

The burdens of clinical practice left their mark on the agenda of annual meetings of the Association. Discussions veered away from general and philosophical expositions of the nature of insanity which would have interested laymen, and rested more and more on methods of administration and housekeeping, on the management of general paresis and epilepsy, and on the use of chloroform, bromides, and chloral ether. Disillusionment with moral management may be seen in such discussions as that on forced feeding, since greater clinical experience revealed the inadequacy of persuasion to deal with obstreperous behavior. It was found that some patients who refused to eat for long periods remained deaf to the blandishments of staff, and unless forcibly fed, died of starvation. A movement may thus be perceived away from one of the most noteworthy techniques of moral treatment, the reliance on reasoning with the insane, as a method of evoking good behavior.

The use of trust and of social expectations and demands to control patients also declined, as may be seen in the increased use of mechanical restraint. This issue will be discussed more fully later, when the controversies that it engendered are described.

The impact of changing professional theory on the patient community was to denigrate the importance of social organization in the etiology and cure of insanity. By the late nineteenth century, the history of a case contained a record of the patient's physical development and diseases, and any instances of insanity among his antecedents. It seldom included any social data. Changing professional theory altered the practitioner's approach to his patient, because clues to the nature of insanity were increasingly to be sought not by observation on wards or in conversations with the patient and his family, but on the dissecting table. This removed one of the forces that had aided the close relationship of practitioners to their patients, that of scientific curiosity.

The necessity of standardizing and disciplining fellow alienists in order to provide guidance for younger members of the guild and to draw on a wide pool of epidemiological data lowered the spontaneity of individual practitioners and produced rigidity and an intolerance of the all-embracing humanitarianism that had engendered the Association. It also failed to encourage any original work, for American psychiatry continued as a derivative system, relying on Europe for its discoveries.

As dramatic illustration of the degree to which the Association had become preoccupied with its own members and with the technical, scientific, and administrative aspects of the role of alienists, to the virtual exclusion of the society of patients and the society of the outside world, in 1881 the Association formed eight committees to report on the following areas at annual meetings:

1. Annual necrology of the Association
2. Cerebrospinal physiology
3. Cerebrospinal pathology
4. Therapeutics of insanity
5. Bibliography of insanity
6. Relation of eccentric diseases to insanity
7. Asylum location, construction, and sanitation
8. Criminal responsibility of the insane.[36]

This list may be compared with that of the committees formed by the early members of the Association in the 1850's, which reported on such issues as moral and medical treatment, restraints and restraining apparatus, the construction and organization of mental hospitals, laws governing insanity, prevention of suicide, preparing a manual for attendants, statistics, support of the pauper insane, asylums for idiots and demented, post-mortem examinations, the comparative advantages of hospitals and private practice, asylums for Negroes, insanity and prisons, and the causes and prevention of insanity.[37]

NOTES

1. *The American Journal of Insanity*, XXI (1864–1865), 159.

2. *Ibid.*, p. 244.

3. *The American Journal of Insanity*, XXIX (1872–1873), 82.

4. *The American Journal of Insanity*, XXI (1864–1865), 232.

5. *The American Journal of Insanity*, XXIX (1872–1873), 78–79.

6. Pliny Earle, *An Examination of the Practices of Bloodletting in Mental Disorders* (New York: Samuel S. and William Wood, 1854), p. 119.

7. *The American Journal of Insanity*, XIV (1857–1858), 68.

8. *The American Journal of Insanity*, XXI (1864–1865), 158.

9. *Ibid.*

10. Pliny Earle, *A Visit to Thirteen Asylums for the Insane in Europe* (Philadelphia: J. Dubson, 1841), p. 36.

11. *The American Journal of Insanity*, XIV (1857–1858), 36.

12. *Ibid.*, p. 152.

13. *The American Journal of Insanity*, XIX (1872–1873), 85.

14. *The American Journal of Insanity*, XXI (1864–1865), 250.

15. *The American Journal of Insanity*, XXIX (1872–1873), 87.

16. *Ibid.*, p. 90.

17. *Ibid.*, p. 168.

18. *Ibid.*, p. 172.

19. *The American Journal of Insanity*, XIX (1862–1863), 229.

20. *The American Journal of Insanity*, XXI (1864–1865), 359.

21. *The American Journal of Insanity*, XXXVI (1879–1880), 387.

22. Benjamin Rush, *Medical Inquiries*

and Observations Upon the Diseases of the Mind (New York: Hafner Publishing Co., 1962), p. 23.

23. *The American Journal of Insanity*, XVIII (1861–1862), 11.

24. *Ibid.*, p. 12.

25. *Ibid.*, pp. 12–13.

26. *The American Journal of Insanity*, XXXI (1874–1875), 31.

27. *The American Journal of Insanity*, XVIII (1861–1862), 70.

28. *The American Journal of Insanity*, XX (1863–1864), 28.

29. *The American Journal of Insanity*, XVIII (1861–1862), 13.

30. *The American Journal of Insanity*, XXXIX (1882–1883), 61.

31. *The American Journal of Insanity*, XIV (1857–1858), 391.

32. *The American Journal of Insanity*, XV (1858–1859), 2.

33. *The American Journal of Insanity*, XIX (1862–1863), 2.

34. Edward Jarvis, *Relation of Education to Insanity* (Washington, D.C.: Government Printing Office, 1872), p. 7.

35. *Ibid.*

36. Henry M. Hurd (ed.), *The Institutional Care of the Insane in the United States and Canada* (Baltimore: Johns Hopkins Press, 1916), Vol. I, p. 42.

37. Albert Deutsch, *The Mentally Ill in America* (New York: Columbia University Press, 1945), p. 194.

Chapter 15

CHANGING PROFESSIONAL
ATTITUDES TOWARD
THE INSANE

One of the most profound, though gradual, changes in mid-nineteenth-century American psychiatry was the virtual reversal of alienists' attitudes toward the insane. As wards became chronically overcrowded, as more immigrants and paupers filled asylums, and as public laws obliged superintendents to accept alcoholics, criminals, and other "undesirable" patients, a return may be seen in psychiatric speeches and writing to some of the earliest stereotypes of lunatics as indecent, inhuman, and menacing. This was, of course, profoundly ironic, because alienists had long attempted to dispel similar notions in the lay population. Their own negative attitude helped to confirm laymen in old prejudices about the bestial and hopeless nature of insanity, and about the inhuman treatment by alienists of their charges.

In part this negative view of insanity among superintendents arose from the etiological theory which held that an overwhelming number of cases were due to faulty heredity engendered by vice and dissipation among ancestors. Masturbation, excessive drinking and smoking, or the reading of lascivious or sadistic novels were thought to produce insanity, transmittable to future generations.

The hereditability of brain damage was an early concept, and was found, for instance, in the work of Esquirol, who had noted that the children of women crazed by the French Revolution were unusually prone to insanity. A number of subsequent studies seemed to confirm the fact that children of lunatics had a poor prognosis for maintaining mental health, as had the children of those who had endured major social trauma. It was believed that political, social, and financial upheavals, like wars, revolutions, or the South Sea Bubble, inevitably disequilibrated minds on a mass scale. During the Civil War, alienists expected an increase in asylum admissions. When, however, the forecasted epidemic failed to occur, it was predicted that the trauma would take its toll in the next generation.[1]

Emphasis on vice as a major cause of insanity altered the earlier, nonjudgmental view of patients as innocent and helpless, and returned practitioners to a traditional concept of madness as one of the wages of sin. The public was warned to avoid dangerous habits in highly emotional terms in books and articles about such issues as "the secret vice," or masturbation. Gray thus hailed *A Warning to Fathers, Teachers and Young Men, in Relation to a Fruitful Cause of Insanity, and Other Serious Disorders of Youth*, by W. S. Chipley, superintendent of the Eastern Lunatic Asylum, Lexington, Kentucky, as a book in which "an unwelcome and almost repulsive task has been admirably performed." [2]

G. C. S. Choate, superintendent of the asylum at Taunton, Massachusetts, wrote in an annual report,

There can be no question, that those who disregard the moral law and the laws of nature, are not only more liable themselves to insanity, but also transmit this disability to their descendants. The parent who indulges in the excessive use of poisonous substances, or who gives way to enervating or debilitating indulgences, even if not made insane himself is exceedingly liable to pay the penalty of his transgression in witnessing the horrible epileptic convulsion, or the pitiable imbecility, or the more awful maniacal paroxysm of his child. And if the child follows the evil course of the parent, which is too apt to be the case, an hereditary family tendency is formed, which develops into disease, upon what, under other circumstances, would be very far from being a sufficient exciting cause.[3]

Vice as a prime originator of hereditary insanity was discussed in a number of books for laymen, such as Isaac Ray's *Mental Hygiene*. Here the author sought to "expose the mischievous effects of many practices and customs prevalent in modern society, and to present some practical suggestions relative to the attainment of mental soundness and vigor." Ray believed that intemperance was a prolific cause of hereditary insanity, leading not only to a repetition of patterns of drunkenness in children, but also producing a tendency to cerebral degeneration, immorality, and criminality. He cited the case of a patient of R. Hills, admitted to the Ohio Lunatic Hospital in 1861 to prove his point. This man had begotten four children in his youth, all of whom were normal. He then became an alcoholic, and during this time had four more children, two of whom were currently in a lunatic asylum, the third was an idiot, and the fourth an epileptic. The unfortunate father had meanwhile reformed; and during this recent temperate period, had sired three more children, all of whom were normal.[4]

Although such writings may conceivably have taught individuals to avoid a life of drunkenness and vice, they are more likely to have encouraged them to regard those who were, or had been, insane as walking evidence of the wages of sin, thus negating the attempts of practitioners to ameliorate the attitude of the public toward the unfortunate. Moreover, alienists themselves and their families, once noted for living closely with patients, also began to withdraw the hems of their garments from the corruption of the insane, thus further isolating their patients.

The concept of hereditary insanity lent a fatalistic tone to discussions of its nature. Those suffering from mental disorders were no longer seen as ordinary members of the community who had been stricken by chance, but as a race apart that might corrupt the welfare of all society with its tainted blood. John Gray criticized annual reports that continued to tell the public that all were as susceptible to insanity as to any other naturally occurring disease, because, he said, hereditary factors were too important.[5] Similarly, Isaac Ray wrote in the 1864 Report of Butler Hospital that tables of causes of insanity were of little value because hereditary factors were the primary determinants, although often difficult to discover.

If I have succeeded in making myself thoroughly understood, it must be admitted that the causes of insanity which spring up around us are of far less potency than those which we bring into the world with us, and that the only effectual measure of prevention is that which gives them no chance to enter the blood. Most certainly, until this conclusion is adopted, we shall witness little diminution of the amount of insanity in the world.[6]

Long-term prevention of insanity, however, was still thought possible with the aid of eugenics, in which the union of the handicapped and the "vicious feeble-minded" would be prevented. Some marriages between normal individuals were also considered dangerous, particularly those of cousins. A number of studies had been conducted that purported to show that consanguineous unions produced an unusually heavy burden of suffering and dependency. S. G. Howe, for instance, studied 17 such marriages and the resulting 95 children and found that the latter included "forty-four idiots, twelve scrofulous and delicate, one deaf, and one dwarf." [7] Bemis of Worcester State Hospital combined his own observations with those of others to record that in 833 marriages of cousins that produced 3,942 children, there were "one hundred and forty-five deaf mutes, eighty-five blind, three hundred and eight idiotic, thirty-eight insane, sixty epileptics, three hundred scrofulous, ninety-eight deformed and one hundred defective in one way or another." [8]

Such findings impressed the public, since alienists lobbied successfully in a number of states for legislation forbidding the marriage of cousins. The following is an excerpt from a speech by Governor Magoffin of Kentucky that illustrates the gullibility of the public in accepting sensationally phrased information, and the precariousness of their trust in alienists, because the claims of the latter could not ultimately be fulfilled.

By a single act of the Legislature you can save in the future an immense amount of suffering. You can diminish, according to the opinion of those who have fully investigated the subject, 20 percent of the number of imbeciles, insane, deaf-mutes, and blind children. Render the marriage of cousins illegal, and a great evil is at once eradicated. At least from fifteen to twenty percent of all sufferers are the offspring of cousins. A gentleman of science, of learning and enlarged experience, who has for a long time paid a great deal of attention to this subject, recently informed me that he never yet had seen all the children so related sound in body and mind. There is always among some of them some defect, mentally or bodily. A large number of the pupils (so say the teachers) in the Deaf and Dumb Asylums are the children of cousins. . . .

The state, when the parents or friends of these children are not able to provide for them, has to do it; and the instances are numerous where the burden falls on her to provide for and educate these mutes, insane, blind, or imbeciles. She is weakened by so many of her citizens suffering these privations, and a heavy tax is thereby imposed upon her. It is her duty to protect herself against the evil and expense by forbidding such unions, which nature forbids by the natural penalty she uniformly inflicts. [9]

Increased emphasis on the hereditability of insanity led Ray and others to urge the public to eschew marriage with anyone whose family bore the taint of insanity.

The highest mental and personal accomplishments will prove to be no compensation for the evil; nor will they furnish any excuse for compromising the welfare of those who derive from us their existence. None but they who have a professional acquaintance with the subject, can conceive of the amount of wretchedness in the world produced by this single cause. None can adequately estimate the suffering, the privation, the ruined hopes, the crushed affections, the blighted prospects, that may be fairly numbered among its effects.[10]

Such statements negated the work of alienists who had long been attempting to educate the public to take a more rational and sympathetic view of insanity, to regard it as a natural disease to be treated in a public hospital, not as a family disgrace to be hidden in the attic. But such concepts as this served to reinforce the old prejudice and evasion, because acknowledging a family taint would damage the marriage prospects of a good proportion of the population. Although the old phrenological view held that even a predisposition could be controlled by education, habits, and healthy environment, later writing simplified the concept into a far more fatalistic notion.

The concept of heredity carried with it implications of what in later years would be known as "Social Darwinism," a philosophy of society governed by the concept of survival of the fittest, in which the individual was subordinated to the economic need and the racial purity of the total community. Because intelligence and sanity were thought to be hereditary, they were also racially determined; and hence such groups as the Irish and the Negroes were expected to have higher rates of insanity and lower rates of cure than the allegedly more robust Anglo-Saxons. In 1864, the *Journal* reprinted a review from the *London Intellectual Observer* on "psychological differences which exist among the tropical races of man," in which it was noted that among the colored races, there was inferior mental age and mental agility, with an inability to grasp complex intellectual and moral thoughts.[11]

A corollary of this position was that nature should be allowed to destroy the weaker members of society. It was feared that, if defective individuals were saved by charity or medicine, they would intermarry with, and enervate, the community. At the 1862 Annual Meeting of the Association, for instance, Jarvis noted that although the amenities of civilization, such as better quality and more skillful preparation of food, enable more people to survive childhood, those with weaker constitutions only lived to succumb to later stress.[12] Workman agreed, and described a town in his native Canada whose citizens were noted for their robustness, and where one-third of the children died in their first year. He ascribed this mortality rate to the fact that all children were carried to church for baptism, no matter what the weather, and only the strongest survived the ordeal. He added,

This is one reason why these people are so robust, that from negligence and various other agencies all the delicate ones die. By your artificial treatment you carry these people forward. You do not confer a blessing upon the whole community, but upon the people themselves. For I am sure, in a broad view of the subject, losing sight of individuals, it was much better that they should die before they perpetuated the evil, and left a weak and sickly people to follow them. This evil will rectify itself—will die out in insanity and other diseases in which it is now wearing itself out.[13]

A return may also be seen among alienists of that period to traditional notions that in the past had dehumanized the insane and that had been fought by early superintendents and reformers. Such, for instance, was the idea that those suffering from mental disorder are less sensitive than the sane to pain and deprivation. Andrew McFarland told a meeting of physicians in Illinois in 1862,

The suspension of physical pain, for instance, which occurs in many cases of mental disease, is so great as to mask and conceal bodily injuries of an extreme character. The nerves of sensation seem actually paralyzed.[14]

The same message was also conveyed more subtly by the fact that the insane, when placed in the most unpleasant surroundings, appeared oblivious to their misery, surviving for years. This gave those accustomed to such sights an impression of the ability of the insane to withstand inhuman stress. James Leonard Mount, of the Hamilton County Lunatic Asylum, Cincinnati, wrote in an annual report,

When we look around us, and observe nearly 300 persons crowded into apartments but ill suited to indifferently accommodate one-third the number, forced, for want of space, to remain closely and constantly pent-up and unoccupied through the day, and at night crowded together in large numbers in small rooms, in too many of which there is no method of ventilation whatever, (for, owing to the fact that we have no means of heating the sleeping rooms of two of our buildings, the windows must be kept closed, particularly during the winter months, to prevent our patients suffering from cold, knowing the ordinary effects of breathing such a vitiated atmosphere, poisoned by the nauseous effluvia arising from so many human bodies)—we are led to conclude that the freedom from sickness among these old demented people, and the tenacity of life manifested by them, must be accounted for on the ground that derangement of the mental faculties renders the system less vulnerable to the ordinary causes of disease and death.[15]

From such a view, it was too easy to reach the conclusion that more comfortable, and hence more expensive, accommodation for the insane was unnecessary. This was already the tendency of planners erecting institutions for the poor. It was felt that the lower classes were unused to comfort in their normal life, and that therefore they had no need of it when they became dependent on public charity.

Another factor separating the mentally disturbed from the sympathy of the community was the expression by alienists of a need to protect the public against the presence of lunatics in their midst. Institutionalization was thus restored to its traditional role as a method of isolating a dangerous and corrupting class. This may be seen in Isaac Ray's remarks about the contagious nature of mental disorder, a notion derived from instances of mass hysteria. It was felt that the safety of the sane, and particularly of children, demanded the extrusion of lunatics from families in order to prevent spreading of their disturbance.

It is incumbent on all, therefore, who know these facts [of epidemics of insanity], so to regulate their work and conversation, as to expose themselves to no unnecessary danger. Intimate association with persons affected with nervous infirmities, such as chorea, hysteria, epilepsy, insanity, should be avoided by all who are endowed with a peculiarly susceptible nervous organization, whether strongly predisposed to nervous disease, or only vividly impressed by the sight of suffering and agitation. Not one of the least evils incident to insanity is, that the poor sufferer cannot receive the ministry of near relatives, without endangering the mental integrity of those who offer them; and the common practice of removing the insane from their own homes is required, not more for their own welfare than the safety of those immediately around them.[16]

The burden of the insane on relatives was also discussed by McFarland in his address to the Illinois State Medical Society in 1862, when he spoke of the imposition by hypochondriacs of their illusions on families:

The extent to which such persons will sometimes impose their imaginings upon others as realities, is one of the curiosities of human experience. The patient martyrdom of the sympathizing mother, regarding it as her pious duty to forego every earthly pleasure in order to confine herself to the bedside of a daughter thus afflicted, whose condition constantly becomes more deplorable by witnessing this very self-devotion on the part of the parent, is a truly affecting instance of a double delusion, in which it is difficult to say which case is the more pitiable.[17]

Thus institutionalization was again advocated to relieve the sane of an unwelcome burden. Such arguments contributed to professional opposition to a plan much discussed during the late nineteenth century, to board out chronic and harmless lunatics to families in the lay community, because it was felt that innocent children might be endangered. One cannot help wondering whether this particular idea was not the product of the experience of superintendents themselves, living in a world of lunatics and increasingly isolated from rational minds. The discomfort of this, and the high rate of breakdown among alienists in Europe and America, may have led some to feel that life with the insane had acute dangers. It may also have contributed to the increasing distance discernible between superintendents and their patients.

Changing views of insanity because of changing theories and clinical experience took their toll on liberal treatment. The efficacy of moral management and the degree to which patients might be trusted among the public or with the families of alienists became an urgent question as an increasing number of practitioners described experiences in which previously quiet and trusted patients were suddenly revealed to have a capacity for great violence. It thus seemed imperative to protect both hospital personnel and the general public from this source of danger.

The question was discussed at the 1856 annual meeting of the Association. Gray had presented a paper on "Homicide in Insanity," in which he had noted,

A disposition to violence is a common characteristic of mental disease. It is exhibited in every conceivable manner, from harsh words to suicide and the most cruel and brutal murders, and is found in every form of insanity. If then, among the unhappy phenomena or symptoms developed, under the influence of the delusion and hallucinations peculiar to the disease, we meet with a tendency so universal, so destructive of happiness, and so dangerous to society, how important is its careful study, with reference to the welfare both of the patient and the public! [18]

Thomas Kirkbride remarked that the presentation

had served to strengthen his conviction, that the danger to be apprehended from the class known as harmless insane was much greater than the community generally supposed, and that a record of such cases, and the accidents resulting, would present some startling facts. He thought that where there was one such case confined improperly and unnecessarily, ten or twelve were at large who every year commit some great offense against society. What shall be done with those acquitted of deeds of violence on the ground of insanity is an important question. He thought that convicts who became insane should be kept under prison discipline, and that the criminal insane should not be allowed to go at large.[19]

John S. Butler next told of an experience that struck at the practice of having the superintendent and his family mingle freely with patients. He had had a quiet old gentleman under his care who had become a constant companion to one of the superintendent's children. After his recovery, the old man came to Butler and said,

You should be more careful, Doctor, in allowing your children to be with your patients; three or four times I have had a strong inclination to kill H———.[20]

The incident made a strong impression on Butler, who came to treat patients with much greater caution.

He had under his care several robust men of the class of apparently harmless insane, who could accomplish a great deal of work around the premises, but he never allowed them to be trusted.[21]

There was general agreement among participants that great care should be taken in allowing dangerous implements to be issued for work.

Choate remarked that in Massachusetts, where the hospitals were crowded, it was the practice to send quiet, harmless, and incurable patients to one of the three state almshouses, some of which now housed 150 lunatics. While he felt that in the present state of the hospitals this was unavoidable, he questioned the safety of this practice. Gray added that a similar situation existed in New York, where patients were allowed to wander freely away from the hospital only to cause damage in the community. Kirkbride wondered whether homicidal patients and insane criminals should

be confined for a lifetime, rather than risk the lives of the many who might cross their paths if they were at large.[22]

As though to underscore this discussion, Utica Asylum was set on fire and largely destroyed on July 14, 1857, by a patient, a docile, quiet youth who had been known to set fires before a previous admission to the institution, but who had seemed trustworthy after treatment and during an intervening return to the community. The same year, news came of a patient in the Avignon Asylum in France, who had fatally stabbed a physician with a pair of scissors with which he had been working.

Fear of violence was inspired in part by the fact that public institutions were no longer able to select their own patients, and were instead required to accept those sent by the courts and the commissioners of the poor. These increasingly came to include violent, maniacal patients as well as the criminally insane, both those who had been acquitted of crimes of violence on the grounds of insanity, and those prisoners in penal institutions who became mentally disturbed while serving their sentence.

Fear of violence was also the result of feelings of loss of control over patients by alienists; first, when hospitals became overcrowded to the extent that superintendents no longer knew every patient, and when the proportion of attendants to patients declined; and, second, as younger alienists emerged, lacking the confidence, idealism, and the charisma of their predecessors, who had been able to quell violent patients with their eyes.

Fear of potential violence in even the most docile patients led to the establishment of greater distance between alienists and the insane, and greater isolation of the insane from the community. It contributed to the growth of custodial institutions because there was no way of knowing whether a patient was really cured of his violent urges, and whether it was therefore wise to discharge him. Superintendents felt responsible for protecting the public against possible outrage, so they laid greater emphasis on preventing escapes or "elopements." They therefore curtailed work and recreation programs which might allow patients to elude attendants.

Fear of violence produced distance in another way, because the statements of alienists about their patients were now reinforcing the traditional terrors of the public. McFarland, for instance, told the Illinois State Medical Society that the insane do, indeed, resemble children—

children who rob birds' nests, kill cats, and fight savagely over a piece of cake. This characteristic of childhood is removed when the passing years instill the rule of reason; but when reason is lost, the individual reverts to childish cruelty and violence.[23]

NOTES

1. *The American Journal of Insanity*, XX (1863–1864), 477.

2. *The American Journal of Insanity*, XVII (1860–1861), 472.

3. *The American Journal of Insanity*, XXI (1864–1865), 291–292.

4. Isaac Ray, *Mental Hygiene* (Boston: Ticknor and Fields, 1863), p. 45.

5. *The American Journal of Insanity*, XVI (1859–1860), 240.

6. *The American Journal of Insanity*, XXI (1864–1865), 242.

7. Ray, *op. cit.*, pp. 38–39.

8. *Ibid.*, p. 39.

9. *The American Journal of Insanity*, XVI (1859–1860), 360–361.

10. Ray, *op. cit.*, p. 19.

11. *The American Journal of Insanity*, XXXVII (1881–1882), 95.

12. *The American Journal of Insanity*, XIX (1862–1863), 79.

13. *Ibid.*, pp. 52–53.

14. *The American Journal of Insanity*, XX (1863–1864), 14.

15. *The American Journal of Insanity*, XVI (1859–1860), 225.

16. Ray, *op. cit.*, p. 174.

17. *The American Journal of Insanity*, XX (1863–1864), 17.

18. *The American Journal of Insanity*, XIV (1857–1858), 119.

19. *Ibid.*, p. 91.

20. *Ibid.*, p. 92.

21. *Ibid.*

22. *Ibid.*, p. 108.

23. *The American Journal of Insanity*, XX (1863–1864), 23.

Chapter 16

DETERIORATING PRACTICE
IN MENTAL HOSPITALS

By the mid-1860's and 1870's, treatment in most American asylums was poor by any standards. Overcrowding had become the norm, with patients often sleeping on straw pallets on the floors of halls. Annual reports announced the purchase of bedsteads and mattresses as a major accomplishment.

Asylum architecture became gaudy and nonfunctional, as psychiatrists were to complain bitterly in later years. In 1889, W. W. Godding, medical superintendent of the Government Hospital for the Insane, Washington, D.C., told the Association in his presidential address,

Patients find themselves in the midst of oppressive splendor, vast hall spaces lined with settees, in stately gothic, mediaeval in their discomfort, of which good old Dr. Ray once said to me inquiringly, "Nobody ever sits down on these things?"; drafty corridors where they encounter for the first time in their lives the chilly contradictions of the problem of forced ventilation; blank, white walls and ceilings that awe them by their shadowy light; polished floors coldly beautiful in their cleanliness that suggests a skating rink. Amid such unaccustomed environments they should recover at once under the well-recognized curative influence of entire change of surroundings, or failing of cures, pine in nostalgic melancholia for the homely comforts of a cottage, not so imposing in its architecture, but more homelike; or perchance (they may) characterize the whole cathedral pile, after the manner of one of my poor fellows, as a "palatial barn." [1]

Not only were buildings inadequate, but so was personnel. Political jobbery continued to take its toll. Attendants were scarce and of questionable character.

Contemporary scientific advances in brain physiology, neurology, and pathology reached only the elite of the psychiatric profession, though some version of emerging theories filtered down to the rest in *American Journal of Insanity* articles and the like. These papers showed a marked drop in quality from earlier years. They were often badly written and poorly reasoned, repeating over and over older ideas or tortured versions of new theories. These contrast strikingly with articles in contemporary neurological journals, which had clearer focus and a more competent tone. Superintendents were harried by their duties, and perhaps too discouraged by the hundreds of chronic cases under their care and by their own lack of scientific work to write anything inspired. There was also the careful editing of John Gray, which pruned ideas with which he disagreed, particularly those smacking of undue loyalty to moral causality and moral treatment.

The treatment schemes of most superintendents show the same stagnation as their writing. An increasing number of drugs were used in large doses; some surgery appeared, as in experiments in removing ovaries; and purges, diets, and enforced rest remained as popular as ever.

In the absence of significant advances, and following an already established pattern in American psychiatry to hail a favorite remedy or treatment scheme as the new panacea, fads developed that helped to negate the claims of alienists that they practiced the scientific method. This tendency in his colleagues had been noted and attacked by Isaac Ray. He felt that few superintendents were ever wise enough to maintain a middle course; instead, they often seized upon untried ideas, and used them to excess, while dropping older methods of proven utility because they would not cure every case.[2]

A dramatic example of a fad in full cry may be seen in records of the 1874 meeting of the Association, when favorite medications were discussed. It was disclosed that in a majority of asylums, the most popular item in the pharmacopoeia was chloral hydrate. One member warned his colleagues that

In some institutions it is given in large doses, and, in many cases continued for a long period. Its great popularity in connection with the fact that so many physicians regard it free from danger, I fear, has already caused many grave results attending its use to be overlooked.[3]

Cautious alienists noted that experience in English hospitals had demonstrated a danger of poisoning and of paralysis of the respira-

tory system. The enthusiasts at the meeting, however, rose to the
defence of chloral hydrate, both as a soporific and as a therapeutic
tool, because it was said to diminish cerebral arterial circulation, a
finding that would have pleased Benjamin Rush. What is fascinating in this discussion is the passion with which users of chloral
hydrate defended their favorite drug, and the vehemence with
which they discounted caution:

In [chloral hydrate's] administration, I do not feel that I am required
to observe more caution than in the use of opium, or any other harmless drug, if used within due bounds. I seldom use it in doses larger
than thirty grains. But thirty grains seem to be regarded by yourself as
an absolutely large dose.[4]

When a resolution was proposed advocating the use of chloral
hydrate "with great caution," a chorus refused to affirm it unless
the word *caution* were removed. When it was pointed out that the
public was buying the drug from apothecaries for the thrill of
experiencing an alteration of consciousness, another member demanded, "Why single out chloral hydrate?" and asked that all medications be included in the resolution.

It is hardly surprising that psychiatrists were complacent about
established remedies. During the nineteenth century, there was no
machinery to follow up cases and assess the long-term outcome of
treatment, unless the patient were recommitted to the same hospital
and were remembered by the staff. Thus, even when interest re-
vived in experimental clinical work, psychiatrists were seriously
handicapped, as a young doctor from Taunton Asylum in Massachusetts complained in the 1880's. He had tried to ascertain empiri-
cally the best length of stay for alcoholics in asylums. In the absence of available evidence, he eventually was forced to make a
guess of two to three years.[5]

One of the characteristics of psychiatric practice at this time
appears to have been a marked detachment from patients. Superintendents referred to them as objects to be manipulated, rather than
as individuals to be motivated and led. A certain brutal jocularity
may be seen in the following characteristic article of the period, a
"Report on the Therapeutics of Insanity," by J. G. Rogers, superintendent of the Asylum for the Insane, Indianapolis. It is typical
of its time for repeating old remedies; for the way in which patients are regarded as virtually inert or, perhaps, as creatures
obstructing their own treatment; and for referring to the insane

not as individuals, but as members of generalized categories, for whom prescriptions were made en masse, with little or no variation from one case to another.

The lower intestines [of maniacs] are usually loaded; they should be emptied by very large enemata of water at 90° of temperature, in gallon portions if necessary, repeated incessantly till successful and retained by a tampon around pipe or syringe if there be a disposition to prematurely discharge. This system of "hydraulic mining," so to speak, if skillfully used, will excite evacuation of the entire canal, often discharging enormous scybalae. This may, in cases of active cerebral hyperaemia, be advantageously supplemented by an active purgative *per os.*[6]

The major emphasis of psychiatry became diagnostic, the ability to place a patient in his proper category as quickly as possible, for upon this his subsequent treatment depended. The degree of professional preoccupation with categorization may be seen, for example, in an 1874 article by R. P. Hughes, assistant physician of the Alabama Insane Hospital, "Psychological Medicine Considered as a Specialty." The author suggested that clinical experience be a necessary prerequisite for high office in asylums and for appearing as an expert witness in criminal trials. Such experience might be assessed, he wrote, by an examination conducted by the Association, in which the candidate, after showing his general knowledge of insanity, would tour a ward with the examining committee, to classify patients according to some normative scheme.[7]

The most important categorization was that which divided the few curable patients from the majority of chronic ones. In an article on the "Treatment of the Insane," Orpheus Everts, medical superintendent of the Cincinnati Sanitarium, limited his remarks as follows:

It may be understood . . . in advance, that the recommendations and suggestions to follow in this report, pertain to the treatment of such of the insane as are supposed to be curable by treatment; any allusion to the other class being simply incidental.

I shall assume that the physician called upon to treat the insane, is capable of differentiating the curable from the incurable; or, if not, treating them tentatively, as if curable.[8]

During this period, thoughtful alienists still considered the total environment of the hospital, rather than individual components of physical treatment, as the most important element of therapy.

Everts, for example, noted that the basis of the effectiveness of a mental hospital was restraint—not specific forms of straps and muffs,

but restraint in a general and comprehensive sense. Restraint—that falls upon the patient as he approaches the hospital, as the shadows fall from its facades and towers upon the lawn beneath. Restraint—that becomes more appreciable when expressed by the attitude of persons in authority, superintendent and subordinates, physicians, attendants, nurses, and others, acting under orders, whereby the patient is placed at once, and unequivocally, upon the footing of a person laboring under some kind of disability—as requiring care and treatment—as an invalid—as insane. A whole system of restraints, making it possible to secure, for the benefit of the insane, more or less perfectly, by general and special means, persuasive or coercive: (a) regularity of habits, including eating, drinking, bathing, exercise, and rest; and (b) an abandonment of pernicious practices. All of which, to an intelligent observer familiar with the homes and habits of our people—the assumptions, intolerance of environment, insubordination toward authority, and indifference to consequences of conduct, characteristic of the insane; and the attitude of concession, evasion, and downright lying generally occupied by relatives, friends, and physicians, toward the patient, justifies the presumption in favor of hospital, over home-treatment, upon which the recommendations of this report are based.[9]

Everts continued that if institutionalization were impossible, relatives must turn the home into a hospital:

So far, at least, as to effect a recognition of the fact, on the part of the patient, that he, or she, is regarded, and will be treated, as a person incompetent to direct affairs pertaining to him, or herself; and to secure observance of the most important regulations, respecting conduct, and conditions of person and surroundings, essential to health.[10]

Although the earlier system of moral management was authoritarian, imposing on patients rules of regular life and habits, its goal was to elicit and reinforce sane, controlled behavior. In this later system, on the other hand, the pressures of the total environment were mobilized to impress the patient with his own illness and subservience to authority. His strength and that of the community of other patients were discounted; recovery could be effected only by compelling passive acquiescence to the management of the staff by persuasion, mechanical restraints, or drugs, by means of which the damaged brain would be cured with hardly any participation by the patient himself.

The concept of moral management was remembered, but it was now called "moral restraint." Everts felt it was a weak prop, first because it depended on the doubtful skill of those using it, a clear indication of the lack of trust with which attendants were held by the medical staff; and, second, and more frequently, "because of the impairment of organs, on the part of the insane, upon which reflex mental capabilities depend." [11] Everts saw rewards and punishments as the chief component of "moral restraint,"

by which lower human and higher brute beings are ever influenced. He may be said to have attained a lofty intellectual eminence who can see clearly other data of ethics than rewards and punishments, immediate or prospective.[12]

Most lunatics, Everts concluded, have such powerful delusions that exposing them to music, lectures, religious services, and sports would be useless.

Just as the attitude of practitioners of moral treatment toward the asylum environment reflected their view of the total community, one demanding freedom and self-reliance within a framework of fixed standards of work, religion, and regular life, so the system of mental hospitals conceived of by Everts and his colleagues reflected a later *Weltanschauung*. This was a Darwinian, or rather Spencerian, system in which human destiny was restrained by the laws of heredity and natural selection.

Nature, of which we are a part, yet heed so little, is full of suggestions on this as on other subjects; were we but wise enough to see and comprehend them. For example—the conditions of our being are all coercive. Our environments are all restraints, imposed by nature. This world, in which we have our being and prate of liberty, is but a grand old hospital for the insane; and we are, all of us, but so many inmates, suffering limitations, each in accordance with his own infirmities, incompetences, or delusions. Incompetency throughout the universe implies subordination, from which neither love nor pity can redeem it.[13]

Therefore, all those who called for reform of asylums in order to give the insane more freedom were indulging in wishful thinking, which, if implemented, would only harm the unfortunate.

It is sweet and gentle to be interested, sentimentally, in the condition and welfare of the depraved and vicious—who are depraved and vicious because of an arrest of human development short of the higher and more complex intellectual capabilities that are essential to high, complex intellectual perceptions. Yet there is danger of sacrificing the best interests, not only of society, but of the vicious themselves, by permitting our conduct toward them to partake more of sympathy than of judgment.

For, continued Everts in inimitable prose,

Children or savages, according to the degree of deterioration effected by the disease, or the violence of activities manifested, are the insane.

As children or savages, according to conditions, tenderly or rigidly, they must be treated, for their own good and the welfare of society.[14]

This same message, that the will of the insane must be restrained to promote sanity, was echoed by Stephen Smith, the New York Commissioner of Lunacy, when he addressed the first graduating class of the training school for attendants at the State Asylum in Buffalo in April, 1886.

How shall . . . a man be brought to obedience—perhaps the very first step toward recovery? . . . He is overcome by superior strength, and the first link in the chain of disorderly thoughts and feelings is broken. . . . [The attendants] have done their duty well and faithfully, according to the rules and regulations of asylums, and have not abused their trusts. But patients in their insane state very naturally construe these efforts as gross forms of abuse.[15]

Subsequent complaints and investigations, however, were to prove that some attendants had been brutal, and even homicidal, in their attempts to restrain patients, and, by the late 1880's and early 1890's, a number had been jailed for assault and murder.

In 1867, the Massachusetts Board of State Charities reported,

One cause of the sadness felt in visiting our hospitals . . . is the sight of so many persons of each sex, in the prime or middle of life, sitting or lying about, moping idly and listlessly in the debilitating atmosphere of the wards, and sinking gradually into a torpor, like that of living corpses.[16]

Work programs were one of the major characteristics of moral treatment, providing a method by which the physical and social environment of the hospital had been structured in order to re-educate the insane. The work program had also served to reduce the dangers of alienation from the surrounding culture, because it enabled patients to re-enter a society in which labor was the rule of life, success in occupation a measure of grace, and idleness an invitation to mischief or to become an unwelcome burden on the resources of the community. The fate of the work program during this period provides a microscopic view of the melange of forces that eclipsed moral treatment in most institutions, and of the responses of superintendents to these pressures.

During the early days of moral treatment, work programs theoretically fitted the culture of patients. Even in those early days, however, rich patients and their relatives resisted labor, and overseers of the poor objected to indigents working unless the fees paid by the localities to the hospital were lowered. The *Journal* was thus forced to emphasize the benefits to patients from manual labor and to stress the fact that such programs were therapeutic rather than designed to profit the institution.

These problems foreshadowed the fate of the program. The system of work soon reflected the same economic problems and propaganda excesses of other aspects of moral treatment. Superintendents complained in annual reports of idleness on their wards because of a paucity of suitable tools and occupations, particularly during the winter months when outdoor labor was impossible; and they begged for funds to expand their programs. Moreover, work, like other facets of the movement, shared in the hyperbolic claims of curability, as in the following remark by R. Hills:

The sight of ten, twenty or thirty of the patients thus employed in these rural labors, engaged as if each and all had a decided interest in the results, cheerfully following the direction of their leader, and incontinently dropping one after another of their insane ideas, is pleasant to behold. It matters but little what the delusions are,—one may be sure that the millennium is at hand; another has committed an unpardonable sin; another is the King of Tartary; another the Son of God; another is dispensing millions; all are harmoniously hoeing the crops, or digging potatoes, not thinking of the inconsistency of their labors with their fancied callings and conditions.[17]

Hills' ebullience inspired an acid comment from John Gray, arbiter of guild standards. The latter objected to his colleague's raising public expectations to an unrealistic level, and he attacked the use of physical labor indiscriminately for classes of patients for whom work was no longer considered desirable or safe in view of new categorized indications for somatic therapy. Gray, after poking fun at Hills' overly vivid metaphor wrote:

But does it not matter a little what the delusions are? Or rather, are the classes of patients entertaining the delusions noticed, those in whose treatment field labor is safe and beneficial? He who has "committed the unpardonable sin," is a victim of melancholia, worn out and emaciated from the pain of perhaps some visceral disorder, and who needs rest, passive exercise and tonic regimen. If, as is likely, he is impelled to labor by delusions of a penalty to be self-inflicted, so much the more certainly should he not be allowed by Dr. Hills, to assist in hoeing the crops or digging potatoes. The "King of Tartary" is the chronic case, who is properly set at such labor, but he will not drop his delusions into the soil which he cultivates. The "Son of God" is not an acute case, is at least a very dangerous chronic one to use the hoe among a number of his fellows. The case of general paralysis, or of partial dementia with expansive delusions, who is "dispensing millions," will be quite as likely to cut up the crops as the weeds which are about him. The colors of the picture are put on quite at random.[18]

Gray's comment alludes to two further factors that altered the nature of hospital work programs as well as other aspects of moral treatment and its relations with the lay community. First, it was feared that patients might erupt and damage themselves and others; and, second, it was felt that programs were unduly expensive because much patient labor was unproductive and was even destructive of the equipment with which they were working.

The economic issue was a subject of particular urgency, embroiling work and other therapeutic modalities in the financial complications of asylum management. Work programs were particularly vulnerable because their therapeutic intent was liable to be overshadowed by their potential financial role. On the one hand, asylums were apt to call on patient labor to produce necessary goods and services to supplement tight budgets. On the other hand, superintendents curtailed such programs, afraid of exploitation of the insane, particularly if legislatures were tempted to lower appropriations when they discovered that hospitals were drawing on a pool of unpaid labor.

All these problems were discussed at the 1862 meeting of the Association of Medical Superintendents; and the degree to which the original purpose of the system had been modified became evident. The discussion started when Edward Jarvis presented a paper on his observations of English work programs, which were far more comprehensive and effective than those in American hospitals.

One of the first comments was made by John Curwen, who talked of the special problems in American asylums. First, treatment had been disrupted by changes in the ethnic composition and social class of patients in many hospitals and by the consequent preponderance of inmates not committed as their predecessors had been, to the gospel of work and other middle class, Protestant New England ways. Second, there was a belief that patients in American asylums were unusually violent and obstreperous, refusing co-operation to their guardians, so that, in the absence of enough attendants, superintendents feared loss of control over their charges in any but the most structured situations.[19]

Another contributor to the discussion was Isaac Ray, who pointed out that lack of incentives to work reduced the productivity of patients and noted that English institutions issued beer and tobacco as payment, a practice that he would not copy because the consumption of alcohol and tobacco was highly debilitating. This was characteristic of the moralistic stance adopted by many American superintendents and their uncompromising emphasis on decency and virtue. Ray also pointed out that patients nowadays were an unusually restless lot, who were apt to "elope" if allowed to work without constant supervision. He concurred with the view that immigrant patients produced grave problems and remarked,

The amount of labor obtained in institutions in New England, it appears to me, has been steadily diminishing, owing to various causes, such as the increase of foreigners who do not feel that obligation to work in any institution.[20]

The next contributor was Merrick Bemis, the superintendent of Worcester State Hospital, whose remarks show the increasing tendency among administrators to confuse means and ends—to subordinate the needs of patients to the efficient running of the institution. It also shows the overwhelming concern of superintendents with financial affairs.

The labor we get at Worcester costs more than it yields. I could carry on all the operations of the farm in a better manner and with less paid labor, without the assistance of the patients than with. It is true that we do certain kinds of work which we should not do with paid labor, and thus the value of the State property is increased, and we perhaps procure for our patients some luxuries which we should not expect but for their labor. But it is a kind and quality of labor which we should not purchase. . . . It is for us to determine whether, on the whole, we can afford the introduction of labor as a remedial measure, to any very great extent . . . whether the incidental difficulties and dangers are not greater than the benefit to be derived. We all know the great liability to accident from the use of tools among the insane, and also the increased danger from fire when a large number of patients are permitted the privileges necessary to induce them to labor. Then again, friends will soon require pay for the labor performed by the patients. In the month of May, we had 1827 full days' labor performed by the patients in the hospital, and shall probably have 20,000 days' labor performed in the course of the year. At this rate, outsiders will soon regard our insane asylum as self-supporting, and it will be very difficult for them to believe that all this labor is worth really nothing. This question we must meet in all its forms, and I apprehend that it will be difficult and annoying. . . . Pecuniarily, the work done by the insane is of no value. It is always unsteady, full of imperfections, and the cause of a hundred annoyances, and subjects the institution to very severe risks.[21]

Bemis next alluded to the danger of lay interference in internal asylum affairs,

What must always interfere with the pecuniary benefits of labor with us, is the fact that as soon as an incurable patient has been taught to work to advantage, he is removed by the Commissioners of Overseers of the Poor, thus depriving the hospital of any benefit.[22]

A young superintendent, James H. Woodburn, who felt that work was an important part of treatment, explained his own concern with the financial aspect of the matter.

He did not think that with the small appropriation they had for the support of their institutions, they could get along without the labor of patients. They had a farm of 160 acres of very fine land, and to cultivate it employed but one farmer and a gardener, besides the labor of patients. The profits of the farm amounted at least to between five and six thousand dollars. His plan was, not to suffer the patients to work long enough to make them weary. He had not had long experience, but had observed that the out-door workers . . . were always the most likely to be cured and go home.[23]

Then Gray brought the focus back to the welfare of the patients:

I have never been accustomed to look upon labor principally in the light of its pecuniary value to the institution, but as an important remedial measure, beneficial to the patient in promoting his comfort, facilitating his recovery, and producing quiet and order throughout the house. If the question was asked, whether we did not receive pecuniary benefit from this labor, I should reply affirmatively. We undoubtedly are able to take better care of the patients, expend more on their behalf, securing to them advantages they otherwise would not enjoy, from having their labor to assist that of the hired attendants.[24]

The danger of lay interference was again noted, with the implication that greater secretiveness and distance from the friends of patients was a necessary safeguard to ensure recovery of inmates and to protect professional autonomy:

It is not uncommon for friends of patients, hearing by our letters or otherwise that they are engaged in useful employment, to ask whether or not the charges will be less for their care, or they will propose their removal at once, supposing that because they are capable of labor, they are well, or at least, would recover at home, so with many of the county officers. As soon as they ascertain that a patient is quiet and comfortable, and inclined to employ himself, they are anxious to remove him, supposing that such a course is for the interest of the public, not understanding that this is one stage of his recovery.[25]

The discussion ended after several desultory remarks by other participants, including a Canadian superintendent who saw nothing wrong with the British custom of issuing beer and tobacco to working patients. His institution had even planned to build a brewery to supply mild intoxicants to cooperative inmates.

The question of work programs continued to fester, now taken up by those, both among the superintendents and within state legislatures, concerned about the burden of the chronically insane on the community. It was suggested that separate institutions be established for such cases whose cost would be defrayed by the labor of patients, who would, in essence, be self-supporting. Professional outcry was loud and sharp, in spite of the fact that many members of the Association apparently used patient labor for other than therapeutic ends themselves. After such a plan had been presented at the 1865 annual meeting by John S. Butler, Curwen snapped that "he did not believe in the idea of the insane being self-supporting." [26]

In order to oppose the danger of "forced labor," expectation of which was fairly realistic in view of the history of almshouses, superintendents united to prove that, in fact, work performed by the insane was quite worthless and that such "exploitation" would be a waste of public money. They showed here striking evidence of guild solidarity, of the ability to call upon a large body of unanimous opinion and to mobilize protests from all over the country to

support the dominant view. Annual reports were filled with de-
nunciations of such schemes. Gray wrote:

A very mistaken view prevails as to the productiveness of work performed by the insane. Some of the best authorities estimate the labor
of three insane men as equivalent to that of one sane person; while
others place the ratio as high as five to one. On this basis of calculation,
bearing in mind also that the insane are suffering from bodily disease,
and that there is, in reality, no such condition with them as "robust
bodily health," the absurdity as well as the cruelty of any attempt to
make the insane self-supporting, becomes apparent.[27]

In these statements there was a tendency to so denigrate the
value of work in order to support a dialectic position that the therapeutic benefits of such programs were barely mentioned. The
major emphasis was placed on the economic unsoundness of the
venture and on the damage to which patients would be liable if
forced to support themselves against their will and beyond their
physical strength. Superintendents were apparently unconcerned
by the danger that, after taking so adamant a stand, they might
then find it difficult to draw legislative appropriations to support
and enlarge existing therapeutic work programs. The already widespread idleness was thus in danger of being indefinitely perpetuated. Moreover, the proclivity for fads among superintendents
meant that ideas and practices were rejected in short order when
new theories appeared to question their benefit; thus, practitioners
seemed eager to curb work programs because their indiscriminate
use was suspect.

The polemic against patient labor was continued by Isaac Ray in
an 1865 article, "The Labor Question and Hospitals for the Insane." He pointed out that experience in such penitentiaries as that
at Charlestown, Massachusetts, proved that even with long working
hours, on jobs unaffected by weather, with physically fit inmates
all of whom were obliged to work, with no comforts, amusements, or varied diets to add costs, prisoners failed to be self-
supporting in the absence of willingness and incentives to produce.
Ray held that English asylums were not self-supporting, even
though almost all their patients worked. He also claimed that conditions in Europe and America were not analogous anyway, because insanity in England was less marked by physical prostration
and violence than in the United States; because beer and tobacco
provided incentives; and because the natural subservience of Eng-

lish patients made them amenable to regimentation and to control by superiors. In a final blow at the utility of work programs, Ray listed the experiences of some Massachusetts colleagues:

Nearly thirty years ago, Dr. Woodward prepared a work-shop in the Worcester Hospital for shoe-making, regarding that craft as more likely than any other to be remunerative and though the account showed a small profit, it was quite too small to be regarded as a financial success. About the same time, Dr. Bell, of the McLean Asylum, provided similar arrangements for making candle-boxes, with much the same result. Two or three years ago, Dr. Prince of the Northampton Hospital, desirous of giving the experiment the fairest possible trial, pitched upon basket-making as that which furnished, in the highest degree, the elements of success. The materials were cheap, the tools few and simple, the art was easily learned and required but little strain on either the mental or bodily powers. Even under these favorable circumstances, the result was no better. "Pecuniarily," says the Report, "it was a total failure. There was no money made, but there was not much lost." There were other consequences of this experiment—a fair specimen, no doubt, of what may be reasonably expected from the employment of the insane in skilled labor—that ought not to be left out of the account. An overseer was discharged for abusing a patient, one patient eloped, and one threatened another with a knife.[28]

In spite of all this protest, however, hospital farms became common under the economic exigencies of the late nineteenth century. Institutions did become to some extent self-supporting, producing much of the food and many of the services and utilities of the hospitals in workshops, laundries, power plants, and so on. In 1890, Alabama Insane Hospital even reported working its own coal mine, while Stockton Asylum in California was tapping its own natural gas. These were in truth total institutions, more isolated than ever from the community because they had fewer needs for supplies and services. In the twentieth century in England, where asylums had undergone a parallel evolution, it was found difficult to introduce modern medical appliances, because many hospitals had their own electric generators, which produced a different current than that of the surrounding community.[29]

Moral management did not, however, vanish entirely. It continued successfully in such asylums as Utica State Hospital, where John Gray, in spite of a violent distrust of such "unscientific" ideas as moral causality, nevertheless remained a firm believer in humane management, and at Northampton Hospital, under the superintendency of Pliny Earle, which was a good example of the coexistence of the older system with custodial care.

NOTES

1. *The American Journal of Insanity*, XLVII (1890–1891), 5.

2. *The American Journal of Insanity*, XX (1863–1864), 485.

3. *The American Journal of Insanity*, XXXI (1874–1875), 209.

4. *Ibid.*, p. 231.

5. *The American Journal of Insanity*, XLVI (1889–1890), 56–57.

6. *The American Journal of Insanity*, XL (1883–1884), 345.

7. *The American Journal of Insanity*, XXXI (1874–1875), 267.

8. *The American Journal of Insanity*, XL (1884–1885), 159.

9. *Ibid.*, pp. 161–162.

10. *Ibid.*

11. *Ibid.*

12. *Ibid.*

13. *Ibid.*, p. 164.

14. *Ibid.*, pp. 164–165.

15. *The American Journal of Insanity*, XLIII (1886–1887), 73.

16. Gerald N. Grob, *The State and the Mentally Ill* (Chapel Hill, N.C.: University of North Carolina Press, 1965), p. 193.

17. *The American Journal of Insanity*, XVII (1860–1861), 85.

18. *Ibid.*

19. *The American Journal of Insanity*, XIX (1862–1863), 57.

20. *Ibid.*, pp. 60–61.

21. *Ibid.*, p. 63.

22. *Ibid.*, p. 64.

23. *Ibid.*, p. 65.

24. *Ibid.*, p. 66.

25. *Ibid.*, p. 67.

26. *The American Journal of Insanity*, XXII (1865–1866), 70.

27. *Ibid.*, p. 211.

28. *Ibid.*, pp. 449–450.

29. Maxwell Jones, *Social Psychiatry in the Community, in Hospitals, and in Prisons* (Springfield, Ill.: Charles C Thomas, 1962), p. 79.

Chapter 17

NORTHAMPTON UNDER

PLINY EARLE

The Massachusetts State Hospital at Northampton under the superintendency of Pliny Earle, from 1864 until 1885, provides an example of the coexistence of moral management and custodial care. Northampton is a particularly good test case because, unlike private and even corporate institutions, it faced the full complement of pressures that in other state hospitals combined to undermine moral treatment and to promote custodial care.

The asylum intended for pauper and incurable insane had opened in 1858, the third and largest public mental hospital in Massachusetts. Its early administration had been unsatisfactory and wasteful, a situation that had been foreshadowed by the fact that its construction costs had been immense. F. B. Sanborn recalled that the first superintendent, William Henry Prince (married to a cousin of William James), had been typical of many in the new generation of alienists. He was generally held to have been a political appointee; and

though an agreeable man, [he] had no special fitness for the position and no proper training in the management of large expenditures. Consequently, the hospital was usually in debt. Its medical staff was unequal to the moderate requirements of that period,—so much less exacting than our day—and the discipline of attendants and patients left much to be desired. Finally, public criticism, too long withheld, led to the resignation of Dr. Prince.[1]

Among those who no doubt influenced the superintendent's removal was Dorothea Dix, who paid one of her unheralded visits of inspection, and later wrote to her host, warning him against his practice of allowing the public into the building to gape at the inmates.[2]

In 1864, when Earle was appointed superintendent, the asylum was in a shambles:

He found the bonds of discipline much relaxed, and a very small proportion of the patients apparently curable. Out of more than 200 whom the state supported there from its own treasury, only seven were reported to me [Sanborn] in September, 1864, as curable, of whom, in fact, only four did recover. The farm was not large enough, and had been ill-cultivated. In short, everything needed the eye and hand of a skillful master.[3]

Northampton was from the first a custodial institution, filled with chronic cases from the other state hospitals at Worcester and Taunton, which in turn drew their patients from the densely set-tled, industrial urban areas of eastern Massachusetts, with their heavy influx of Irish and other immigrants. Few were admitted to Northampton from the surrounding, sparsely populated counties, as local authorities preferred to place the few dependent insane in poorhouses while most families kept diseased members at home. When any local cases were brought to the asylum, their illness was well entrenched by years of neglect, and they were generally held incurable. Earle noted in his second annual report of 1864 to 1865,

Out of 134 admitted in the year, the disease of only 34 was of less duration than one year. In all the rest it had passed into the chronic stage of comparative incurability.[4]

By the 1890's, the hospital still housed ten of the original patients transferred thirty years earlier; for years, the death rate at North-ampton was higher than the recovery rate. Earle's difficulties were compounded by the opening of another public asylum at Tewks-bury, for chronic and quiet insane. Less troublesome cases were siphoned off to the new institution, leaving the violent and noisy to Northampton.

Northampton thus appeared a ripe case for developing the worst features of custodial care. Its population included immigrant, pauper, violent, and chronic patients, all highly unevocative of public sympathy and all apparently most unsuited to moral treat-ment. It had serious financial problems; insufficient farmland; un-trained and undisciplined attendants; and all the constraints of a state institution whose patient flow was regulated by external authority. Nevertheless, Northampton retained moral management. Earle continued to give his evening lectures to patients and to encourage religious services. Equipment for work and amusements was available; adequate food and clothing were provided; proper discipline of attendants and patients was maintained; and Northampton boasted the most effective patient work program in the United States.

Earle's success depended in large measure on his own personality, which nicely balanced conservatism and flexibility. A founding member of the Association of Medical Superintendents, and a deeply religious man, he never abandoned opinions basic to moral management, such as the value of humane treatment, the importance of dealing honestly and respectfully with the insane, and the correct social and moral tone to be maintained in asylums. He continued to associate closely with his patients, joining them in such games as billiards, to which he was addicted, and observing their symptoms as a way of discovering the nature of insanity. He lectured to them frequently, even discussing with them the nature of their own maladies. In a period of growing materialism in science and psychological medicine, and while himself one of the early proponents of pathological studies, he continued to believe in the essential separation of brain and mind. He told an audience of physicians,

Were the arguments for the hypothesis that in insanity the mind itself is diseased tenfold more numerous than they are, and more weighty, I could not accept them. My ideas of the human mind are such that I cannot hold for a moment that it can be diseased, as we understand disease. That implies death as its final consequence, but mind is eternal.[5]

In many other areas, however, he remained flexible and was able to reverse earlier opinions on the susceptibility of insanity to cure and to modify his grave opposition to schemes such as family care, designed to diversify the conditions under which chronic patients were kept. He was particularly adaptable to the practical problems of his position, which mobilized his flair for mathematics and administration. One of his greatest accomplishments was not only to free his institution from financial difficulties but also to make a profit:

At the end of Dr. Earle's fourth year not only had the valuation of the hospital property increased by nearly $30,000 since he came, but the trustees were able to say, "For the first time since the founding of the hospital we have passed a year without borrowing money;" and they closed the year with a balance of nearly $10,000 in hand. This balance went on increasing—though often drawn upon for other than current expenses—until, when Dr. Earle resigned in 1885, it stood at $34,000; while the valuation figures had gone up from $272,000 in 1864 to more than $440,000 in 1885.[6]

Earle managed this economic triumph in a number of ways. First, in order to meet the lack of working capital, he enlisted the aid of the Board of State Charities to obtain advance payments of costs for most of the patients at the hospital. This allowed him to make cash purchases, thus reducing expenditures. He also adopted various administrative practices that he had admired in German asylums. On a visit to the mental hospital at Leubus, Silesia, for instance, Earle had noted the method of distributing supplies and later described in his book on German and Austrian asylums:

In supplies even of a handkerchief, a shoe-string, a broom, or an ounce of salt, nothing can be obtained without an order from the proper officer. If a garment be torn or worn so as to make a new one necessary, or if any article has become unfit for use, these must be produced as evidence. A regular account of debits and credits is kept between the various departments; and thus unnecessary consumption, carelessness, and "sequestration" are guarded against. No institution can ever attain that perfection of good order which is a chief beauty in a public or private establishment without such a system.[7]

This system was instituted at Northampton, and it eliminated much waste and theft. When it and a number of Earle's other administrative innovations were adopted by other institutions, however, they led to the rigidity of stereotyped custodial care, although, in their original form, they had helped to preserve moral management by producing economic independence.

Earle also copied the German work programs, in which idleness of all but the most infirm patients was forbidden. He decried the failure of American colleagues to compel patients to remain active, claiming that work was a cornerstone of moral treatment and as necessary for the well-being of the insane as the medicines and baths that alienists commonly forced on their charges.

With his well-directed patient labor, and with a knowledge of agriculture gained during his youth on the family farm at Leichfield, Massachusetts, Earle made his institution virtually self-supporting. He saved enough to expand buildings and purchase additional land, and he supplied a much fuller diet to patients than did many other public facilities. He doubled the hospital's acreage and crop yield, so that, although in 1864 40 tons of hay and 6,256 pounds of pork had been produced, by 1885, when Earle retired, Northampton yielded 251 tons of hay and 17,544 pounds of pork.[8]

Economic success not only prevented the shortages of food, equipment, and space common to other large asylums, it also gave Earle a specially favored position among lay regulating authorities, who regarded Northampton as a model institution. As Sanborn, Chairman of the Board of State Charities wrote,

By this prudent management of the hospital, Dr. Earle disarmed criticism on the economic side, and made his establishment popular with the legislature and the State authority, who had been accustomed to see it a frequent applicant for appropriations, not only for repairs and new buildings as was the case with other hospitals, but for deficiencies in its current expenses.[9]

Earle further endeared himself to lay leaders, though not to colleagues, by his criticism of extravagance in other institutions, such as the new State Hospital at Danvers. This asylum cost over $1.5 million to build, double the estimate; and Earle felt that much of this money was paying for the fancies of architects and engineers and for palatial staff quarters that would benefit neither patients nor taxpayers. As a result of strenuous complaints by Earle and others, public inquiries were made into the plans for Danvers, and a new board was appointed to manage its affairs.

Earle, however, never compromised his standards of good practice for economy. For example, he remained opposed both to institutions exclusively for the chronic and to mammoth hospitals that reduced per capita cost by assembling hundreds of inmates under one roof. He felt that, although such schemes might appear to save money, they would sacrifice the comfort and well-being of patients, as well as the optimum professional functioning of alienists.

Earle's excellent relations with laymen, and particularly with Sanborn, of the Board of State Charities, stood him in good stead when, like many of his colleagues, he was threatened with public scandal. A former patient alleged that sane people were imprisoned at Northampton, that treatment was neglectful and abusive, and that certain state regulations dealing with notification of distant relatives of patients had been ignored. Official investigations revealed that Earle had indeed infringed the latter "needless requirement of the law," as Sanborn described it; and that he maintained discipline strict enough to be mistaken for unkindness. Nevertheless, he was exonerated and praised for his humanity and deft administration. The strain of the inquiries, however, had been severe enough to drive Earle into one of his periodic depressions.[10]

With the blessings of lay authority, Earle managed over the years to change the composition of his patient body. He attracted paying patients, thus further improving his financial condition. He admitted some middle-class cases, proving that in fact a sufficiently high level of care did exist in his institution to counteract its former reputation as a dumping ground for the pariahs of other hospitals.

Earle also attempted to change the latter characteristic of Northampton by drawing more of his patients from the four surrounding rural counties, rather than from the distant urban, industrialized East. This project was in accord both with the plan submitted to the state by Edward Jarvis and with the preference of the Association of Medical Superintendents, which held that asylums should be local institutions drawing a diversified patient body from a surrounding locality. During the twenty years of Earle's superintendency, the population of these western counties doubled, producing more cases and more local revenues to support them at Northampton. After Earle's retirement, his successor, Edward Nims, reported in 1888 that of the 166 patients admitted that year, only one had come from outside this catchment area.[11]

It has previously been noted that one of the forces that mitigated against moral treatment was the psychiatric guild; and although Earle was one of the founding members of the Association, he stood, for much of his career, outside the mainstream and influence of fellow professionals. A frequent contributor to the *Journal* under Amariah Brigham, his work was no longer published under John Gray, because Earle, like Isaac Ray and others, remained incorrigibly attached to notions of moral causation and moral insanity. Because of his "treachery" in criticizing extravagant buildings, and particularly after he delivered the *coup-de-grâce* to the curability myth, he was attacked by colleagues and regarded as "one that troubleth Israel." [12] His successful ideas, however, were eventually accepted, and he was even elected president of the Association the year before his death; but during most of his career he remained aloof from contemporary guild pressures and fashions. It is significant in this regard that he selected Sanborn as his biographer, not only a layman, but a leader of a regulating authority, the Board of State Charities, distrusted by many alienists.

The history of Earle's Northampton shows that custodial care was not inevitably linked with the degeneration of moral management. A strong and innovative superintendent could still control his own institution. Ironically, however, many of Earle's expedient and liberating measures, such as meticulous attention to finance and to the distribution of supplies, proved, when adopted by less imaginative men, restrictive and stultifying, although his exposure of the emptiness of the myth of curability inadvertently made a laughing stock of idealistic predecessors, as well as of less honest practitioners, and further discredited moral management.

NOTES

1. F.B. Sanborn (ed.), *Memoirs of Pliny Earle, M.D.* (Boston: Damrell and Upham, 1898), p. 261.

2. *Ibid.*, p. 262.

3. *Ibid.*

4. *Ibid.*, pp. 264–265.

5. *Ibid.*, p. 281.

6. *Ibid.*, p. 263.

7. *Ibid.*, p. 172.

8. *Ibid.*, p. 266.

9. *Ibid.*, p. 263.

10. *Ibid.*, pp. 273–274.

11. *Ibid.*, p. 266.

12. *Ibid.*, p. 278.

PART THREE

Late Nineteenth Century:

Reformers and Their Impact

Chapter 18

PUBLIC OUTCRY AGAINST

THE QUALITY OF

PATIENT CARE

In 1907, Clifford W. Beers published *A Mind That Found Itself*, an account of his mistreatment as a patient in a number of mental hospitals. With the encouragement of Adolf Meyer and William James, and with the support of an aroused citizenry, Beers founded the National Committee for Mental Hygiene to sponsor reform in asylum management and research into methods of prevention and cure of mental disorder. The mental hygiene movement has generally been seen as a turning point in psychiatric history, when community forces made a concerted attack on institutional stultification and mismanagement, and when psychiatry began to move out of asylums into schools, into child guidance and out-patient clinics, and into the army in an attempt to eradicate insanity in the general population.

This movement, however, was the culmination of a process that began in the 1860's and 1870's, when laymen and practitioners in other branches of medicine attempted to improve mental hospitals, to break the monopoly of asylum staffs in managing the insane, and to promote innovative research and treatment. As in the later mental hygiene movement, the impetus for reform came first from outside psychiatry, from the crusades of indignant laymen, often spurred by the shocking stories of former patients. Such stories gave concrete form to pre-existing prejudices of the public and led to the formation of leagues of would-be investigators and reformers. The zeal of such associations was strong because their members were driven by the confirmation of deep-seated fantasies.

During the later nineteenth century, American psychiatry had stagnated, and the old alliance between alienists and lay reformers, which had created the public mental hospital movement in the 1830's and 1840's and had sped the tenets of moral treatment across the country, had broken down. Dorothea Dix remained highly respected by the Association of Medical Superintendents, although she was felt by younger men, such as F. B. Sanborn, Chairman of the Massachusetts Board of State Charities, to be conservative and schoolmarmish.[1] When she died in 1884, the profession adopted no lay reformers into its ranks to fill her place.

Psychiatrists became associated in the public mind with conservative and injurious patient management; with political corruption; with failure to evolve scientific insights and treatments at the same rate as other branches of medicine; and with a stiff-necked self-importance, fostered by the guild, which held alienists aloof from fruitful interchange with members of the community.

During this period, public concern with insanity was high. Books on psychological matters sold in surprising numbers,[2] and many asylums were supported by generous contributions and bequests. Nevertheless, prejudice against the insane continued, hardly dispelled easily at a time when alienists were themselves so ambivalent about their patients. Thus, in spite of much professional propaganda, the public continued to regard insanity as shameful, and residence in an asylum as an indelible stigma. This produced recurring complaints in psychiatric literature. Some practitioners tried to minimize the importance of this problem by denying its existence among the enlightened, as Thomas Kirkbride did in the 1858 report of the Pennsylvania Hospital for the Insane:

Another error—formerly very prevalent and altogether now discarded by the most intelligent portion of the community, still occasionally alluded to—is that of regarding insanity itself, or the residence of an individual in an institution for its treatment as a reproach, or as destructive of future prosperity in life.[3]

This prejudice, however, had not been discarded, and Edward Jarvis, in a paper on the place of private asylums in the United States, suggested that such institutions were particularly helpful in the care of those who shared this mistaken notion and who might therefore be unduly agitated by commitment to a recognized insane asylum.[4] Isaac Ray noted in discussion of legislation governing commitment that many people defended the right of families to secretly isolate sick members in their own homes, on the grounds that they would suffer bitterly if their shame were exposed to the world.[5]

Feelings about the shamefulness of insanity were also reinforced by the increased use of mental hospitals as dumping grounds for a variety of then unmanageable conditions, such as alcoholism, criminality, epilepsy, and retardation. The public tended to so shun asylums that in England Lord Shaftesbury proposed legislation to force those who committed a patient to visit him periodically.[6] Later in the century, when Massachusetts inaugurated a limited boarding-out system, it was reported with surprise that relatives who had never shown any interest in patients before were now going so far as to buy them new clothes.[7]

The persistence of prejudice and neglect was acutely troublesome. Psychiatry was considered an undesirable and dangerous profession; and one alienist reported meeting a wild animal trainer who told him, "I would rather be shut up in a cage with my cats than do your work." [8] Various aspects of the work of superintendents were treated with disrespect. The public and the press ridiculed and attacked the role of alienists in criminal trials. At an annual meeting of the Association, G. C. S. Choate reported that the public objected to the performance of post-mortems; and relatives of deceased patients often withheld permission for such study, seriously hindering research.

Far more alarming to alienists, however, were persistent charges that patients were mistreated by attendants and fellow lunatics. The popular view of treatment in an asylum may be seen in the following early, but typical, description, an excerpt from *Melmoth, the Wanderer*, by C. R. Maturin, which appeared in 1820 and was one of the last of the great Gothic novels. In one of the episodes, an Englishman named Stanton is falsely confined in Bedlam by a greedy relative.

He [Stanton] was in complete darkness; the horror of his situation struck him at once, and for a moment he was indeed almost qualified for an inmate of that dreadful mansion. He felt his way to the door, shook it with desperate strength, and uttered the most frightful cries mixed with expostulations and commands. His cries were in a moment echoed by a hundred voices. In maniacs there is a peculiar malignity, accompanied by an extraordinary acuteness of some of the senses, particularly in distinguishing the voice of a stranger. The cries that he heard on every side seemed like a wild and infernal yell of joy, that their mansion of misery had obtained another tenant.

He paused, exhausted—a quick and thundering step was heard in the passage. The door was opened, and a man of savage appearance stood at the entrance—two more were seen distinctly in the passage.

"Release me, villain. . . . Will you dare to detain me?"

"Yes, and a little more than that," answered the ruffian, applying a loaded horse whip to his back and shoulders, till the patient soon fell to the ground convulsed with rage and pain. . . . They [the other attendants] then were advancing into the room as he spoke, with fetters in their hands (strait waistcoats being then little known or used), and showed, by their frightful countenances and gestures, no unwillingness, to apply them. Their harsh rattle on the stone pavement made Stanton's blood run cold; the effect, however, was useful. He had the presence of mind to acknowledge his (supposed) miserable condition, to supplicate the forbearance of the ruthless keeper, and promise complete submission to his orders. This pacified the ruffian, and he retired.[9]

There follow descriptions of Stanton's fellow inmates, foul and bestial creatures, shrieking and moaning caricatures of human beings.

Despite attempts by superintendents to educate the lay community to believe in the humane and therapeutic intent of asylums, the public acted on its fears. In 1862, for instance, Utica State Hospital found itself the target of public scandal when a patient died of internal injuries a few days after admission, injuries subsequently proved by legislative inquiry to have been inflicted the day before the unfortunate man arrived at the asylum. The scandal was so great, however, that John Gray used the case as an example fifteen years later at an annual meeting of the Association when these by now commonplace legal battles were discussed.[10]

Alienists were eager to blame the circulation of evil rumors about asylums on sensational novels, or on newspaper accounts based on the tales of prematurely discharged patients with delusions of persecution, or on those still hospitalized who told lurid tales to visiting relatives. However, movements in Europe and America were spawned by a general atmosphere of public distrust, which was not generated but was only inflamed by the findings of governmental investigations and newspaper exposés. In England, this movement produced such oddities as "The Alleged Lunatic's Friend Society," described by John Connolly as "holding public meetings, publishing transactions, offering premiums for antimedical essays, the great—nay sole, object to the Association being, to destroy what its members imagine to be, the existing medical despotism towards the insane." [11] As Isaac Ray remarked,

Indeed, so far has this prejudice gone, that if we do not greatly mistake the present state of public sentiment, the mad doctor, as he is elegantly termed, is classed by multitudes of people with rogues and charlatans. Novel writers seeking fresh stimulus for the jaded sensations of their readers, find it in depicting the horrors of the *mad house.*[12]

Public fears were confirmed by cases of alleged brutality, which led to one legislative inquiry after another. Some of the most sensational of such disclosures appeared in the 1880's, the product of muckraking reportage. A series of firsthand exposés began in April, 1889, when a reporter from the *Chicago Times* set a pattern for his colleagues by having himself committed to the Jefferson Asylum in Cook County. He later wrote of his treatment there and at the Detention Hospital where he had been held before commitment. Among other enormities, he described the murder of a patient by three attendants. A coroner's inquest was held at the insistence of the newspaper; and a post-mortem found a number of fractures, sufficient to cause death, in a melancholia patient "dying of phthisis and exhaustion." The attendants were arrested, and two of them were bound over to the Grand Jury for murder.[13] In the same year, the *Philadelphia Inquirer* sent a reporter to the insane wards of the Philadelphia Hospital (Blockley). The reporter

alleges many instances of cruel treatment, kicks, blows, cuffs and profanity from attendants being, according to his statement, the rule on the excited wards.[14]

The story produced an investigation, but apparently failed to reveal any evidence of misconduct by the medical staff. The attendants, however, were tried and found guilty of assault.

The same year, further reports of brutality were circulated. In Minnesota, two attendants were tried and sentenced to prison for killing a Negro patient in the asylum in Rochester. It appeared that the medical staff had known of the case but had suppressed the facts. They were all suspended during official investigations. The superintendent, J. E. Browers, however, was eventually vindicated.[15]

A particular target for reform, one that confirmed public fears of mistreatment, was the by-now virtually routine use of mechanical restraints in American asylums. This was an inflammatory issue during the mid- and late nineteenth century, because British asylums, in a much-publicized movement led by John Connolly, were abandoning and decrying the use of these methods as cruel and self-defeating. This controversy was not only significant as an indication of how far American alienists had moved from the dicta of moral treatment, but showed also how influential the guild had become in imposing a relatively uniform and distinctive flavor on American psychiatry, which in this case ran against European currents.

The original members of the Association had repudiated the routine use of restraints as basically inimical to moral treatment, but they had, nevertheless, refused to outlaw sleeves, bed straps, and so forth because they felt that a potentially valuable avenue of treatment should not be closed to superintendents. At the 1844 meeting of the Association it was therefore resolved that

It is the unanimous sense of this convention that the attempt to abandon entirely the use of all means of personal restraint is not sanctioned by the true interests of the insane.[16]

By the late 1850's and early 1860's, discussion of this question among American superintendents had become acrimonious. As wards became overcrowded, force was more often used; in Worcester State Hospital, for instance, restraint and isolation rooms were in general use by the 1850's.

American reformers, protesting their local system, pointed to the greater calm and industry found on European wards, in contrast to the chaos of American mental hospitals, as evidence that restraints roused patients rather than tranquilized them. An article in the *North American Review*, for example, noted that "The degree of freedom from physical restraints . . . is at once the test and measure of good asylum management." [17] Reformers were particularly incensed by a recently developed form of restraint, the Utica Crib, which became a symbol of asylum cruelty and helped protestors to brand John Gray, editor of the *Journal* and therefore a doubly convenient target, as the arch conservative. Thus a petition for asylum reform brought before the state legislature by the New York Neurological Association in 1879 suddenly lost its third-person, judicial tone, when it demanded,

Do you ever employ the barbarous and injurious means of restraint known as a "crib"? [18]

The reaction of American superintendents to these charges was violent. Not only were laymen seen to be meddling in asylum affairs at a time when the professional identity of superintendents was developing and therefore tender, but critics unfavorably compared American with European systems of asylum management, thus further injuring the pride of the developing guild. Moreover, practitioners in their overcrowded and culturally heterogeneous wards were afraid of being deprived of an instrument for suppressing violence. The use of restraints and isolation also fitted some contemporary theories of therapy, because some patients were thought to require enforced rest in order to restore depleted bodily forces that were thought to lie at the root of their disturbance. Superintendents rallied, therefore, to an emotional defense of mechanical restraints. One nevertheless feels from their papers that many were unwillingly carried forward to support extreme positions by the force of polemic although in more sober hours they might not have held such unqualified views.

To those who admired the success of English hospitals in maintaining discipline while abandoning force, supporters of restraints, like Ray, had a number of answers. First, he felt that freeborn Yankees were naturally harder to control than Europeans, who were brought up to show subservience to authority; thus, American patients could not be dealt with by moral persuasion alone. Second, he felt that the harsher climate of the northern United States produced a more maniacal form of insanity, with symptoms of greater noisiness, combatability, and propensity to suicide than did Europe. Third, he felt that English institutions made fraudulent claims when they insisted that they had banished restraints entirely, because they had merely substituted the strength of attendants for the impersonal force of strait jackets or the silence of isolation. The Association held that mechanical restraints would quell a patient more quickly and safely than would attendants who might injure him and that the calm and quiet of isolation would be more soothing than the presence of other patients, who might both irritate a combative individual and might themselves be stimulated to copy him.

Any evidence of the failure of the nonrestraint system was collected. The *Journal*, for example, reviewed all books and articles, particularly British, denouncing nonrestraint. In the review of two of these, "The Theory and Practice of Non-Restraint in the Treatment of the Insane," by W. Lauder Lindsay, Physician to the

Murray Royal Institution at Perth, and "Restraint in the Treatment of Insanity," by G. F. Bodington, a member of the Royal College of Physicians, Isaac Ray noted that nonrestraint was not in fact the universal rule in England. Such statements were publicized, the *Journal* continued, because

We only wish to show that the statement so confidently made, both here and abroad, respecting the abandonment of all mechanical restraint, is not true, and that the obloquy attempted to be fastened upon us for preferring the old ways is utterly undeserved.[19]

Nonrestraint was said to be a source of danger.

Dr. Bodington, the honored superintendent of a large private asylum, charges the non-restraint system with being the parent of many mischievous practices—violent struggles between patients and attendants, wounds, bruises, broken ribs, and prolonged irritation.

Ray concluded,

What we prize most in these pamphlets is their outspoken protest against the arrogant assumption of the advocates of non-restraint that they alone are wise, even beyond any possibility of mistake or doubt, while their opponents, including most of the honored names in this field of professional labors, in Germany, France, and America, are behind the age, guilty, every day, of cruel and barbarous practices.[20]

The following editorial comment in the *British Medical Journal* of June 26, 1880, on a review of the "Asylums Without Locks" at Barony Parochial Asylum, Woodilee, near Glasgow, was likewise reprinted gleefully:

There must be some limit to the removal of restrictions on the insane; if not, the simplest and wisest course would seem to be to abolish lunatic asylums altogether and at once; for, disguise it as we may, they are, after all, but costly and elaborate engines for the imposition of restrictions.[21]

With the same sense of gathering ammunition to defend a beleaguered position, American psychiatrists who toured British asylums brought back stories of dissatisfaction with the system. J. E. Browers, for example, of the Minnesota Hospital for the Insane, told on his return of seeing a patient struggling frantically with two attendants who were holding him down. When the visitor had asked his host whether he did not think sleeves might have been more effective, the superintendent replied, "Unfortunately with us the restraint is on the superintendent instead of the patients." [22]

Browers himself used restraints, but only "when imperatively demanded." He wrote in his 1881 annual report that with 112 patients and 5 attendants, "there had been but two instances of restraint during the week just closed." [23]

The use of restraints became almost a test of whether or not a superintendent held to the true faith, whether he remained loyal to his colleagues and to the founding members of the Association who had refused to outlaw them. American hospitals that attempted to unlock doors and remove bars from windows, such as McLean Asylum for the Insane in Massachusetts under Edward Cowles in 1880, were regarded with considerable distrust by others. A great reaffirmation of the value of restraints took place in the face of such criticism as the reports by J. C. Bucknill of his trip to America in the 1870's, and of subsequent lay anger. Jamin Strong, for example, in the 1881 report of the Cleveland Asylum for the Insane, wrote,

It is well known that we have in this asylum the boldness to practice and the audacity to advocate restraint.[24]

To a British colleague who had claimed that a low mortality rate among his patients was proof of the efficacy of nonrestraint, Strong answered that the still lower death rate in his own hospital must, on the contrary, prove the superiority of restraints.[25]

The course of this controversy, as of others at this time, shows the way in which community criticism caused psychiatrists to invest greater value in their practices than they might otherwise have done, as though by acknowledging the justice of one critical suggestion they might destroy their entire system.

Superintendents reacted to nonpsychiatric reformers with extreme disdain and bitterness. Change and self-examination were evaded by abusing the critics and by withdrawing from attack into dignified, but bristling, silence. For example, John H. Callender, a president of the Association and the medical superintendent of the Hospital for the Insane, Nashville, Tennessee, spoke in 1882 on the first occasion when a president of the Association was required formally to address the group before relinquishing his office. He discussed the "History and Work of the Association of Medical Superintendents of American Institutions for the Insane," saying of the early refusal of the Association to outlaw restraints,

The importance of this subject, the mischievous errors and consequences which a departure from this salutary and conservative dictum has caused, and the ignorant and prejudicial censure it has called forth from mountebanks not of the specialty who know little or nothing of the matter practically, will require yet further allusion in this review.[26]

In this, as in other controversies, superintendents accused their detractors of insanity, stupidity, mischief (a strong word in the nineteenth century), and of being totally incompetent to judge mental hospitals because of their lack of professional qualifications. Psychiatrists may well have been right in judging that the protests of muckraking journalists and civic leaders were often based initially upon prejudice against the insane and irrational fears of asylums and their administrators. Public fears were often buttressed by wild stories of former patients, some of which at least were delusional. But these concerns stimulated investigations of asylum management that exposed actual conditions of abuse and neglect. The fact that laymen were prejudiced did not prevent the content of their fantasies from being true. And when superintendents attempted to evade and discredit the accusations on the grounds that they were irrationally based, they further inflamed an already aroused citizenry.

NOTES

1. F. B. Sanborn (ed.), *Memoirs of Pliny Earle, M.D.* (Boston: Damrell and Upham, 1898), p. 306.

2. *The American Journal of Insanity*, XXVI (1869–1870), 110.

3. *The American Journal of Insanity*, XVI (1859–1860), 216.

4. *The American Journal of Insanity*, XVII (1860–1861), 26.

5. *Ibid.*

6. *The American Journal of Insanity*, XXXVII (1880–1881), 46.

7. *The American Journal of Insanity*, XLV (1888–1889), 185.

8. *The American Journal of Insanity*, LIII (1896–1897), 195–196.

9. Charles R. Maturin, *Melmoth the Wanderer* (Lincoln, Nebr.: University of Nebraska Press, 1961), pp. 36–37.

10. *The American Journal of Insanity*, XXIII (1866–1867), 84.

11. *The American Journal of Insanity*, VI (1849–1850), 336.

12. *The American Journal of Insanity*, XXI (1864–1865), 36.

13. *The American Journal of Insanity*, XLVI (1889–1890), 132.

14. *Ibid.*, p. 137.

15. *Ibid.*, p. 134.

16. Nina Ridenour, *Mental Health in the United States* (Cambridge, Mass.: Harvard University Press, 1961).

17. *The American Journal of Insanity*, XXXVIII (1881–1882), 130.

18. *Journal of Nervous and Mental Disease*, VI (1879), 343.

19. *The American Journal of Medical Sciences*, LXXVII (1879), 213.

20. *Ibid.*, p. 214.

21. *The American Journal of Insanity*, XXXVII (1880–1881), 95.

22. *The American Journal of Insanity*, XXXVIII (1881–1882), 104.

23. *Ibid.*, p. 103.

24. *Ibid.*, p. 88.

25. *Ibid.*, p. 89.

26. *The American Journal of Insanity*, XL (1883–1884), 9.

Chapter 19

THE COMMITMENT
CONTROVERSY

Reform movements in the history of psychiatry often arose when documented accounts of injustice corroborated public fears. One example of such a process may be seen in demands for change in commitment procedures and inspection of asylums. This was based initially on widespread fantasies of sane people being imprisoned in asylums and was supported by a number of well-publicized lawsuits.

The issue provided plots for popular horror novels in which rapacious guardians or husbands consigned their defenseless ladies to the wild and brutal world of the insane with the collusion of alienists, often versed in mesmerism and the use of soporific drugs. This may be seen in one of the enduring books of this genre, *The Woman in White,* by Wilkie Collins, or in the much earlier *Melmoth, the Wanderer.*

A number of court cases throughout Europe and America were brought by former patients or by relatives against asylums during the 1850's, 1860's, and 1870's, the prosecution claiming either false confinement or mistreatment. In 1863, for example, alienists were upset by reports of a case in Valencia, Spain, in which three physicians and three relatives of a lady suspected of insanity, her husband and two brothers, were condemned to twenty years hard labor for alleged false commitment. Eventually it was discovered that "expert" testimony at the trial had been negligent and that the lady was in fact insane; the six men were released, but not before suspicions had been aroused against alienists in other countries.[1]

In England, another spectacular case involved Lytton Bulwer, a politician and a friend of Disraeli, who had his wife confined in a private asylum after she had made speeches against his candidacy in an election. This lady was also released after much public scandal.[2]

One of the most notorious and significant of the American false commitment cases occurred in the mid-1860's when such a charge was successfully brought in Illinois by Elizabeth Packard against her husband and the superintendent of the asylum to which she had been confined, Andrew McFarland. Not only did Mrs. Packard win her case, a fact which horrified the superintendents, who always insisted that she had been, and still was, insane, but she launched a national crusade to prevent false commitment of others. She thus initiated a pattern, that was to be carried on by such significant figures in the history of American psychiatry as Clifford Beers, of the former patient who, after publicizing his own mistreatment during hospitalization, became a focus for reform.

In 1867, Illinois passed the "Personal Liberty Law," popularly known as the "Packard Law," and a number of other states followed suit with similar legislation requiring a jury trial of the fact of lunacy before any patient could be admitted to an asylum. Alienists protested this ruling on a number of grounds, that the privacy of the patient and his family was violated, that commitment procedures were unduly delayed by relatives who feared the trial, and that judges and juries were not competent to identify insanity.

Twenty years after the passage of the law in Illinois its defects could be assessed more clearly, and a number of state legislators communicated their disillusionment with the ruling to members of the Association of Medical Superintendents. In twenty years, 1,500 people had been declared insane, at an estimated total cost to the state of $600,000, money that many felt could have been put to better use in the service of patients.[3] Moreover, the system did not succeed in preventing precisely that abuse for which it had been passed, because a number of sane persons were regularly committed. Not only was the record of juries in improper commitment held worse than that in asylums not subject to such provisions, but several erroneous admissions in the late nineteenth century, such as the commitment of muckraking journalists, had serious repercussions.

Not only were improper commitments not prevented, but the human rights of patients were said to be scandalously abused. As an Illinois state official complained in the 1880's,

As to counsel appearing at these trials, the attorney is often assigned to the alleged lunatic by the court as a perfunctory matter. In exceptional cases, the alleged lunatic engages counsel and makes a legal contest. I should say from my experience that a large majority of those who go through this form in court are wholly unaware of the nature of the proceedings, and in quite a percentage of these pains are taken to so obscure the facts or pass them over in a hurried way that the alleged lunatic, even though fully capable of appreciating the bearings of the legal process, is unaware that he or she has been declared insane.[4]

In a larger view, however, one of the most damaging outcomes of these "Personal Liberty Laws" was the official investiture of the act of hospitalization with the language of criminal prosecution and imprisonment. The patient was called "the accused" or "the defendant," "charges" were read against him, the case for his commitment was argued by a "prosecuting attorney," the judge and jury rendered a "verdict," and so forth. Such language, and the fact of public hearings in a courtroom before judge and jury, served to confuse further the already delicate distinction between the asylum as a hospital or as a prison. It further exacerbated the delicate issue, which is still argued by psychiatrists and lawyers in the twentieth century, of whether the confinement of the insane against their will is an infringement of constitutional rights; and whether an individual has a "right to be ill" if he is harmless. It also raises the question of whether society is justified in institutionalizing someone who medical authorities infer might, if left at large, be a danger to himself or others. This involves the larger issue of the propriety of preventive arrests at a period when the indexes of behavior prediction are grossly unreliable.

Many of these issues were acutely troublesome to mid- and late nineteenth-century alienists, who resented the limiting of their own professional autonomy, as well as the outcome of such doubts on an already prejudiced and fearful public. The battle was fought in many states through the courts, with decisions going both ways, and was reflected in the progressive refinement and elaboration of commitment procedure.

In spite of the propaganda of the Association, public distrust could not be stilled. When the Massachusetts legislature, in 1863, appointed a Commission of Inquiry into the Condition of Lunacy, a group free to inspect all receptacles for the insane in the Commonwealth, the first question they were asked to examine was whether they found any individuals wrongfully committed. It happened that they did not.[5] Nevertheless, fears were not quieted, and in 1870 the Massachusetts Board of State Charities issued the following statement in its annual report:

The post of superintendent of an institution for the insane exposes its occupant to criticism, to censure, and to scandal, and perhaps more in this country than abroad. He has to take in charge, and to restrain, persons of disturbed faculties and morbid fancies, to whom, of all others, restraint is hateful, and who invoke license in the name of freedom. Moreover, the blood relatives of such persons are apt to be of like temperament. . . .

The tenacity of life in popular bugbears is shown in the credit readily given to stories about our lunatic hospitals being used as bastilles for the imprisonment of sane persons, for wicked purposes.

The Board has given to this matter specific thought and investigation, during many years, and it is convinced that the notion of our State Lunatic Asylum's being used for such wicked purposes is a bugbear used to excite or frighten the public.[6]

A characteristic response of superintendents was to seek and follow the most explicit commitment rules possible, in order to leave no loopholes for future prosecution. This issue was discussed, for example, at the 1866 Annual Meeting of the Association, at the height of Mrs. Packard's crusade, and in the wake of a number of similar cases in which superintendents were prosecuted. The immediate cause of the discussion was a paper presented by W. H. Stokes, resident physician of the Mount Hope Institution, on the ordeal of his own institution as a result of charges of conspiracy to defraud the public brought the previous year by six lunatic women. Superintendents concluded that their main safeguards were explicit legal commitment procedures and meticulous record keeping. On the latter point, John Gray said,

The great safeguard against unpleasant trials or difficulties of any kind is a faithful and careful record of the conduct and symptoms of persons under treatment. In a number of instances where false impressions have been made, based upon the stories of uncured patients, a simple transcript of the case has generally been all that has been necessary to satisfy reasonable people.[7]

Explicit commitment laws had been under discussion in the Association for some time. Ray, for example, in an article, "American Legislation on Insanity," had been concerned about both protecting the rights of the insane and avoiding unnecessary legislation. He noted the dangers inherent in any system that must be "limited and hedged around by a multitude of restrictions." On the other hand, the privacy of the patient and his family must be respected. Ray, therefore, advocated the system in effect in such states as Massachusetts, which required certificates signed by two physicians and an affidavit by some authoritative person of good character, usually the trustee of an asylum.[8]

In many states, however, there was inadequate legislation, because the insane had traditionally been secreted away by families, or had been confined in prisons and poorhouses under other legal provisions. In time, however, this vagueness became dangerous, both to those who might easily be unjustly deprived of their freedom and to asylums receiving patients in good faith, but later accused of malpractice. At the 1866 Annual Meeting, S. Van Nostrand of the State Hospital for the Insane, Madison, Wisconsin, suggested

that we might avoid some of these difficulties by strict legislative provisions for receiving patients. I think our Legislatures should give us laws which, if complied with strictly, would relieve us from liability to these infernal prosecutions. In my own state the law is specific, and I feel when I receive a patient and lock him up, if necessary, that I am just as safe from prosecution as if I locked up my horse or anything else. I think if these gentlemen who have such difficulties would ask their legislatures to give them more specific laws in regard to the admission and discharge of patients, it would relieve them from troubles of this character. We all have a class of patients who are ready to make trouble for us if they can, and those of us who are positive men will have enemies ready to assist these people in making trouble. I always insist upon complying with the law specifically, even to the cancelling of the last stamp, and I believe that will be found a remedy for many of the difficulties in respect to this class of cases.[9]

Thus, fear was producing a greater reliance on such administrative issues as meticulous record keeping, not for the good of the patient, but for the protection of the hospital; greater reliance on detailed commitment laws; and a certain fear of voluntary admissions, which, by evading the legal formulas, might render superintendents more vulnerable.

There was, however, a further defense adopted by superintendents that contained the germ of much danger and contributed to an ever-growing public outcry against their practices. This was the systematic and deliberate curtailment of communication between asylums and the outside world. This policy was intended not only to evade undue interference by public officials in the internal affairs of institutions but also to stop public rumors and prejudices by giving them as little fuel as possible.

Curtailing the flow of information from asylum to community began after superintendents had realized that all their attempts to inform the public had failed to shake traditional fears and stereotypes. John Gray, like many alienists, was so disgusted with the failure of the public to accept his teachings that he advised his colleagues to drop the attempt. In his critique of the 1864 report of the New Hampshire Asylum, in which a by-now conventional appeal was made for early institutionalization to ensure prompt recovery, Gray wrote,

We reluctantly adopt the opinion that . . . [Dr. Bancroft's] appeal to the public will produce but little good. Repeatedly of late years, have asylum superintendents urged this matter with all the force its importance demands. The futility of their efforts in this direction is seen in the gradual increasing number of the incurably insane seeking admission to the hospitals. The annual report, it is true, reaches only a comparatively small proportion of the community, but the great mistake lies in supposing the general public capable of appreciating the medical facts presented, and in attempting to form an "enlightened public opinion," when, from the nature of things, such illumination is impossible.[10]

Isaac Ray also advocated fighting prejudice by narrowing the flow of information from the hospital to the community and by excluding carping and interfering laymen from professional preserves. He had noted in an 1852 article, "The Popular Feeling Toward Hospitals for the Insane,"

None but those who have our opportunity of knowing, can have any adequate idea of the amount of bad feeling, gross misconception, scandalous gossip, and even fierce hostility, that quietly pervades the community, with the effect of circumscribing more or less . . . [the hospital's]sphere of usefulness.[11]

Ray noted that there was some legitimate basis for complaint because of the hospital's air of mystery and seclusion, cheap construction, a too-frequent prison-like appearance, and the poor discipline of attendants. His remedy, however, was a curious one. Besides rectifying such matters as staff discipline and procuring a conscientious board of directors to ensure high standards, he advocated further isolation, from neighbors who spread rumors and from state capitals with their political commissions of inquiry. He demanded an end to the practice of inviting the public to visit hospitals, because this unnecessarily agitates patients, while failing to dispel ingrained prejudice. In later years, Ray implemented these ideas in his own institution and reported public reaction with surprised resentment. Relatives, whose visits were discouraged "for the good of the patient," proved tiresomely persistent in their attempts to enter the asylum. In 1856, Ray wrote,

It seems to be impossible for some people to appreciate the motives that lead us to discourage indiscriminate visiting. When advised not to see a patient, they feel as if they were debarred from exercising an inalienable right, and from learning something which they ought to know, and which we are desirous of concealing. Hard feelings are produced, harsh remarks are made, a story passes round, and we are actually regarded by many worthy people as having committed an outrage on the rights of humanity. Even those who have seemed to be convinced by our reasons and disclaimed all desire to see the patient contrary to our advice will, not unfrequently, go away and fill the community with their complaints.[12]

Forbidding free access to patients had other rationales than just that of preventing the circulation of highly colored rumors. One was the traditional idea that allowing patients to see those associated with the onset of the malady would negate the value of institutionalization.

They who have charge of hospitals for the insane will tell us that the sight of a bundle of old clothes from home is sufficient to reproduce all the original excitement and agitation in many a patient, calm, quiet, and apparently convalescing.[13]

This idea received official sanction by the 1860's, when the Massachusetts Commission on Insanity as a result of its findings dismissed suggestions of appointing a "Protector of the Insane" who would, among other duties, grant patients permission to write home, because indiscriminate permission to do so would increase restlessness, impede recovery, and lead to premature withdrawal by relatives who felt that the cure had been completed.[14]

The latter point was felt by superintendents to be an acute problem, as more and more relapses occurred, casting doubt on the professional reputation of alienists. Relatives and Overseers of the Poor, all of whom were anxious to withdraw patients from asylums as soon as possible, were constantly warned that the first signs of returning sanity were not to be taken as evidence of recovery, and that only the alienist could judge the proper time for discharge.

This idea of excluding the public was symptomatic of the failure of alienists to appreciate the concern of nonprofessionals in the issue of insanity, whether it was due to family feeling, humanitarian sentiments, economic need, or concern about public safety and the enforcement of civil liberties. There was wholesale rejection of all outside influences, in spite of the fact that some of these might have materially enhanced the therapeutic task of alienists and have shielded them from some public distrust. Leading laymen often blamed the psychiatric guild for this. F. B. Sanborn, an early chairman of the Massachusetts Board of State Charities, years later wrote angrily of the obstructiveness of alienists when faced with outside inquiries,

Such was the state of things . . . when the first Boards of State Charities were created, with a general power of inspecting hospitals and asylums, from 1863 to 1870. In every instance, probably, the heads of these establishments opposed the visitation and resented the criticism of the earlier Boards of this class. Instead of welcoming a new ally . . . this medical trade-union of alienists received them as meddlesome critics, and at first thought to put them down. But from that day to this [1893] the question of insanity has gradually acquired a fuller and wiser discussion in America, though the treatment of patients still leaves much to be desired. A superficial and often pompous display of knowledge has given way to an earnest search for truth.[15]

As pressure on superintendents increased, more alienists adopted silence and a pose of disdain for the outside world as a defense. Some superintendents, such as D. Tilden Brown of Bloomingdale Asylum, developed such contempt for the press, for example, that they no longer attempted to protest sensational stories. Brown himself told an annual meeting of the Association that he had once treated an editor, when the press had attacked his institution. The editor had apparently told him that newspapers pursue stories only so long as public interest endures. Such interest dies quickly unless excited by fresh disclosures; and an apologia from a superintendent might thus prolong a passing sensation and should be avoided.[16]

The idea that there was defense in silence became increasingly common, and even acquired chivalric overtones. John Gray, for example, declared it beneath the dignity of a gentleman to reply to stupid or libelous attacks. At the Annual Meeting of the Association in 1880, in which members discussed recent criticism of the superintendent of Utica State Asylum, Gray said that he never answered detractors, because

No advice that they have ever given me, I can safely say, is worth the paper on which it is written.[17]

Furthermore, he added,

The man who gives himself up to personalities and detraction and envy, who makes these the basis of any proposition of reform or conceals them behind propositions of reform, places himself beyond the pale of reputable criticism, and should be left to himself without argument or answer, where he will die under the weight of his own defamatory work, sooner or later.[18]

NOTES

1. *The American Journal of Insanity,* XXI (1864–1865), 331.

2. Robert Blake, *Disraeli* (New York: St. Martin's Press, 1967), p. 385.

3. *The American Journal of Insannity,* XLVI (1889–1890), 16.

4. *Ibid.,* p. 17.

5. *The American Journal of Insannity,* XXI (1864–1865), 259.

6. *The American Journal of Insanity,* XXVIII (1871–1872), 110.

7. *The American Journal of Insanity,* XXIV (1867–1868), 21.

8. *The American Journal of Insanity,* XXI (1864–1865), 23-25.

9. *The American Journal of Insanity,* XXIII (1866–1867), 87–88.

10. *The American Journal of Insanity,* XXI (1864–1865), 230.

11. *The American Journal of Insanity,* IX (1852–1853), 37.

12. *The American Journal of Insanity,* XIII (1856–1857), 378.

13. Isaac Ray, *Mental Hygiene* (Boston: Ticknor and Fields, 1863), p. 323.

14. *The American Journal of Insanity,* XXI (1864–1865), 264.

15. F. B. Sanborn, ed., *Memoirs of Pliny Earle, M.D.* (Boston: Damrell and Upham, 1898), pp. xii–xiii.

16. *The American Journal of Insanity,* XXX (1873–1874), 242.

17. *The American Journal of Insanity,* XXXVIII (1881–1882), 211.

18. *Ibid.,* p. 212.

Chapter 20

THE REFORM MOVEMENT
GATHERS MOMENTUM:
AN ATTACK ON ISOLATION

By the late 1870's and 1880's, criticism of asylums had become organized and powerful. Reform societies included many professionals and intellectuals, philanthropic businessmen, lawyers, clergymen, and medical practitioners, particularly members of the rising specialty of neurology. Articles calling for reform were no longer the exclusive province of the popular press but now appeared in church and general medical journals as well as in such prestigious literary periodicals as the *North American Review*.

Formal pressure groups organized for reform. One of these appeared in 1880, and was called the National Association for the Protection of the Insane and the Prevention of Insanity. It sought to unify forces to supervise and reform public asylums throughout the country,

First, by encouragement of special and thorough clinical and pathological observations by the medical profession generally, as well as by those connected with asylums.

Second, by enlightening public sentiment as to the nature of the malady, the importance of early treatment, improved methods of management and treatment at home and abroad.

Third, by recommending an enlightened State policy, which, while neglecting no one of its insane population, shall so administer relief and protection as not to lay unnecessary or undue burden upon the taxpayers.

Fourth, by holding public meetings, wherever needed, to stimulate legislation that will secure efficient state supervision of all public institutions for the care of the insane, as a mutual safeguard for the protection of society—the patients, as well as those who have them in charge.

Fifth, to further the perfection of laws relating to the treatment of the insane, and their rights while patients in the asylum.

Sixth, by efforts to allay the public distrust in relation to the management of insane asylums, by placing them on the same footing as that of other hospitals, both in the matter of freer communication with the outside world, and the privilege of a consulting medical staff of general practitioners.[1]

Another powerful group attacking American psychiatry was the New York Society of Neurology, whose petitions to the state legislature for reform of local asylums, and whose own publication, the *Journal of Nervous and Mental Disease*, were eventually successful in shaking some of the security and privileges of the rival profession.

If there was a common denominator to the complaints of reformers during the 1870's and 1880's, it was protest against all the forms of isolation to which they felt contemporary American psychiatry was prone. They attacked superintendents for their isolation from the mainstream of American medicine. This isolation was shown by their failure to conform to newly standardized qualification requirements, to use outside consultants in the general medical care of patients, and to engage in scientific research, one of the priorities of contemporary medicine. Critics decried the failure of psychiatrists to deliver the cures that had been promised if more "palatial asylums" were constructed.

Critics also attacked the isolation of asylums from public scrutiny, by the barriers set up between patients and public, and by inadequate measures for official supervision, which too often appeared to mask, rather than expose, patient abuse and corrupt management. This was seen as linked to political collusion between superintendents and inspectors appointed by the same party machine.

One of the most powerful and telling attacks made on psychiatry at this period came from fellow physicians, and, like the calls for change by other groups, it was part of a larger movement; for an attempt was being made to raise the standards of general medicine in America. During the second half of the nineteenth century, the gap between scientific education and research in the United States and Europe became more noticeable. The relative crudeness of contemporary American practice, which, for example, was still ignorant of asepsis, may be seen in periodicals addressed to average physicians, such as *The American Practitioner*, and from the curricula of such medical schools as Harvard in the 1860's and 1870's, when Oliver Wendell Holmes, professor of anatomy and physiology, used to say,

If the whole materia medica (*excepting only opium and ether*), as now used, could be sunk to the bottom of the sea, it would be all the better for mankind—and all the worse for the fishes.[2]

Qualification requirements were low. Two years of classroom study, one of internship, a thesis, and a cursory oral examination were the steps to a medical degree. The degree itself gave the license to practice.[3] By 1870, however, President Charles Eliot of Harvard began to improve his medical school by adding courses in basic sciences, often against the wishes of his faculty.

During the next two decades, the standards of American medicine began to rise, as curricula and qualification requirements became more demanding. Institutions that sold diplomas to unqualified applicants were attacked by new regulatory legislation. Reformers also battled powerful groups who were felt to withstand modern science and hence to debase the field, such as homeopaths and Christian Scientists, whose great popularity was itself an indication of the low confidence of the public in contemporary medicine. Alienists were often put in the same class.

The latter were attacked in part because their professional qualification and education were not only held inferior to the rest of medicine, but their daily work left them no opportunity or incentive to supplement their poor preparation. The 1879 petition of the New York Neurological Society to the state legislature, for example, concluded with the following points:

1. Superintendents of insane asylums are, nearly without exception, not chosen from among medical men who have pursued special studies in neurology at home and abroad, and who are well trained physicians, but from among assistant physicians of asylums who, after having been badly chosen. . . , have passed a number of years immured in an institution.

2. Assistant physicians of asylums [future candidates for the position of superintendent] are nearly always men just issued from our too elementary medical schools; men who have not served in civil hospitals (which can be entered only by severe competitive examination); their qualifications are not submitted to any test; when in the institution they

are not furnished with means of study (medical journals, books and instruments); and, inevitably, as years go by, they forget what general medicine they knew on graduating. . . .

4. Superintendents and their assistants, with hardly an exception, are not versed in the new anatomy and physiology of the nervous system, the part chiefly concerned with insanity.

5. Superintendents and their assistants, with hardly an exception, are not believed to be skilled in the modern methods of diagnosis and of post-mortem examination. Few of them are able to read in the original the invaluable contributions to insanity and its treatment which we owe to the German and French scientific physicians for the insane.

6. The little pathological work which has been done in our asylums at enormous cost has been of the most elementary sort, and has been ridiculed at home and abroad. With the liberal aid it receives from the state, the pathological laboratory in one of our asylums did not furnish the materials for successful competition for the great Tuke prize, for the best essay on the pathological anatomy of insanity, offered in England last year.[4]

One of the major grudges held against superintendents by fellow professionals was the paucity of scientific work carried on in asylums. Alienists had a virtual monopoly over the institutionalized care of the insane, and they received public funds. Other practitioners, such as neurologists, neuropathologists, and psychologists, attacked this privileged position of superintendents, claiming a share of the field by virtue of their own more substantial researches. These professions maintained that the failure of the alienists to discover new methods of prevention and treatment of insanity was wasting the lives of patients and the resources of the public as well as disgracing the United States in the eyes of Europe by failing to match the advances of foreign scientists. As Clark Gapen, professor of medical jurisprudence at the University of Wisconsin, wrote,

It is humiliating that while the greatest activity prevails, the world over, in this field, we, here in America, who pride ourselves upon our activity and originality, are not only *not* advancing, but find those engaged in the work unspeakably ignorant as to what is going on in this direction in other parts of the world; the present work of institutions, so far as the patients are concerned, consisting, as an observing medical man, a former resident officer in a Hospital for the Insane has well said, "in feeding and grooming." [5]

Some thoughtful critics blamed the isolation of both staff and patients behind asylum walls for the paucity of research findings and treatment results in American institutions. John Van Bibber, for example, a Baltimore physician, wrote an article, "Intermediate Hospitals for the Treatment of Acute Mental Diseases," one of the earlier suggestions of a plan later embodied in psychopathic wards and hospitals. He attacked the quarantining of the insane, isolated not only by the wall around the asylum, but also by the custom of having staff live in the hospital, thus reducing outside contacts. Van Bibber felt that this isolation in the company of lunatics was stultifying to alienists, and accounted for the poor showing that psychiatry made beside other branches of medicine.

In other hospitals where patients are received, diseases treated, sufferings mitigated, and cures fortunately brought about, communication with the outside world is constant and beneficial. It comes through the medical officers, who call daily, fresh from the varied experience of life, from friends who are not frightened away by too stringent rules, through members of associations, whose benevolent purpose is to make the dreary time of sickness less heavy and insupportable. But none of these healthy regulations exist in the management of these institutions. . . . Though it is claimed as necessary for the medical head of an asylum to live in the institution, and that his peculiar responsibilities require him to be always on the spot, I think this regulation is a decided mistake, and has been the cause of many of the most serious objections to the present system.[6]

Van Bibber suggested that alienists share the freedom of other specialists, such as surgeons, who leave their hospitals to have "a more liberal and extended practice."

As critics of alienists generally noted, one of the obstacles to research and proper treatment in American asylums was the fact that superintendents spent so much time on administrative and housekeeping chores that they had little left for professional work. Other doctors found the apparent preference of their colleagues for nonmedical work mysterious and suspicious. Some wondered whether superintendents did not cling to their farms and architectural plans in order to excuse their inability to do creative professional work.[7]

In fact, American superintendents had long viewed their administrative role with ambivalence. The early superintendents had shared the management of their hospitals with boards of trustees, and, because the establishments were small, their jobs were not onerous. Moreover, some, like Pliny Earle and Amariah Brigham, had been trained in orderly and thrifty management in their youth on farms or business, and by the surrounding society of small entrepreneurs. As asylums grew in size, as governmental appropriations added complexity to financial planning, administration became a larger, more time-consuming task. Superintendents resented this drain on their time but realized that anyone with power of the purse would have a stranglehold on the asylum. Thus, they were unwilling to let control of asylum affairs pass to those who might interfere with medical autonomy. Consequently, many superintendents came to spend most of their time on accounts, on purchasing supplies, and on managing kitchens and farms, while assistant physicians managed the wards. Treatment suffered, and research virtually disappeared.

Vocal critics asked why medical talent was squandered on jobs more fittingly done by bookkeepers. The burdens of administration were thought to fall particularly heavily on the young alienists, those who might otherwise be expected to do original research and bring fresh ideas into the closed world of the asylum.

One critic, Gaspen, therefore suggested a system, in which asylums would have two superintendents, a medical director and an administrator. He realized that this suggestion would displease "many superintendents [since] this would deprive them of the sweet morsel which they roll so consolingly under the tongue." [8] But the "better class" of alienists would, he felt, welcome their new freedom.

This suggestion, based on an existing British model, was regarded with increasing favor by the public. Laymen disapproved of the administrative activities of superintendents, not only because they isolated psychiatrists from their patients and from the scientific community, but also because sufficient irregularities in bookkeeping had been revealed by investigations to cast suspicion on the competence and honesty of asylum management.

The honesty of superintendents was particularly questioned, because they were usually political appointees and because this was an era of gross immorality in public life. Corruption ran through all levels of government, long a prey to mismanagement in the absence of a trained civil service, and with the spoils system awarding jobs by patronage rather than by experience. By the 1870's, public confidence had sunk to new low levels, as corruption and collusion with industrial powers could no longer be hidden. Irregularities in national politics were reflected on state and local levels by machines, such as that run by Boss Tweed in New York, and by the pocketing of public funds through the collusion of politicians and business interests. Abuses, and the fury of reformers, inevitably extended to asylum management, because the hospitals received significant appropriations and, by their requirements in construction and provisioning, gave scope to many thieves.

Superintendents were suspected of living luxuriously on hospital appropriations, of running asylums not as public trusts,

but as personal estates or petty sovereignties, the main purpose of which they seem to regard is to contribute to their comfort, pleasure and social exaltation. The petty sovereign air, the luxurious apartments and equipages, the indulgences of aesthetic or whimsical tastes at the expense of the state, are all too common to admit of dispute.[9]

Suspicions were reinforced by such episodes as the following. In 1892, the Alabama Insane Hospital announced,

We have just commenced the erection of a residence for the superintendent of the hospital and his family, which will be located on the lawn in front of the present building. . . . It will cost between fifteen and twenty thousand dollars when completed, and what is of more importance, will be paid for out of the funds saved from the allowance of $2.25 for each patient per week, without asking for any special appropriation from the state.[10]

Superintendents were further suspected of defrauding the states when purchasing supplies and services and in the very building of their institutions. In New York State, for example, public works were at the mercy of contractors and their friends in high office who made fortunes on such projects as the canal system and, it was suspected, also on the construction and maintenance of asylums.[11] In 1879, the report of the State Charitable Institutions of New York noted that in the past decade, four million dollars had been spent on the construction, repairs, and improvements of four state hospitals, but that little work had in fact been accomplished.[12]

Superintendents were also suspected of moonlighting, of drawing handsome salaries but neglecting their patients in order to collect fat fees as expert witnesses in criminal trials, or as private practitioners. These charges were reflected in the 1879 petition sent by members of the New York Neurological Society, and signed, by a number of prominent citizens to the state legislature, demanding investigation of recurring questions about asylum management, which they claimed had been long left unanswered by superintendents.[13]

The plan to introduce a separate administrative officer into asy-

lums, which became known as the "two-headed" system of management, was advocated by the public, but was bitterly fought by
superintendents and increased the tenacity with which they clung
to their administrative jobs. Just as in the case of nonrestraints, the
superintendents were carried to extremes by polemic. Some experiments with this system were made, however, and they confirmed
the worst fears of alienists.

In 1884, for example, the Board of the State Asylum for Insane
at Morristown, New Jersey, succeeded in having a bill passed by
the state legislature separating the medical and administrative jobs
of the superintendent. Their first step after passage was the removal of Horace A. Buttolph, the old superintendent, and the appointment of two new men, a "medical director" and a "warden."
The chaotic outcome was described by William L. Russell, one of
the assistant physicians, in a letter to the *Journal.*

If the warden had been an ambitious person, with only private aims, he
could hardly have succeeded more effectually in alienating the two
departments from each other. The medical department was looked on
with a jealous eye; any attempt of a medical officer to suggest any
measure, or do any activity which would have any visible effect on the
management of the asylum, was termed, "officiousness"; and soon it
was quite plain that the medical department was expected to occupy a
subordinate position. The medical director was seldom or never consulted by the warden on any matter whatever. He was simply ignored,
and the warden even went so far as to advise the friends of patients on
matters of which he was totally ignorant, and which could only be
properly dealt with by a medical officer. It is easy to imagine the
confusion that resulted from such a state of affairs as this.[14]

Matters degenerated further when, in 1886, the position of matron
was abolished, and when the first medical director resigned,

it being generally believed that he could no longer remain and retain
his self-respect. He was succeeded by a gentleman who, in spite of
many difficulties and mortifications, has stood bravely at his post up to
this time.[15]

The warden next created havoc by nepotism. He made his wife
"supervisor of the centre," in which ambiguous post she began to
take on the duties of the matron. By concerted action on the part
of the medical department, she was kept out of the wards; but the
officer in charge of the sick and of supervising special diets in the
kitchen was discharged, and she took his place.[16]

The medical staff attempted to take action over the head of the warden. The medical director, armed with letters of resignation from his assistants, appealed to the Board of Managers, who in turn appointed an investigating committee. After a cursory examination, the committee left, and nothing further was ever heard on the matter. The assistant physicians, unable to tolerate the warden's behavior further, resigned. Meanwhile, the warden continued to rule, now reinforced by his son who occupied the position of storekeeper, refusing to fill requisitions unless they were countersigned by his father.[17]

Although the fate of this asylum was extreme and perhaps gained somewhat in the telling, nevertheless it and a number of similar cases wedded alienists more firmly than ever to their administrative tasks, because they feared that an "outsider" would profiteer at the expense of the patients and would displace medical primacy in asylums.

Another major criticism of American asylums was that their stone walls were impermeable, that it was impossible to learn the truth about their management. Their isolation, particularly in private hospitals, came from real disdain for the public. Some superintendents believed that they should only communicate with the public when they needed money and that otherwise their affairs were their own business.

An example of this attitude may be seen in the case of D. Tilden Brown, superintendent of Bloomingdale Asylum, who, in 1863, issued an unusually brief annual report. He explained his action by three reasons, first, the *Journal* provided a medium for the exchange of professional gossip, so reports were redundant; second, the rich of New York, unlike the elite of other cities, were not interested in making charitable contributions, so issuing reports for their benefit was a waste of effort; and, third, the institution was private and did not depend on state funds, so there was no need to inform the community of its programs in order to attract legislative appropriations.[18]

Brown's statement caused a furor. John Gray quoted Isaac Ray to prove that in fact many colleagues did find useful information in each other's reports, which did not duplicate material in the *Journal*.[19] The trustees of Bloomingdale issued their own much bulkier report, in which they noted that, although indeed independently endowed, they were still anxious to justify a "moderate augmentation" to the "annual bounty" from state funds.[20] No one, however, suggested that an asylum had a duty to inform the community on its activities.

Public anger over the dearth of trustworthy information about hospitals stimulated reform movements with two goals, establishing the right of patients to communicate unhindered with the outside world and the right of the public to expect adequate official inspection of asylums. A number of states passed laws to enable patients to write some sealed letters. In 1875, the Commission of Lunacy of the Commonwealth of Massachusetts suggested in its report that patients should be allowed to write to their guardians, because this was analogous to their inalienable right of petition.[21] This issue was later espoused by some of the more extreme reform movements. In 1890, one such group appeared with the revealing name of "The Anti-Kidnapping League and Lunacy Reform Association," whose membership was characterized as follows by the *American Journal of Insanity:*

This recently organized association appears to be made up of (1) at least one paranoiac; (2) that large semi-responsible class who spend their lives in depths of social degradation which their own morbid imaginations have created and who are forever wailing out, in pharisaical protest, against the ungodliness of all the world except their own select coterie; and (3) a few (a *very* few) real philanthropists who are eager to do good in any way but who are not possessed of the true data concerning this subject.[22]

The group attempted to get bills passed that would allow patients to name their own correspondent, who might be changed every three months. They also asked that patients might have the privilege of sending sealed letters to the governor, attorney-general, judges of courts and record, district attorneys, and the State Commission on Lunacy.

Alienists indignantly refuted the statements of lay critics that their asylums were closed against the outside world, claiming that all those with official concern, like trustees, state boards of charities or lunacy, and legislators, had free access. But here also it was held by reformers that the public was being misinformed. It was felt that asylums had inadequate supervision and that superintendents had unrestricted power over their institutions, successfully hiding abuses from the public and establishing petty tyrannies over staff and patients. In theory, the superintendent was controlled by the board of trustees, but critics doubted the honesty and adequacy of

such bodies. A critic named Dorman B. Eaton summed up this issue
as follows:

Let us see . . . what the American system is, by showing the theory
and method of governing the Asylum at Utica . . . nine trustees, a
majority of whom must reside within five miles of the asylum, are to
govern it. They make such by-laws and regulations as they deem expedient. They appoint the treasurer and the superintendent. They, by
approval, determine the number of employees, and their salaries. They
keep the only record of their own doings. They inspect their own
work. They (or their subordinate, the superintendent) make all purchases. They audit their own bills. They report to the Legislature the
only authorized version of their own conduct. Neither their report,
nor that of their subordinate, the treasurer, is required to contain such
particulars as would disclose extravagance or other abuses. As private
owners of the institution, they could not have power more absolute
and irresponsible. . . . But . . . the authority of the asylum superintendent is, if possible, more dangerous and unchecked than that of the
trustees. He is an autocrat—absolutely unique in this Republic; supreme and irresistible alike in the domain of medicine, in the domain of
business, and in the domain of discipline and punishment. . . . He
. . . is monarch of all he surveys from the great palace to the hen-
coops, from pills to muffs and handcuffs, from music in the parlor to
confinement in the prison rooms, from the hour he receives his pris-
oner to the hour when his advice restores him to liberty. . . . This
unparalleled despotism extending to all conduct, to all hours, to all
food, to all medicine, to all conditions of happiness, to all connections
with the outer world, to all possibilities of regaining liberty, awaits
those whose commitments may be easily unjust, if not fraudulent . . .
is over prisoners the most pitiable of human beings, whose protests and
prayers for relief their keepers despise, and many good people believe,
no man is bound to respect.[23]

Another critic, Clark Gapen, held similarly that boards of
trustees were inadequate. Unlike Eaton, he did not openly accuse
them of dishonor but felt that, because members of such boards
were not paid, they could not afford the time necessary for exhaustive investigations. Moreover, board members feared that

Frequent visitation and extended inquiry are synonymous with meddling, which idea is not unlikely to be encouraged and fostered by the
officer in charge.[24]

Nor did Gapen think highly of the practice of placing a doctor
on the board, with the title of Chairman of the Visiting Committee.
From such a figure, reports

averse to the management [of the asylum] . . . [were] an unheard of thing, his peculiar relations and the nature of his appointment being such that a report less than laudatory would preclude the necessity of his ever preparing another. Indeed it is extremely amusing to run through the reports of various institutions, and see what excellent characters are invariably given to such by those whose especial business, as in this case it is, to criticize the management.[25]

Such an environment, Gapen held, encourages autocracy, because, in common with most Americans, he believed that unchecked power always becomes oppressive. He felt that these conditions made the task of regulatory agencies doubly difficult, because staff and patients were afraid to reveal actual conditions.

It is rare to find a hospital in which any freedom of speech is tolerated. The rule is evasion and a guardedness which savors strongly of servility, secured by a system of government which can only be compared to that of Russia.[26]

Gapen thus suggested that boards of trustees pay surprise and protracted visits to hospitals and assess, in some way, the true feeling of the hospital toward the superintendent.[27]

During the late nineteenth century, therefore, public suspicions of asylum management became focused into reform movements. Citizen forces mustered to take formal political action against the status quo in mental hospitals by petitioning existing regulatory authorities and by lobbying for new laws. The results of their efforts will be discussed presently; but two obstacles to success were incorporated into the methods of such groups. First, the political system was partly responsible for many of the deplorable conditions attacked; yet citizens turned to government to regulate those offenses with which it was itself intimately linked. They appeared able to divorce the system from the shortcomings or excesses of the individual office holder and to believe that more regulatory statutes and agencies, more checks and balances, would control corruption. Second, the withdrawal of superintendents behind asylum walls and into a closed guild was in part a defense against the irregularities of laws and governing agencies, and their interference in asylum affairs. The pressure of reformers for more statutes and more levels of official supervision only exacerbated the very causes of such isolation.

NOTES

1. *Cincinnati Lancet and Clinic*, V (1880), 566.

2. Gay Wilson Allen, *William James* (New York: The Viking Press, 1967), p. 99.

3. *Ibid.*

4. *Journal of Nervous and Mental Disease*, VI (1879), 344–345.

5. *Ibid.*, p. 446.

6. *American Journal of Medical Science*, LXXXIX (1885), 39.

7. *Journal of Nervous and Mental Disease*, VI (1879), 445.

8. *Ibid.*, p. 449.

9. *Ibid.*, p. 447.

10. *The American Journal of Insanity*, XLIX (1892–1893), 139.

11. *Journal of Nervous and Mental Disease*, VI (1879), 488.

12. *Ibid.*

13. *Ibid.*, p. 342.

14. *The American Journal of Insanity*, XLIV (1887–1888), 429.

15. *Ibid.*

16. *Ibid.*

17. *Ibid.*

18. *The American Journal of Insanity*, XX (1863–1864), 493–494.

19. *Ibid.*

20. *Ibid.*, p. 494.

21. *The American Journal of Insanity*, XXXI (1874–1875), 474.

22. *The American Journal of Insanity*, XLVII (1890–1891), 442.

23. *The American Journal of Insanity*, XXXVIII (1881–1882), 121.

24. *Journal of Nervous and Mental Disease*, VI (1879), 443.

25. *Ibid.*

26. *Ibid.*, p. 448.

27. *Ibid.*

Chapter 21

THE PSYCHIATRISTS'
INITIAL RESPONSE TO
CRITICISM: EVASION,
DENIAL, AND COUNTERATTACK

During the 1880's, massive criticism of American institutions for the insane, accompanied by court battles and legislative inquiries, frightened superintendents. Their plight was described by John B. Chapin, medical superintendent of the Willard Asylum for the Insane in New York.

So frequent, causeless, undeserved and unexpected have been the attacks upon the asylums for the insane, and those connected with them, that it has, probably, been the personal experience of some here present to enjoy a momentary sensation of relief after gleaning the morning papers to find they have not been publicly charged with the commission of some grave offenses; or, during a session of the legislature that no inimical measure has been proposed.[1]

Although many of the complaints of critics were undoubtedly justified, the insecurity of superintendents and their resentment of community pressures were heightened by the excesses of many would-be reformers. This was the period in which newspaper empires were being built; and the magnates of the press were known to print sensational and often improbable stories in order to boost circulation. The complaints of former patients and employees had sometimes been circulated in a garbled form; and those who spread the stories ignored all attempts to correct the record. Even reputable reformers admitted privately that their charges against asylums were unreasonable and exaggerated;[2] but they had thought this the only way to arouse public opinion, much as the proponents of moral treatment had felt it necessary to overstate their case half a century earlier in order to alarm an apathetic people.

Superintendents charged that those attacking asylums recklessly and perhaps falsely did incalculable harm. They frightened the friends of patients and hindered many from committing their relatives until cure was impossible; they ruined the careers and reputations of asylum personnel, and discouraged qualified young doctors from entering this "honorable and humane work." They demoralized all institutions, because even the most cautious superintendents were never secure:

It has been correctly observed that every superintendent of an asylum reposes among hidden forces of a volcanic nature, which may at any moment be moved to great activity. He may have discharged his whole duty, as he understands it, to the best of his ability, be more familiar with the defects of his institution than his detractors can hope to become, but in his hour of trial, no good service record of a lifetime, or careful and faithful administration can be relied upon to shield him from suspicion and detraction. His tenure of office is at best of the most precarious nature, and during its continuance, it has not unfrequently happened that a superintendent of an asylum who has devoted more or less of the best days of his life in its service has suddenly found himself put upon his defense against merciless and unwarranted attacks upon his character and professional reputation, on which he may set a higher estimate than he would place on his usually limited earthly treasures.[3]

Even when superintendents were exonerated by an official hearing, the damage to careers and institutions might be irrevocable. As one critic of American psychiatry pointed out, such cases roused so much hatred and prejudice in communities around asylums, that even the people themselves were startled by the force of their own passion.[4] Moreover, particularly in cases where false commitment had been charged, exoneration was always doubtful, because many judges shared popular ignorance and distrust. As one psychiatrist complained,

I find many judges have an idea that a person is not insane except he be a raving maniac and requiring manacles, etc., to control him; that any person who can sit quietly in a chair and witness his own trial and perhaps give testimony in regard to himself, makes it impossible for the court to believe that he is insane, unless he gives evidence in the courtroom of his insanity.[5]

The fear of adverse judgments that might set ruinous precedents was intensified by such cases as one that came to trial in 1877 in Michigan. Two years earlier, Nancy J. Newcome, a physician, had been admitted to the Michigan Asylum at Kalamazoo by the superintendent, E. H. Van Deusen. The patient had been accompanied to the asylum by the superintendent of the poor in Calhoun County, who had signed the order for admission. It was later realized that such an order should have been signed by a majority of the superintendents of the poor in the state. As the story was later told to the Association by H. M. Hurd, Superintendent of the East Michigan Asylum at Pontiac:

In 1877, nearly two years after her discharge, she brought an action against the medical superintendent for trespass, false imprisonment and malpractice, and asked damages in the sum of $40,000. In her declaration she complained of assault on the part of the medical superintendent, "with force and arms," and of being "seized," "dragged about," "struck many violent blows and strikes," and forced to remain imprisoned in the asylum for ten months contrary to her wishes, and to the great detriment of her health and professional reputation. She further charged him with conspiracy with the superintendent of the county poor and her son-in-law, to detain her in the asylum; and also that while there she was compelled to swallow large quantities of calomel (of which she took none) and other drugs; that she was obliged to bathe in foul water; that her clothing was taken away; and that by means of this improper treatment she was debarred from attending to her business as a physician.[6]

The judgment in this case was significant. It was ruled that no patient could be hospitalized or secluded against his will without due process of law.

In other words, any detention of a person, sane or otherwise, unless actually dangerous, is false imprisonment.[7]

A further point was even more significant, for the judge ruled that

Intentional wrong was not essential to create a right of action. If the defendant (the superintendent), acting in good faith, intentionally caused the plaintiff to be imprisoned, such act was presumed to be unlawful and he should be held responsible for all the damages which the plaintiff suffered, as a natural consequence of such imprisonment. Beyond this, it was charged that if she (Mrs. Newcome) was thus confined without lawful authority, sick and in need of medical treatment and subjected to improper medical treatment, he (Van Deusen) was responsible for all damages which followed. As the result of the trial and the charge to the jury, a verdict was rendered for $6,000 damages.[8]

Alienists at once realized that a dangerous precedent had been set, and Van Deusen appealed to the Michigan Supreme Court, pleading that the good faith of the superintendent should be a protection. This time, the judgment was favorable, and the ruling of the lower court was reversed. Nevertheless, much damage had been done to public confidence and professional security.

The threat to asylums and their staff from community criticism was undeniably serious; but the nature of professional responses formed an equally significant chapter in the history of relationships between mental hospitals and the surrounding world. During this period, the major answer of psychiatrists to critics was abuse and countercharge.

Reformers were accused of hypocrisy—of shirking their own responsibilities toward the mentally ill, and then criticizing those who had taken the burden off their hands. Critics, superintendents claimed, grew sentimentally morbid over the use of restraints, after they had themselves abandoned their insane relatives as unmanageable.[9] Reformers blamed asylum policy for poor communication between patients and community, but they frequently neglected their own friends, as J. C. Bucknill had shown in a book published in 1880, on the *Care and Legal Control of the Insane*. Bucknill had pointed out that many patients were "entirely abandoned to the care of others," citing the findings of Lord Shaftesbury, in England, who had urged in 1859 that a law be enacted compelling the person who had committed a private patient to visit the patient "once at least in every six months during his confinement." [10]

Superintendents further charged that the growing rate of chronic insanity was not because of professional incompetence, but of pig-headed prejudice among laymen and general practitioners against asylums. Psychiatrists complained that doctors, so ready to blame superintendents, created tragedy themselves by their failure to learn the early signs of mental disorder and by undue delay in committing patients. In the 1880 report of the West Pennsylvania Hospital for the Insane at Didmont, for example, the superintendent, Joseph A. Reed, wrote,

Go back to the admission of patients to the hospitals, and see if society and its laws, as well as the persistent efforts of those who are industrious in prejudicing the public mind against hospital treatment, are not immediately responsible for the large and increasing army of chronic cases brought to the hospitals after their day of cure has passed—to occupy room intended for others, to be fed, clothed, and cared for so long as they may live.[11]

An even more dramatic attack on the medical profession was made by John Gray in an 1884 paper entitled "Hints on the Prevention of Insanity." Success in this area, Gray felt, hinged on the early recognition of pre-insane symptoms of exhaustion, or "brain-fag," and treating them with sedatives and food. He blamed the ignorance of general medicine for failure to deal with such cases promptly, and hence for contributing to the aggravation of symptoms and hastening the descent to insanity.[12]

Superintendents further charged that community criticism was misdirected. Why, they demanded, were reformers so glib in their advice to public asylums, and so insensitive to the fate of hundreds of insane inmates in poorhouses, jails, and other unsuitable accommodations? As Chapin noted,

The administration of the State asylums has been the subject of extraordinary criticism, while the fact that a system may have an existence with the sanction of the law under which men may be chained in hand-cuffs and shackles in rooms for months; the sexes not separated by any building plan; insane persons kept in seclusion in basement rooms and in considerable numbers in wards without attendants, or proper medical attendance in acute stages of insanity, has nowhere elicited any note or comment from those whose suspicious zeal finds an outlet in exciting and inflaming the public mind with apprehension and prejudice toward the established institutions of the State.[13]

Superintendents also responded to reformers by contradicting specific charges. To those, for example, who wanted to regulate commitment procedure in order to safeguard personal liberty under all circumstances, psychiatrists answered that such indiscriminate, though high-sounding, sentiments were based on a misunderstanding of the nature of true liberty.

The prime and indefensible right of every insane person is to have his or her diseased condition recognized and respected, and all other rights pertaining must revolve about that one. This can only be judged and passed upon by medical men. In the restriction of personal liberty it involves, they have the right to be protected from its undue prolongation, the right to skillful and humane treatment, the right to such exercise and privileges of a wholesome and elevating tendency as they may have been accustomed to, and the right to intercourse with and visitations from friends. All these must be under the direction of medical men.[14]

Fear of critics produced among psychiatrists a heated defense of the status quo and compensatory self-congratulation. One superintendent noted,

That errors of administration, errors of professional opinion and practice, undetected neglect of duty, deceptions and concealments, and even exceptional cruelty of conduct, may and do occur in rare instances in hospitals for the sane or insane, may be frankly admitted. But such things are incidental to human relations of every character. More insane persons are ill-treated, injudiciously restrained, neglected and otherwise abused while among friends in the family relation, than suffer from similar treatment in the least reputable insane hospital in America, proportionately considered.[15]

Psychiatrists, during this period, were rarely able to acknowledge faults in their own practice. When, however, the shortcomings of their institutions became too blatant to be denied, they could only blame them on immutable and external forces, offering no suggestions on how they and their colleagues might modify these conditions. When, for example, charges of brutality by attendants could no longer be denied after several had been convicted in court of assault or murder, superintendents could only regret the fact that they were forced to work through "subordinate instrumentalities," [16] attendants drawn "from a class whom no species of vigilance and discipline can always control in the prescribed line of propriety." [17]

This kind of defense further alienated superintendents from the insane, since practitioners turned part of their anger on certain unmanageable and "mendacious" classes of patients, such as alcoholics, drug addicts, and psychopaths, who were likely to carry tales of mistreatment to the outside world.

These persons prove to be as disturbing an element in the asylum as in the community in which they have resided. It would be the better policy of the asylum administration to refuse to receive these cases when recognized, and rid itself of their presence until public sentiment shall cause their relation to the community to be more clearly defined.[18]

A striking example of the way in which blame could only be directed outward may be seen in the opening address at the annual meeting of 1881, on "Asylum Management," delivered by J. Workman, the former superintendent of the Toronto Asylum for the Insane. He first eulogized a list of dead members of the Association, and paused gravely over the name of the recently deceased Isaac Ray,

the nestor of our grand humanitarian phalanx, the Solon and Socrates of American alienistic jurisprudence, the wise and frank admonitor of the young, the sage and modest counsellor of the aged, and the sympathizing brother of the entire family.[19]

Workman then noted that he was now the oldest member of the Association; and, since he would no doubt soon join his departed colleagues, he begged the young men to listen to these, his dying words, his critique of hospital management in the United States.

One might have expected Workman to attack poor record-keeping, low recovery rates, failure of attempts at prevention, failure to select and train attendants properly, or any number of other matters that might have troubled an old alienist in the 1880's. But instead, Workman attacked community pressures on asylums,

It is my belief that no small proportion of American [U.S.] asylums are too much governed, and that some of them have been sadly misgoverned. I am not blind to the fact that in any country which has achieved free popular institutions, and in which all public affairs must be conducted in conformity to the dominant suffrage of the electoral body, there must be great difficulty in convincing the multitude that there are some affairs in which they may be lacking in that cautious discrimination and stability of purpose, which are essential to final success.[20]

Workman deplored the role of political patronage in rendering the time in office of American superintendents uncertain. He considered this "one of the greatest evils connected with the administration of your asylums." Not only did he suggest nonpolitical appointment of asylum personnel, but also the awarding of pensions to long-term employees in order to encourage staff to remain at their jobs.

Workman next decried all other forms of lay interference.

The next evil to which I would allude, as calling for serious consideration, is that of the interference of the governors or trustees of asylums, with the appointment of assistants of every class or grade; and the same remark applies with even greater force to all higher authorities. I assume it as a certainty that every superintendent is capable of best judging as to fitness and competency of all his assistants, and it is consistent with common sense that he will endeavor to procure and to retain the best he can find; if not, he is unfit for his position, and the sooner he is released from it, the better.[21]

Workman characterized as "an evil of unspeakable virulence in connection with the administration of American asylums" the frequent charges of misconduct and mismanagement brought against colleagues,

the concoctions of discharged, bad servants, or of imperfectly recovered patients, where lingering insanity has underlain their moral obliquity. It is, however, truly lamentable to observe the extent of popular credence awarded to these calumniators, and it is badly calculated to elevate our conception of the primal purity of human nature, to find that so many people are anxious to believe evil of their fellow man, and to rejoice more in the hope of verifying inequity, than of discovering innocence.[22]

Workman called, therefore, not for direct confrontation with detractors, but for

some protecting breakwater that might withstand the force or avert the fury of the wave of popular delusion. That your local boards of trustees have in many instances not proved adequate to this service, will be readily admitted by all who have suffered from the defect. It is my belief that a central governmental supervision by one or more well qualified, discreet officers, whose function should be that of vigilant and thorough, not merely perfunctory, inspection of the condition and treatment of the patients, and of everything relating to their well-being, and whose duty it would be to report, at stated periods to the Governor of the State, whatever they might deem proper or useful to be made known, might meet your requirements.[23]

But even these powers would have to be hedged with restrictions and controls to ensure that they too would not interfere unduly in the province of the superintendent, and would not become involved in scandals that would reflect back on the institution.

It would not be either necessary or advisable that such officers should exercise any immediate control or direction over the financial affairs of the institutions, or have any connection with the giving out of contracts, or the buying and selling operations.[24]

So great had become their fear of the outside world, that alienists were willing to consider any buffer to safeguard their hospitals rather than risk direct confrontations with critics. Workman's suggestion was particularly ironic in view of the number of regulatory boards already formed in such states as Massachusetts and New York, charged with inspecting asylums on behalf of the public, but deeply resented by many superintendents for their interference in hospital affairs.

This was, moreover, a time when psychiatrists constantly reiterated the idea that a superintendent must have complete authority over his asylum, just as a captain controls his ship; and that any sharing of executive power could only produce chaos. This attitude was vividly illustrated at the annual meeting, when a new hospital, organized in two sections, one for male and one for female patients, sought admission to the Association for the woman physician in charge of the female wing. The male superintendent, already a member, was sharply questioned by his colleagues on whether or not he ran a "two-headed" institution." Most members seemed displeased by this divided authority, which might set precedents for other institutions, and the lady's request for membership was temporarily shelved.[25] Superintendents felt so threatened that organizational rigidity became greatly exaggerated, as though any change in procedures might be interpreted as capitulation to detractors.

Most criticism, however, was not answered directly. Rather, psychiatrists reacted with general abuse. Reformers were accused of "ignorance and malevolence," [26] of insanity, of being "in character bisexual," [27] of inventing "crude schemes," of "sermonizing and drooling over imaginary needs for the protection of the insane." [28]

There are some who think with their aid, the counsels of the Almighty in creation or the order of evolution, might have been amended, but usually they do not discern true reform, or effectually accomplish it.[29]

They were "born agitators" and "would-be philanthropists"; they were sentimental, unprincipled, and stupid. They were "professional reformers, who live and move upon the borderland of insanity, being native there." [30]

Although criticism from laymen might be discounted, practitioners were far more sensitive to the pressure of medical colleagues. The neurologists, they dismissed more easily as would-be superintendents, whose lack of qualifications had kept them out of asylum positions, and who were simply crying "sour grapes." This may be seen, for example, in the remarks of A. E. Macdonald of New York at the 1879 meeting of the Association, in which he described fellow members on a board of expert witnesses at a criminal trial. The first "expert" was caught contradicting himself when asked whether delusions were invariably signs of insanity. The second,

who, by the way, after being an unsuccessful applicant for appointments in several different asylums, quite lost his confidence in the present management of such institutions, and has been somewhat obtrusive in the citation and invention of supposed abuses therein, and in the indication of a modest willingness to have the duty of their correction thrown upon him, [31]

was shown some of the handwriting of the patient and asked if it offered any evidence of insanity. He replied that it did and, after giving the changes correctly enough, added that similar evidence was afforded by certain mistakes in spelling. Being asked to name them, he said: "Why, he spells 'amount' with only one M!" [32] Macdonald, at the insistence of his delighted colleagues, admitted that these witnesses were the former president and vice-president of the New York Neurological Society.

Superintendents in New York took a more active form of attack, circulating rumors that the neurologists' 1879 petition was a fraud, that they had appended names without authority, and had misrepresented its purport to the signers.[33]

The criticism of other medical specialties, however, was felt by psychiatrists as a betrayal. They felt that colleagues should have respected

The restraining and conservative influences of professional comity and courtesy . . . [which] should govern the relations of medical men toward their professional brethren, who are engaged in a most difficult work surrounded by embarrassments for the most part beyond their control.[34]

Similarly, John H. Callender said in his presidential address to the Association:

Medical men, regardless of the canons of the code of ethics, have participated in these unjust but futile crusades, and may be left in silence to their chagrin.[35]

Nevertheless, superintendents felt obliged to answer medical critics. They charged that the manner in which complaints against asylums were brought before public tribunals and the press was a breach of professional etiquette. The habit of going outside the professional group to bring added pressure to bear was deemed dishonorable, and the motives of those who did such "mischievous" deeds were held suspect.

Medical and other societies . . . have so far departed from their constituted purpose, as to engage in formulating propositions and charges against the asylum system for presentation to state legislatures. Many of the charges have been pressed with such vigor as to lead to the opinion that they were prompted by personal grievances. . . . Whatever may have been the motives which have actuated medical societies and prominent physicians to go out of their usual way to discuss and accomplish the best methods of treatment of the insane, the tendency has been to excite distrust and destroy public confidence, as well as to bring the parties engaged into questionable prominence.[36]

John Chapin concluded that

If movements of this kind are to receive the approval of the best public sentiment—if every disaffected portion of an organization, profession or calling may carry its grievances and opinions to the legislature or public, all groups will use political legislation to solve internal disputes, and the results would be chaotic.[37]

In their fear and frustration, practitioners responded during the late 1870's and early 1880's to attack from the community by evasion and counterattack. They failed at this time to take constructive action to remedy the abuses exposed by reformers, and instead frantically defended the status quo. Eventually, however, community pressures on the one hand, and hospital conditions on the other, began to break the monolithic opposition of the Association to reform.

NOTES

1. *The American Journal of Insanity*, XL (1883–1884), 33.

2. *Ibid.*, p. 35.

3. *Ibid.*, pp. 37–38.

4. *Journal of Nervous and Mental Disease*, VI (1879), 445.

5. *The American Journal of Insanity*, XXXVIII (1881–1882), 150.

6. *The American Journal of Insanity*, XXXVII (1880–1881), 27.

7. *Ibid.*, p. 28.

8. *Ibid.*, p. 29.

9. *The American Journal of Insanity,* XXXVIII (1881–1882), 129.

10. *The American Journal of Insanity,* XXXVII (1880–1881), 46.

11. *The American Journal of Insanity,* XXXVIII (1881–1882), 85.

12. *The American Journal of Insanity,* XLI (1884–1885), 300.

13. *The American Journal of Insanity,* XL (1883–1884), 36.

14. *Ibid.,* p. 30.

15. *The American Journal of Insanity,* XXXVIII (1881–1882), 133.

16. *The American Journal of Insanity,* LIV (1897–1898), 82.

17. *Ibid.,* p. 83.

18. *The American Journal of Insanity,* XL (1883–1884), 44.

19. *The American Journal of Insanity,* XXXVIII (1881–1882), 3.

20. *Ibid.,* p. 5.

21. *Ibid.,* pp. 9–10.

22. *Ibid.,* p. 10.

23. *Ibid.,* pp. 11–12.

24. *Ibid.,* p. 12.

25. *Ibid.,* p. 17.

26. *The American Journal of Insanity,* XL (1883–1884), 28.

27. *Ibid.,* p. 29.

28. *Ibid.*

29. *Ibid.,* p. 30.

30. *The American Journal of Insanity,* XXXVIII (1881–1882), 117.

31. *The American Journal of Insanity,* XXXVII (1880–1881), 149.

32. *Ibid.*

33. *Journal of Nervous and Mental Disease,* VI (1879), 534.

34. *The American Journal of Insanity,* XL (1883–1884), 35.

35. *Ibid.,* pp. 29–30.

36. *Ibid.,* p. 42.

37. *Ibid.*

Chapter 22

IMPACT OF CRITICISM ON
THE GUILD—AN EVENTUAL
BREAK IN THE UNITED FRONT

Over the years, a major target for reformers had been the Association of Medical Superintendents itself and John Gray, who, as editor of the *American Journal of Insanity*, was regarded by the public as spokesman for the group. The guild had been assailed for promoting "unparalleled despotism" in asylums and for being

unscientific and selfish in character and purpose, a close corporation which has tended to become a power as autocratic and domineering in asylum medicine and asylum politics throughout the Union, as are the authorities of each institution behind their own walls and locks.[1]

By the late nineteenth century, the guild had grown into a visible target. By 1883, the eve of its fortieth anniversary, there were 150 members representing 130 institutions in the United States and Canada. It had become a recognized pressure group, whose suggestions were held weighty on matters of legislation and hospital construction and management. Individual members invoked its edicts to sway opinion at home. By holding annual meetings in different states, and by inspecting and criticizing local institutions, the Association became visible to many of the leading citizens of the country. At the same time, individual superintendents became less prominent in their home communities because they now spent most of their time within their institutions and thus intervened less often in lay affairs.

The guild and the allegedly conservative ideas of Gray were frequently blamed by critics for the stagnation of American psychiatry; and the defense of the guild became a convenient way for alienists to repudiate reformers. This defense was often passionate in the extreme and contributed further to the centrality of the Association in American psychiatry. Praise of its founders, of its liberality, of its members, of its scientific contributions furnished topics of many lectures, a trend reinforced by the fact that the guild was commemorating its fortieth anniversary. During this period, a committee was established to maintain a necrology; and elaborate eulogies were prepared, a practice, one feels, whose significance to the organization transcended the normal Victorian fascination with death.

A characteristic defense of the Association was made in 1882 by John H. Callender. To claims that superintendents were unduly complacent about their results in treatment and administration and that they sought to hide lapses from the public, he answered,

The Association in wise regard of the interests of the great cause of which it is properly esteemed to be the overseeing minister and guardian, and mindful of the necessity of preserving a just and favorable temper of the public mind with reference to all forms of provision and modes of treatment of the insane, has never hesitated, when a sense of duty demanded, to remark upon inefficient and faulty institutions and practices, and in a becoming manner to convey rebuke therefore, whether it fell upon the parsimony and neglect of the people and state, county or city authorities, where, indeed, grievous faults of this kind most frequently inhere, or upon boards of management, or upon executive officers. The frank expressions of the body touching such matters, have been so justly and temperately, yet so firmly pronounced, as to carry conviction and arouse no resentments, and to eventuate in improvements and reformations in many instances.[2]

To those who accused the Association of countenancing jobbery and political alliances, Callender said that the guild had

Set its face as a flint against all manner of political jobbery in the dispensation of public charity in this humane behalf.[3]

Of accusations that the Association suppressed variant ideas among its members, he said of Association meetings,

In this species of refreshment of the spirit, the meetings of this Association are to its members what pilgrimages to Mecca are to the devout Mussulman, and the blessing is diffused to the recipients of their labors. . . . It is of the history of this body that its convocations have been characterized by remarkable freedom from all personal, professional or rational jealousies and antipathies. Here has been a common altar, on which has been laid the contributions of each as the common property of all, and upon it the fire of professional zeal is perpetually aflame.[4]

Finally, to complaints about the paucity of scientific advances made by superintendents, he wrote of the Association,

Its papers, published and unpublished, and the debates thereon, comprise every important topic, and evince an erudition and ability proudly comparable with those of any scientific body in Europe and America.[5]

Similarly, another practitioner had written in defense of superintendents within their organization,

They are in their associated capacity less dogmatic, dictatorial, or limited by fixed ideas, constitution, creed or code, than any other organized society on earth.[6]

Praise of the Association served not only to repudiate critics and to comfort beleaguered members by assuring them of the rightness of their thinking and the humanity and self-sacrifice of their lives; it was also an attempt to maintain unity in a sprawling and heterodox organization. Most members might agree in praising "the loftiness of the motives and the wisdom of the councils of this Association," in its "great philanthropic mission." [7] Most might accept the leadership of the vocal group around John Gray, who controlled much of the public image of the profession through the *Journal* and through contacts with legislatures and other visible forums. Nevertheless, a strong dissident element did exist, made up of those who opposed Gray's "Utica School," and who were hence excluded from the *Journal*. And there were many others, who, because of the difficulties of travel and because of the vagaries of political appointments that replaced superintendents at short intervals, had only peripheral contact with the Association. Constant reiteration of the traditions and aspirations of the guild bound together a shifting membership and, it was hoped, stressed those aspects of the organization to which even dissidents owed allegiance. Callender ended his speech of praise with the following prayer for unity:

Its past at least is secure, and in duty to itself, it should preserve the just temper and moderation which has been so eminently displayed in its proceedings, and permit no internal dissention as to matters trivial, to deflect it from its leading objects, and no external disparagement and denunciation, however ingenious or vehement, to discourage its purpose, or sow the seeds of its dissolution.[8]

Evidence of disunity and the consequent attempt of the guild and particularly of John Gray to restore order may be seen in some episodes of the annual meeting of 1881. The group had early been jolted by Orpheus Everts of the Cincinnati Sanitarium, who had given an excited and indignant speech about an article published in the prestigious *North American Review* in 1881, by Dorman B. Eaton, which vehemently attacked the Association as

an organization ably and adroitly managed, [which] has lulled and misled public opinion; shutting out light by artificial methods, defying exposure and change by the exercise of despotic authority which ought never to have been conferred upon the managers of asylums.[9]

Everts had laboriously reviewed and refuted every charge of the critic; and he had waxed particularly indignant over the article's attack on John Gray. Everts asked the Association to support his refutation of Eaton, but the group seemed displeased by his enthusiasm, by his raising an issue more comfortably forgotten. Members mildly rebuked him, then lulled themselves with characteristic speeches praising the Association and its work and denigrating critics. One alienist, for example, Charles H. Hughes of St. Louis, who had retired into private practice but still retained his loyalty to the guild, said,

This Association needs no defense. . . . The point of the paper, that this Association has been obstructive or retrogressive, or not progressive, certainly needs no defense.[10]

Hughes held that if one takes a historical view of the improvement of the lot of the insane,

It was the work done inside asylums. There is where it began, inside of the asylum circles, and where it has resulted in benefit to the race. It was the beginning of that reform in psychiatry, that practical and beneficent form which has been going on from the days of Pinel to the present time within the asylums.[11]

A. E. Macdonald of New York dismissed further the importance of Eaton, who, he said,

Has reached now an age and a frame of mind when he takes upon himself the role of a common scold, and generally behaves as though the whole world had been laid at his feet with the injunction—"O, reform it altogether."[12]

Eaton's article, he continued, was based on garbled testimony before a board of inquiry and was not worth answering.

Suddenly, several speeches took another tack. A young psychiatrist, new to the Association, J. Z. Gerhard of Harrisburg, Pennsylvania, observed,

There is a feeling sometimes among men who are engaged in any special work that they are doing just right, that they have reached the highest point of excellence, and that there is no room for progress or advancement. Yet I believe that in the course of time (particularly with those who are young) we shall see many things differently from what we do now, and be able and willing to admit ideas that we now consider very absurd.

In the state from which I represent an institution, there is a feeling that something different should be done in connection with our hospitals. This feeling has manifested itself in such a strong manner that the administration of some hospitals has been changed to a certain extent.[13]

Gerhard was ignored by his elders. The discussion was continuing along its former, reassuring track, when another interruption came, from a frontiersman, H. P. Mathewson, of Lincoln, Nebraska, who remarked,

One thing we may do well to consider, and that is, the proposition that reform "generally comes from the outside," and we ought to be willing to accept the situation. All suggestions coming honestly and conscientiously, we ought to take in good faith.[14]

He apologized for entering the discussion, because he was a complete outsider:

Every man is strange to me. There is not one person here that I have ever seen before; but I am very glad to see you, gentlemen, and to make your acquaintance.[15]

The meeting continued to ignore these views of virtual outsiders, which were in direct contradiction to the general discussion. But then a change took place, for the minority opinion was picked up by an old, established member of the guild, Richard Gundry of the Maryland Hospital for the Insane at Catonsville, and member of the faction of Isaac Ray, with whom John Gray was feuding.

I believe the best means of reform is to let the light into every place. However much it may cause a temporary depression in our case, it will eventually result in a greater and more favorable movement in our behalf. All advance movements are met with walls of stone before the great asylums themselves. We do not make progress in this. We are, by straight line or by curves going backwards, and I recently overheard an intelligent friend make a remark to this effect. It is the one great obstacle in our profession. . . . It is only from the fact of going out and looking in, that we get the views of others.[16]

Gundry challenged the facile self-congratulation of his colleagues' earlier speeches. Psychiatrists and the Association, he pointed out, were not the creators of enlightened patient care. Laymen, and foreigners at that, were the originators of their methods:

All reform in asylums came over to the United States through the unobtrusive action of Tuke (a layman) and it is to Tuke, really, that we owe all the improvements in management which have come down to us. It has simply been improving and developing the germinal seed that he deposited. It is all very well to recognize the great claims of Pinel (a physician) and others, but we cannot avoid recognizing the efforts of the family of Tukes. They were called to them by certain language of a persistent member before the House of Commons, so it will not do to argue that the efficacious reforms came from within, when, in fact, the greatest reforms have come from without.[17]

Gundry continued in the same heretical vein, showing that many of the accusations of critics against existing systems of hospital supervision, against political jobbery, and against dishonest administration were, in fact, true and therefore warranted the serious attention of superintendents.

He next compounded his heresy by turning on John Gray and the *Journal*. He held it unfortunate that the Association had no official publication to represent it. The *Journal*, which had been until recently the only organ in the field, was in fact the voice of only one institution but was assumed by the rest of the world to speak for the profession.

Now, I say that is unfortunate, because we do not all wish to be held responsible for the opinions of that organ, or the editors of that paper. The editors of that paper have a perfect right to state what views they choose. They have a perfect right to adopt any one of them and when they choose; but it strikes me some of the methods they use are hurtful to this body.[18]

Gundry concluded by noting that

The best sort of reform is that made from within, and if we all do that, I do not think it matters who attacks us—whether it be the highest or the lowest. I think it better we should be sure of our foundation before we attempt to rout the supposed enemy, especially as that enemy has taken the offensive. We can bear everything as long as we can say we have never blushed before.[19]

Now John Gray rose to a lofty attack. He eulogized the Association and dismissed Gundry's remarks about the partisanship of the *Journal* as irrelevant. The Association represents, he said, not individuals, but

official life and action and offices. . . . It does not intend, therefore, either to build up or to drag down, or to defend the mere personal interests of men. It has to do with superintendents in their public duties and capacities; it has to do with the laws which govern these institutions and the great principles which underlie them.[20]

To the applause of the meeting, he rejected the idea that major advances in the care of the insane came from laymen.

History will clearly show that nearly all the steps of real progress in this great cause were the results of consultation and discussion in their annual meetings. Since that time from year to year, as experience has taught us their work has been enlarged, and the series of propositions and special resolutions of this body stand now today untouched by the sophistry of a single one of all the would-be reformers. My friend, Dr. Gundry, shakes his head. I repeat, not a single proposition has been gainsaid or overturned. They stand today above all contradiction as a part of the constitution, so to speak, of this body, and they are interwoven as a part of the fabric of our laws and their practical application is felt in all parts of this country.[21]

Gray continued to refute Gundry's argument point by point and, in the process, ridiculed and embarrassed his opponent. Gundry, for example, had not named states or persons when discussing political corruption in asylum affairs. Gray supplied the missing information over his colleagues' anguished cries for silence before the outsiders in the room. Gray accused Gundry of cowardice and of putting "himself into the shoes of the reformers run mad." He evoked the repeated applause and laughter of the meeting, all of which was recorded in the next issue of the *Journal*.

By his eloquence, Gray won the day, but the battle continued; soothing self-congratulation and invocation of guild traditions and solidarity proved powerless to silence progressives and dissenters. At the 1883 meeting of the Association, another demand was made that colleagues break away from the isolation of the guild's official policy of silence. Everts, in direct contradiction to those who attempted to ignore public outcry, made a plea for greater contact with the community, even if that meant consorting with the press.

> The remedy of some of [these] evils . . . is publication, but not in the *Journal of Insanity*. This reaches men of science, only. This reaches the select few. A very dignified few. We must reach the public. As we used to fight fires on the prairies by setting back fires, so we must appropriate these channels by publication ourselves. We must go into the daily papers. We must present the other side of the matter, fully, and make the side profitable to the publishers by interesting the public. There is no trouble in reaching public opinion through the public press if we take the trouble to do so. But we must unbend—we must come down from our dignified and scientific stand, and meet the enemy upon his own ground. We cannot draw ourselves into our own shells like dumb sawrians, expecting the "Journalists" to admire our dignity and defend our reservations. They will not do it. It is not profitable for them to do so. So I see no other way than to appeal to the people. And I think the true way to get at the people is by the secular press. We need have no fears of public sentiment if we take the pains of educating the public. The public will trust us if we trust it, show it what we are doing—and why we do so.
>
> If the whole truth were known about our institutions, we would have no trouble at all. It is the comparative secrecy of hospital conduct that excites suspicion. . . . Throw open our institutions and invite the press. When a reporter comes, treat him as a reporter likes to be treated. Make him at home, give him a good dinner and good cigars, and tell him all you know, and he will give better reports of your institution. . . . Send him away knowing more than he ever knew before and he will not malign you.[22]

Everts ended his remarks with even greater daring, by noting that his greatest anxiety from adverse publicity concerned the friends of the insane; he was not at all concerned by the sufferings of superintendents.

This unfraternal statement was so shocking that at first no one could return to the point. In time, however, Macdonald of New York did so obliquely, by complaining about the treachery of fellow alienists to their peers, because some of the reform societies were using the names of various superintendents on their membership lists. He explained that he had recently brought suit to suppress a scurrilous article against himself, whose original was written under a letterhead of one of the reform societies that listed the names of certain colleagues as members.[23]

The ice now broken, other practitioners turned to attack Everts with some heat.

I do not agree with the idea that it [asylum management] shall be made public by welcoming these newspaper foot-pads with their cry "Stand and deliver, your money or your life," "Your cigars and your dinner, or your reputation!" I do not believe in welcoming them thus.[24]

Everts, however, delivered one parting shot in favor of entertaining newspapermen. Just as the session adjourned, he snapped, in frontier fashion,

If you had to have a set-to with a rattlesnake that you could not kill with a blow, it would be thought wise to draw its fangs as a preliminary operation, would it not? [25]

The complaints of the community and the manifest evils of the status quo in hospitals were disrupting the complacency of the Association, despite the attempts of the leaders to maintain unity and silence. This period of resistance of psychiatrists to change, however, was succeeded by a more dynamic one of development and self-criticism and, strangely enough, by a return to certain features of a now-defunct system of moral treatment.

NOTES

1. *The American Journal of Insanity*, XXXVIII (1881–1882), 118.

2. *The American Journal of Insanity*, XL (1883–1884), 11.

3. *Ibid.*, p. 12.

4. *Ibid.*, p. 26.

5. *Ibid.*, p. 28.

6. *The American Journal of Insanity*, XXXVIII (1881–1882), 137.

7. *The American Journal of Insanity*, XL (1883–1884), 32.

8. *Ibid.*

9. *The American Journal of Insanity*, XXXVIII (1881–1882), 124.

10. *Ibid.*, pp. 194–195.

11. *Ibid.*, p. 195.

12. *Ibid.*, p. 199.

13. *Ibid.*, p. 187.

14. *Ibid.*, p. 190.

15. *Ibid.*, p. 191.

16. *Ibid.*, p. 205.

17. *Ibid.*

18. *Ibid.*, p. 209.

19. *Ibid.*, p. 210.

20. *Ibid.*, p. 212.

21. *Ibid.*, p. 213.

22. *The American Journal of Insanity*, XL (1883–1884), 303.

23. *Ibid.*, pp. 306–307.

24. *Ibid.*, pp. 307–308.

25. *Ibid.*, p. 308.

Chapter 23

PRACTICAL RESULTS

OF CRITICISM—

REFORM LEGISLATION

Despite the fulminations of a large part of the leadership of the psychiatric guild, outside reformers won the day. In such states as New York, they lobbied successfully for legislation that they hoped would correct the abuses of the "American system" of hospital management. These critics had further impact on psychiatrists, because their propaganda was one of the forces contributing to reorientation of professional thought and practice, and even to reorganization of the psychiatric guild itself. The history of lay concern with mental illness during the nineteenth century shows that, however isolated institutions may appear to have been geographically, professionally, and socially, in fact, the surrounding community continually impinged on them, molding and governing the most fundamental aspects of their organization.

In a number of states, such as Massachusetts and New York, legislation was enacted in an attempt to remedy what critics felt to be the deficiencies of psychiatric practice. Despite opposition from psychiatrists, for example, reformers in Massachusetts, led by Mrs. Leonard of Springfield, a member of the State Board of Health, Lunacy, and Charity, lobbied successfully for a bill, which was enacted in 1885, to permit the boarding-out of harmless, chronic pauper insane in private families, after the model of Gheel and Scotland.

Another goal of reformers was achieved in Massachusetts when, in 1874, the legislature ordered that locked mailboxes be placed on each ward in which patients might post letters to the superintendent or the State Board of Charities. The latter body was empowered to open these boxes monthly.

It was in New York, however, that some of the most comprehensive legislation was passed that became a model for provisions in other states. A major target for reformers here, as in other parts of the country, was the system of local and private asylums, over which public authorities wielded no control. In such states as New York, an elaborate county care system had evolved as an offshoot of the state hospital network. During the mid-nineteenth century, when state governments were erecting public asylums to remove the insane from the neglect of regional poorhouses and jails, there was, ironically, an even faster patient flow in the opposite direction. As governmental institutions became overcrowded, and as a backlog of chronicity filled the beds intended for acute and curable patients, "harmless" cases were returned to county and municipal asylums. A rash of substandard receptacles mushroomed over such states as Massachusetts and New York, accepting acute as well as chronic insane. Reformers later in the century described a visit to such an establishment:

Shall we soon forget the insane man, crouching in a dark cell, so small that he could not stand up in it; or the woman, in midwinter, nearly frozen by the broken window; "It was useless to mend it, she always broke it again"; or one tablespoonful of fish and one potato called a meal, while water spilled in the same room froze upon the floor; or the foul wrongs suffered by those unprotected women; such cruelties one can never forget.[1]

By the 1870's the public institutions in New York were so crowded that an attempt was made to make use of local institutions and to provide them with adequate supervision. A trial of the "county care system" was officially sanctioned. Twenty years later, enlightened men admitted that the experiment had not only been a failure but that the custody of the insane in many localities had reverted to the very abuses that had fired the crusade of Dorothea Dix. By the late 1880's it was realized that, even in the richest counties, such as Kings, the weekly allowance for each patient in a local institution was from one to two dollars less than in state hospitals, and the comparison was far worse in the smaller and poorer localities. As one critic noted,

The lay keeper of one of the largest of these county establishments boasted to the writer that he maintained his insane patients for the munificent sum of 90 cents a week per capita.[2]

The staff of such institutions were generally untrained, and usually the recipients of political patronage; attendants were frequently paupers detained in the same poorhouse. And in the absence of proper standards and adequate supervision, even a well-run institution was unusually liable to retrogression if a change in management took place. Reformers believed that the standards of even the best county hospitals could never equal those of state institutions.

Many of the keepers of these county asylums in the State of New York freely admitted that if they were required to maintain a standard of care equal to that of the State institutions, their per capita cost would largely exceed the rates then charged by the State asylums for the chronic insane. In truth, it may be said that not one of the twenty or more so-called county asylums licensed by the New York State Board of Charities prior to the passage of the State Care Act in 1890, had proper facilities in any essential particular for the care and treatment of insane patients, most of them being only parts of the poorhouse proper, and without even a resident medical officer.[3]

The response of reformers to the abuses of county care was to create public demand for an expansion of state responsibility for the insane and for a tightening and elaboration of the ordinances governing public institutions. This movement began, like many others before and since, with a voluntary nonsectarian organization, founded in 1872 and called the State Charities Aid Association. Its object was

to bring about reforms in our public institutions of charity through the formation of an intelligent, educated, and organized public opinion.[4]

It was composed of members representing nearly all the counties in the state and was led by Louise Lee Schufler, whom many felt to have assumed the mantle of Dorothea Dix.

One of the first successful attacks against county care took place in 1865, with the founding of the Willard Asylum to receive chronic insane from the entire state. Localities, however, appealed for and got exemptions from the Willard Act, a task made easier by a lack of accommodations in state asylums. By 1887, nineteen counties had been exempted from this act by the State Board of

Charities, the counties promising "to give their insane just as good care as the State gave." [5] When, in 1889, the newly formed State Commission of Lunacy was granted the power, previously held by the Board of Charities, to exempt localities from the Willard Act, the Commission refused to make any such exceptions and, instead, recommended that the county asylums be closed.

One successful outcome of the struggle of reformers was the inclusion of mental hospital positions under the Civil Service laws in New York. It was hoped that competitive examinations might be substituted for political jobbery and nepotism when asylum positions fell vacant and that some level of previous training in the care of the insane might be ensured. In New York, therefore, in 1893, the following prerequisites were listed for those wishing to take the examinations: A candidate for superintendent was to be a physician not less than thirty years of age, and to have had at least five years of experience in an asylum; a first assistant physician was to be at least twenty-five, and to have served at least three years in an asylum; a junior assistant was to be at least twenty-one, with one year's experience in the care of the insane. All candidates for top staff positions were to be graduates of a legally chartered medical school and to be citizens and residents of New York. Analogous qualifications were drawn up for lower staff grades.[6]

Opposition to full state guardianship over the insane came not only from pychiatrists wary of outside interference and the proprietors of county asylums who were directly threatened but also from officials of localities, who found here a constitutional issue. This paralleled analogous twentieth-century battles between states and the Federal Government. Local officials brought the matter to court, claiming that the law violated the principle of "home rule." To this, the supporters of state care answered by citing the following three points: First, it was a well-established principle that localism must, in certain circumstances, give way to overriding powers to prevent disorganization and to further the public good. Therefore, the principles of local self-government must give way to the superior powers and resources of the state when the latter could cope with a situation more effectively. Second, common and statutory law supported the premise that the insane were wards of the state, not of localities. The state therefore had the right at any time both to delegate to the localities the task of caring for local dependent classes and to resume support of such individuals itself. Third, because the insane, unlike sufferers from other forms of disease, must be deprived of liberty as part of proper treatment, sufferers naturally fell under the peculiar guardianship of the state.

After fighting for many years, much of the time against organized psychiatric resistance, reformers in New York won passage of a "State Care Bill" in 1890. This law, and supporting legislation passed between 1890 and 1896, sought to attack most of the abuses decried by reformers, not only in patient care but also in asylum management, personnel hiring, supervision, freedom from political interference, and so forth. The State Care Act itself had the following provisions:

The abolition of separate institutions for the *chronic* insane; the designation of all the public institutions for the insane as State hospitals; the division of the State into hospital districts, and requiring that each hospital shall receive all of the dependent insane within its district, whether acute or chronic, providing for the erection on the grounds of the State hospitals of additional buildings to accommodate the inmates of county asylums, then numbered nearly 2,300 at a per capita cost, including equipment and furniture, not to exceed $550; requiring county superintendents to properly prepare patients for removal to hospitals . . . [and] that after such patients have been delivered into the custody of the hospital officials, the care and control of county authorities over them shall cease.[7]

Furthermore, all patients were to be removed from county to state asylums, but there was to be no traffic in the other direction. The Commission of Lunacy was to prevent overcrowding by approving the construction of additional accommodations near existing hospitals or by recommending new facilities.

To satisfy those concerned about waste and dishonesty in asylum management, it was ruled that the commission was to approve all monies spent on new buildings and all extraordinary repairs and improvements. All expenditures of the hospitals were to be itemized and approved, with financial records to be submitted monthly to the commission. The commission was ordered to establish a standardized salary scale; and all books and records in all state hospitals were to follow a uniform pattern. By further legislation in 1895, the practice of making separate legislative appropriations for each hospital was discontinued; instead, a fund was assigned to the commission, which in turn divided the money between institutions.[8]

In 1896, New York passed the Insanity Law, which revised and consolidated all pre-existing legislation into a comprehensive act. It defined methods of appointment, salaries, terms of office, and powers and duties of the commissioners. It created a pattern of uniform organization for hospitals, establishing the numbers and powers of managers, superintendents, stewards, and treasurers and providing the form for monthly financial estimates and accounting. It instructed the commission on the licensing of private institutions. It dealt with the forms of commitment, custody, and discharge.[9] As Stephen Smith, Commissioner of Lunacy in New York, wrote:

No State system for the care of the insane . . . can be considered complete in all its details which does not provide for an independent supervision of all of the insane and of the institutions devoted to their custody. This supervision should represent the sovereignty of the State in the relation of guardian to ward, and should be clothed with powers adequate to prevent wrongs and to secure the welfare of the objects of its care. This purpose can be effectually accomplished only by completely separating these institutions and their supervision from all other classes of public charities, and organizing them on a basis which secures direct and independent supervision by the state.[10]

The Commission of Lunacy became this separate body, established in 1889, and by subsequent modification of the state constitution was freed from dependence on the legislature for its existence. It was to be composed of three men serving staggered six-year terms, and appointed by the governor. The chairman was to be a physician, and the other two members were to be a lawyer and a leading citizen.

The commission was empowered to execute all laws pertaining to the custody, care, and treatment of the insane of all classes except feeble-minded and epileptics. It required effective visitation of all public and private hospitals, with inspection of methods of management, the conditions of buildings and grounds, the accuracy of books and records, the conditions of stores and food supplies, and the quality of the various dietaries of asylums. The commission was to determine the fitness of hospital officers for their duties; it was to see as many patients as possible; and it was to grant private interviews to staff and patients to hear complaints. The commission was to have access at all times to hospitals, and was to make recommendations on its findings. It was also to regulate the correspondence of patients, although the law directed that patients were to be permitted to correspond freely with the county judge and district attorney of the locality from which they were committed.

The commission was also charged to define the hospital districts and to modify their boundaries as conditions might require. They were to keep records of the results of all civil service qualifying examinations in lunacy, as well as all admissions, discharges, and transfers of patients between institutions. Finally, the commission was ordered to appoint a director for the state pathological institute.

In addition to the commission, supervisory boards of managers were to be appointed by the governor for each asylum, with the task of inspecting their own hospitals and reporting their findings to the commission. This body, composed of seven members living in the hospital district, was to appoint and remove the superintendent and treasurer. All other employees, however, were to be chosen by the superintendent from lists of those qualified by civil service examinations.

By no means all the recommendations of reform groups incorporated into law were unpopular with superintendents. The last, for example, echoed the repeated demand of superintendents that they be permitted to appoint their own subordinates, because, under existing conditions, these were chosen by outside authority. This, they felt, undermined their control of asylum practice because it was found impossible to enforce discipline when the superintendent could wield no sanctions over staff. In 1889 the New York Commission of Lunacy had recommended that

The superintendent and chief medical officer of every asylum should be clothed with the absolute power of appointment and removal of all officers subordinate to himself. . . . As the law now stands, boards of managers or trustees of the State asylums have the power of appointment of the superintendent. The power is also given them to appoint, on the nomination of the superintendent, all of the resident officers, so-called, that is, the assistant physician, steward, and matron; and while the superintendent may, for cause, temporarily suspend a resident officer, the right is reserved to the managers to confirm or disapprove such suspension. Instances are not wanting of discord between the superintendent and resident officers. This is not as it should be.[11]

Instances of friction caused by this system were common. An extreme and well-publicized case took place in 1894 at the Missouri State Asylum Number Three, when the superintendent accused both assistant physicians of having committed acts of insubordination, insolence, and profanity in his presence. The second assistant had threatened to kill his superior and had brandished a paper weight "which would have been deadly if used." The first assistant physician had had "personal differences" with the superintendent, which might have mitigated the offense. The murderous second assistant, however, was felt to have been unprovoked and in the wrong; and a member of the Board of Managers publicly stated, after hearing statements from both sides, that in his opinion, " 'the superintendent was clearly in line of duty' when the second assistant insulted him, threatened to kill him, and used profane language unbecoming an officer and gentleman."

The superintendent, powerless to act, took the matter to his Board of Managers. After hearing the case, they passed a resolution calling on all parties to do their duty in the future. The superintendent resigned in fury because the assistants had not been dismissed.[12]

In time, therefore, the recommendations of the New York Commission of Lunacy were viewed with favor when they stated:

The superintendent should be held to a strict accountability for the acts of his subordinates but he cannot be so held unless he is possessed of the power of appointment and removal. The existing methods tend to weaken discipline, to produce a want of harmony, and to create constant friction. The superintendent is appointed on the theory that he is competent for the position. If he is competent, he should be allowed to select and remove his subordinates. If he is not competent, he should not hold the position.[13]

Thus, under the new legislation, the superintendent was confirmed in his personal charge over the hospital. In answer to the charges that patients were neglected, it was ruled that the chief medical officer was to examine every patient within five days of admission and was to regularly visit all wards. He was to establish training schools for nurses and attendants, and he or his first assistant was to meet the commission every month in Albany with the monthly hospital finance record and to discuss any other pressing matters.

The new legislation in New York was felt by contemporaries to promise the following benefits. First, there was greater centralization. The results of civil service exams, for example, were registered, as were figures of patient flow, in a central data bank. Machinery had been created to transfer patients from one institution to another, so that they might be closer to their friends, and so that overcrowding might be minimized. Second, various fee problems were solved. The distinctions between private patients and public charges were reduced when it was ruled that the maximum fees for private patients would be ten dollars a week and that the rich would occupy only one room. Furthermore, the state was able to induce families who could pay to reimburse the Commonwealth for the charges of their relatives.

The legal distinction between acute and chronic patients was removed, and state institutions were called "hospitals" rather than "asylums" to symbolize their new organization on a curative basis. Patterns of regular correspondence for patients were devised. Inmates were permitted to write at least once every two weeks; all letters not forwarded to the addressee were to be sent to the Commission of Lunacy for inspection; and all letters to state officials with jurisdiction in lunacy were to be sent unopened.

Provisions were made for paroling patients for up to thirty days, during which time they might return to the hospital without recommitment. Patients were to be told where they were when they came to a hospital and informed of the fact of their commitment. They were also to be given a hearing by the visiting commissioners.

As part of the new emphasis on making asylums into hospitals, licenses for private asylums were to be granted only to qualified physicians; nurses and attendants were to be given uniforms; and provisions were to be made for the clinical teaching of medical students and of local general practitioners on the wards. There were new directives for the appointment of interns; nonpartisan, civil service examinations were to be the basis of appointments; and there was to be an increase in salaries and wages in all grades of service, with promotion at regular intervals free of favoritism. Female nurses were to be used on male wards. More accommodations were to be provided for attendants. And dentists, opthalmologists, and other specialists were to be consulted by asylum staff. In the interest of greater medical skill, an allowance of one hundred dollars a year was to be made to each hospital for buying medical books; and institutions were urged to subscribe to scientific journals.

In accordance with the latest idea that good nutrition and baths were therapeutic, asylums were asked to employ chefs to improve the cooking; to work out standard dietaries; and to build rain and spray baths. Finally, as a further ensurance of honest management, a system of competitive bidding for supplies was to be used.

To complete this comprehensive code governing insanity, a new commitment law was enacted. Like the rest of the legislation, it reflected the heterogeneity of public fears and prejudice. An early reform had taken place in 1874, when an attempt had been made to emphasize the medical rather than the custodial nature of such institutions. Asylums were to be organized like fever and smallpox hospitals, with patients committed for medical treatment as well as for the protection of themselves and society. They were nevertheless "judicial hospitals," because many patients were admitted after court hearings; however, patients who felt wrongly committed were entitled to appeal to the Supreme Court within three days for a review.

The new ruling on discharging dangerous patients said that they could be released only when superintendents were willing to certify "complete recovery." Furloughs were allowed, and psychiatrists were permitted to send the harmless pauper patient home.[14]

A later commitment law tried to combine the claims of both medicine and law. It also sought to reduce the number of cases brought to the Supreme Court for review.[15] Under the new law no person could be committed to an institution for the insane except upon an order of a judge of a court of record, such order being granted upon a verified petition containing a statement of facts upon which the allegation of insanity was based, and a certificate of lunacy signed by two qualified examiners in lunacy. Notice of application for the order of commitment had to be served upon the person alleged to be insane at least one day before making the application; but the judge might dispense with such personal service or might direct substituted service to be made upon some other person to be designated by him.

If the person alleged to be insane, or any friend in his behalf, is dissatisfied with the final order of the judge or justice committing, he may, within ten days thereafter, appeal therefrom to a justice of the Supreme Court other than the one making the order who *shall* cause a jury to be summoned and try the question of insanity.[16]

In order to limit abuse of the latter measure, it was ruled that those bringing suit for false commitment would be liable for court costs should their suit be denied. This issue of trial by jury, however, still did not satisfy many, who feared the loss of privacy and the fact that a medical decision was here being removed into lay hands.

Initial results of these various laws were heartening. Those concerned with economy in public affairs were delighted. During the first year after passage of the 1890 law, it was credited with saving $300,000 over the previous year's expenditures, while providing better services.[17] Likewise, after initial friction and distrust, many superintendents began to favor the new situation, reporting a sudden rise in standards of allocations of equipment, personnel, and food. In the 1893 report of the Binghamton State Hospital, for example, the superintendent explained a dramatic fall in the death rate among patients, as follows:

To you who have seen the institution grow from a poorly equipped. crudely furnished, poverty-stricken asylum for the chronic insane into the splendid hospital of today, supplied with modern sanitary appliances, provided with good food and raiment for its patients, diversified occupation and amusements to engage their hands and minds, and kind nurses to watch over them, the question needs no answer. Improved surroundings, humane care and treatment, freedom from mechnical restraint, and the largest personal liberty consistent with safety, are the agencies through which the change has been accomplished. Up to the year 1890 it was with exceeding difficulty that the bare necessities of life could be procured for our patients, but when in that year the State care bill became a law, this hospital, scarcely recognized by its sister institutions, was suddenly galvanized into life, and under the beneficent provisions of the act it received a new impetus which enabled it to rise rapidly to high rank in the State. Under the old law anything was good enough for the broken down chronic cases it sheltered; under the new law the arbitrary distinction between acute and chronic insanity was legally annihilated and the doors of the hospital were opened to all for whom admission was sought from the eight counties constituting the district assigned as its bailiwick.[18]

NOTES

1. *The American Journal of Insanity*, LIII (1896–1897), 77.
2. *Ibid.*, p. 73.
3. *Ibid.*
4. *Ibid.*, p. 76.
5. *Ibid.*, p. 81.
6. *The American Journal of Insanity*, L (1893–1894), 441.
7. *The American Journal of Insanity*, LIII (1896–1897), 82.
8. *Ibid.*, p. 83.
9. *Ibid.*, p. 84.
10. *Ibid.*, p. 79.
11. *Ibid.*
12. *The American Journal of Insanity*, L (1893–1894), 451.
13. *The American Journal of Insanity*, LIII (1896–1897), 87.
14. *Ibid.*, p. 90.
15. *Ibid.*, p. 88.
16. *Ibid.*
17. *Ibid.*, p. 97.
18. *Ibid.*, p. 94.

PART FOUR

The Turn of the Century:
The Revitalization
of Psychiatry

Chapter 24

CHANGES IN PATIENT CARE—
RENEWED PSYCHIATRIC
CONCERN FOR
THERAPEUTIC ENVIRONMENT

From the late 1880's to the turn of the twentieth century, the ideas of several leading members of the Association of Medical Superintendents reverted in many particulars to the hitherto ignored or repudiated tenets of moral treatment. More psychiatrists now admitted the truth of lay charges of neglect and mistreatment on wards. They acknowledged the failure of their asylum system, as the rate of chronic cases mounted to 90 per cent of the population of many hospitals. Psychiatrists accepted suggestions for changes in patient management. Individualized care was to replace mass treatment by categories. Programs of work, recreation, and education were to replace mechanical and pharmacological restraints; and patient behavior was to be modified, not only by physical therapy but also by suiting the physical and social milieux of the hospital to the needs of each case.

The fact that these modes of treatment paralleled those of the early nineteenth century was noted, incidentally, with amazement by one or two members of the Association, who had chanced to read back volumes of the *American Journal of Insanity*. They were used to eulogizing the Original Thirteen, but it came as something of a shock to realize that, with all their own vaunted progress, they were so close to the practices of half a century before.[1]

Changes were born, in part, of the experiments of a few innovative and desperate psychiatrists. In 1886, for example, John W. Givens, first assistant physician of the Oregon State Insane Asylum in Salem, explained his use of a "new" method of treatment of making his patients memorize prose passages for later recitation to a physician.

The daily work of the physician in an insane asylum leads him to turn over and over again his resources for the treatment of his patients, hoping to learn of some new factor or of some new combination of old factors which will give him better practical results than he is now obtaining.[2]

The new orientation came also from a loosening of constraints that had earlier bound the guild; and here the justice of much outside criticism of the conservatism of the Association was validated. By 1888, all members of the Original Thirteen but Pliny Earle had died, as had some younger, but relatively authoritarian colleagues, such as John Gray. Many of the restraints long imposed on contributions to the *Journal* and to annual meetings were removed as the so-called Utica School lost influence. Members were now free to discuss matters hitherto suppressed or ridiculed; and they did so avidly. It was felt that a new age was coming, in preparation for which old orthodoxies must be sacrificed. Psychiatrists were urged to reexamine their work and to question their former complacency.

Many of us have been trained under the existing asylum and hospital system of the country or have been identified with existing plans in some way. It is quite natural, and may be more self-satisfying, to believe that what we have done is right than to confess that defects exist. Honest doubts, however, exist whether our work should rest here or be considered finished.[3]

For years, American practitioners had furiously denied that European asylums were superior to those in America, insisting either that claims by foreign superintendents were fraudulent or that a more manageable form of insanity existed abroad. By the late 1880's, however, they could admit that insanity was the same everywhere, that European colleagues were honest, and that the English or French system of asylum administration was frankly superior.

Veneration for the history of the Association was still expressed. For example, John B. Chapin, superintendent of the Pennsylvania Hospital for the Insane in Philadelphia, began an iconoclastic presi-

dential address to the 1888 annual meeting of the Association traditionally enough:

The necrology of our deceased members has been carefully preserved
in appropriate memorial notices and deposited in the archives of the
Association. . . . It should in the future ever be regarded as a sacred
duty, not to be neglected by those who survive.[4]

Nevertheless, during this meeting there was widespread rejection of
earlier dogma. The most dramatic of these purifying gestures took
place when the collected Propositions of the Association were
examined. These were directives passed at previous meetings and
embodying the official guild position on such issues as institutional
architecture, hospital size, and use of restraints. The 1888 meeting,
after much discussion, felt that the propositions were now dated.
Members therefore refused to reaffirm the old directives or to pass
a new set, because they did not want to bind their successors. As
Chapin told the Association in his presidential address,

With all deference to the wisdom of the founders and without calling
in question what they may have thought proper to do . . . I would
now regard it as unwise and a great mistake to make any general
declaration of principles for ourselves or for those who follow us.
. . . Any propositions we might adopt are but announcements of opinions held today, which twenty years hence may come to be regarded
by those who follow us as inapplicable platitudes. . . . Is it just to
those who may follow us to attempt to set a limit to the tendencies of
the future? . . . Ought it ever to occur again that the presentation
and consideration of important subjects at our meetings can be antag-
onized by no better argument than by so-called principles and propositions adopted a score of years previously and under conditions perhaps
entirely changed? Far better would it be to have no principles than
that they should be a bar to progress! [5]

Liberalizing tendencies were proposed and supported by some
psychiatrists who had only weakly adhered to the dogma of the
"Utica School" in the first place; and hence the change in the tone
of Association discussions was in one sense less dramatic than it
might appear. Proposals for reform, however, also mirrored the
latest trends in contemporary scientific and philosophic thought
concerning the role of environment in the development of personality. Thus, the statements of these former dissidents were endowed
with greater authority than they had been earlier.

At this time, there was much theorizing about the effects of sensation and experience on the development of the brain, the nerves, and hence of the personality. As a result of such interest, psychiatrists concluded that if the social and physical environment of hospitals were modified, healthy habits of thought and behavior would be instilled in patients, because the physical organs would be molded anew. This idea, of course, was in striking consonance with those of moral treatment.

Of great importance to this movement was contemporary investigation of psychology and of morbid brain pathology. Attempts were made to localize cerebral functions, thus in essence continuing the work of phrenologists such as Franz Joseph Gall and Johann Casper Spurzheim, whose influence on earlier American psychiatry had been so marked. Four spheres of brain action were delineated: organic, reflex, sensorimotor, and ideomotor; and their respective brain regions were sought by such workers as H. Fritzsch, Edward Hitzig, and Sir David Ferrier. One of the by-products of such research was an improved ability to localize and remove tumors, one of the major advances in brain surgery.

As a result of research into the mechanism of nervous impulses and the function of synapses, the brain was seen by such scientists as Henry Maudsley as a communications center for a complex neural network. Hence, earlier conjectures about the influence of both the body and of external stimuli on brain tissues were reinforced:

Every form of functional activity in the brain is the result of structural changes in its tissues. Every mental operation represents a transformation of energy in the process of which a waste of substance takes place in some portion of the brain cortex. This waste is being constantly supplied in the normal state by the assimilation of nutritive materials; and this restoration has one peculiar characteristic which has been well described by Dr. Tuke and Maudsley: It is a restoration of material with the functional capacity of that previously transformed into energy; *plus* an added intensity to its former tendency to expend its energy on certain lines.[6]

In other words, habits were thought to be created by successive generations of cells in the brain inheriting an ever strengthened tendency to function in a particular way. As William James, a major theorist in this area, wrote,

Our nervous system grows to the modes in which it has been exercised.[7]

Environment was felt particularly to materially modify the brains of present and future generations:

Where the influence of the environment is persistent, habits of conduct are formed. Modifications of structure result. By heredity, these are transmitted from generation to generation, and are always undergoing changes produced by the environment.[8]

As Daniel Clark, superintendent of the Asylum for the Insane, Toronto, Canada, noted in his presidential address to the Association in 1892:

Man is ruled by the external influences, from the thraldom of which there is no manumission, being, as Emerson would say, in "the hands of the cherubim of destiny." [9]

This theory led psychiatrists to one that bore striking similarity to that of early nineteenth-century alienists; for insanity was seen again as, essentially, the development of bad habits of cerebral functioning.

I venture to assert further that the abnormal expenditure of energy and the abnormal tissue waste, with the nutritive changes, more or less modified by disturbance in the conditions, which accompany and constitute the disease called insanity, in most instances obey the same general laws. If this be true, it follows that the functional activity of the brain in disease along any particular line, predisposes to similar action under like circumstances in the future.[10]

In an 1888 article, "Tact in the Management of the Insane," A. B. Richardson of Ohio continued this theme, setting forth a theoretical basis for the role of environment in insanity drawn from contemporary psychologists and particularly from the English psychiatrist Maudsley.

It has . . . been established beyond peradventure that our environment makes a decided impression on our desires, and through our desires as the motive forces, modifies the power and degree of the dominance of the will. . . . While the will in insanity is always perverted and often greatly impaired, it's not usually effaced, but continues to exist, maintaining in a greater or lesser degree, some semblance of its normal state; and as Maudsley in his chapter on "Will in Disease" justly remarks, we must "treat its derangements through the body exactly as if it were entirely dependent on the body." [11]

By a long chain of arguments, it appeared that in order to so affect the will through the body, it would be necessary to manipulate the environment.

We all recognize a decided variability in the mental symptoms in most cases of insanity, and we have no difficulty in noting the dependence of this variation, in many cases at least, upon modifications in the diseased processes of the brain. It is a little more difficult, but not the less essential to a right comprehension of the disease in its entirety, for us to go a step further and note the fact that this variability in symptoms is often dependent upon the will of the individual affected, and consequently to a certain degree controlled by his desires. His desires also receive their coloring from his environment, it must follow that the surroundings of an insane person seriously affect the diseased condition of the brain.

Richardson continued,

Bear in mind here that while insanity is a disease of certain of the tissues of the brain, and while this physical disease is often of the same general nature as that of any other organ of the body, and amenable to the influence of medicinal agents in a similar manner, there is no other organ whose functional activity, and consequently whose processes of tissue waste and tissue repair, are so profoundly affected by external conditions.[12]

Insanity, Richardson noted, was the failure of the brain tissues to receive stimuli from the rest of the body and from the outside world in an orderly way that would allow normal cell growth and replacement.

With this theoretical basis, Richardson now defended the idea, so scorned by John Gray and his followers, that a "functional insanity" might exist that would not manifest brain damage; or rather, that tissue damage produced by such disorders could be erased by corrective experience, much like the theories of earlier moral treatment.

Like early alienists, some late nineteenth-century psychiatrists drew from such theories a "final common path" hypothesis. It did not really matter how the original damage occurred, whether by brain damage, disease, or overwhelming sense impressions or emotions; they all produce similar trains of action in brain cells, and they might all be modified by similar methods, both medicinal and moral. This might be seen in laboratory experiments, where it could be shown that under suitable circumstances compensation for brain damage took place in animals that recovered normal functioning after portions of the brain governing particular actions were excised. It could also be demonstrated in mental hospital wards, by observing the clinical picture of a heterogeneous group of patients whose social environment reinforced controlled behavior.

But if the clinical history can be so modified, and the functional activity of the brain even in disease leaves a special impress upon the structure of the brain, it is further evident that the physical basis of the diseased condition may also be modified. Experience in the care of the insane affords abundant evidence of these points. I could mention scores of instances showing the volitional control of the symptoms. In this controllable variability exists one of the most fortunate conditions at our command in our contest with this dreadful and dreaded disease. The study of its scope and capabilities for good becomes imperative— and this opens the whole question of what may be called moral treatment of the insane in contradistinction to the purely medical. Though this is often considered unscientific and unworthy of the investigation of professional men it is now seen to be based upon as purely scientific principles as the application of medical agents.[13]

Two avenues were seen for attacking improper habits of mind:

first, the adaptation of the environment of the patient to the particular circumstances in each case, and second, the attitude toward the patient of the various individuals with which the patient comes in contact.[14]

Attention to the physical environment led late nineteenth-century psychiatrists to take the same precautions in hospital arrangement as had their predecessors early in the century in moral treatment institutions. It also led them emphatically to repudiate the propositions of the Association governing and standardizing hospital construction. The major fault of these old directives

has been a too limited recognition of the vast diversity of demands in the nature of the case for the successful treatment of mental disease.[15]

Measures to control patients had in the past assumed primacy, while those to implement "the more subtle mental and moral demands" had been overlooked. This produced monotonous and forbidding architecture of

Long straight corridors . . . , the walls destitute of any ornament or pictures, scantily furnished, cheerless, monotonous and uninviting. Some here present do not forget the rows of chairs fastened to the floors, as was every article of furniture, . . . which restrained such patients as were turbulent, nor the din and confusion of what were properly called the "Noisy Wards." [16]

Like the practitioners of moral treatment, late nineteenth-century psychiatrists attempted to minimize the shock of institutionalization on damaged nerves and brains. The taboo of advocating separate provisions for the acute and curable insane began to fade. Superintendents realized the danger to acute patients entering chronic wards where all therapeutic functions had been smothered and where recent cases were terrified by the noise, violence, and convulsions of other patients.

Experience has left the settled conviction in my mind that the great mixed ward, as a place to commence healing influence in a recently disordered mind has, to say the least, very grave disadvantages, and I believe stronger terms might be used with truth.[17]

It was therefore urged that separate facilities be provided for acute cases, either in special wards in general hospitals or small separate institutions. This was the beginning of the idea that would culminate in the psychopathic wards and hospitals.

Attempts were made to ameliorate existing asylums, to reduce some of their frightening starkness and monotony. Asylum reports now listed acquisitions of picture collections for their wards, of new furniture, of curtains, and of Edison's "incandescent globes." They also recorded the repainting of rooms, and some structural alterations for greater comfort.

This new plan for patient management called for individualized treatment and furnished grounds for further attack on the Association propositions standardizing asylum architecture.

I am strongly tempted to assert that no institution should be built precisely on the plan of any other institution, and certainly no department in any institution should be similar in general design or in detail, to any other department of the same institution. The individual peculiarities of different classes should be provided for in the construction as far as the number and subdivision of departments will permit. The internal decoration and the furnishing should also have a pleasing variety. The patient's daily life should be relieved of monotony as far as possible by the separation of his different apartments and by the use of different styles of furnishing and decoration in each. His sitting-room and playroom should be entirely separate from his sleeping apartment. His dining-room should be removed from each and resemble neither. His sick-room and his work-shop should each have a distinct identity and special characteristics.[18]

Such modes of construction would be in themselves therapeutic.

It cannot be doubted that under such favoring environments as modern experience in mental disorders is amply competent to devise, the period of hospital residence in curable cases might be materially abridged, and during that period the comfort and satisfaction of the patient greatly enhanced. . . . The sympathetic adjustments become in themselves corrective, tending to undermine delusions, suspicions and unreal fears.[19]

The social milieu on the wards was likewise to be regulated.

His association among patients should be so chosen as will best counteract the morbid tendencies in his own case.[20]

In repudiating the Association's propositions on hospital architecture, therefore, it was hoped that

The hospital for mental diseases, which may be looked for in the future, will not be copied from tradition, a stereotyped structure, but will be the outgrowth of an unbiased study of the ideas and wants suggested by many individual observations and experiences.[21]

A new emphasis on individual treatment of the insane led some psychiatrists to repudiate the older fascination for statistics and categorization of patients that had marked the directives of the Association to its members in past years.

When shall we learn that the individual case is not a matter of general averages or the greatest good of the whole number. I am tired of curing the insane by statistics. . . . What we want to know and to find out by careful study of the individual is, what treatment—exceptional it may be—will save that man or woman . . . and bring back the mind.[22]

Instead, all hospital environments were to be modified to fit individual needs; and the regimentation of patients that robbed them of their individuality was attacked. At the 1888 annual meeting of the Association, one superintendent protested against the routine of mass dining-rooms,

I rather doubt that it is necessary to wait for the tap of the bell if it necessitates the keeping of the food on the plates until it becomes cold. I do not see why a general dining-room should not be served as the general dining-room of this hotel would be. I do not see why it should not be treated like a restaurant; why patients should not be sent in at different hours. Why should that dining-room be shut up except at special hours of meals? Why shouldn't it be open for a variety of purposes.[23]

Interest in individualized care and in instilling appropriate habits produced a resurgence of interest in patient work programs, now

once more regarded by leading practitioners as primarily a therapeutic, rather than an economic, measure. It was found to produce
such improved behavior that the need for mechanical restraints was
reduced.

I do not exaggerate when I state that in a ward where at one period I
had seen from twelve to fifteen women in muffs, securely fastened to
the . . . row of chairs on account of their turbulent and destructive
propensities, on a succeeding visit to the same ward I was most agree-
ably surprised and impressed with the fact that a revolution had occurred. Seated in comfortable chairs about a table in a well appointed
ward were the same number of patients who were well ordered, engaged in useful occupations. The restraints had disappeared, the
psychical storm which characterized the irritation resulting from a
different system had subsided, the attendant, trained to an improved
service, had come to remain, and the environments were restful too for
the eye.[24]

Another strong advocate of a hospital work system was G.
Alder Blumer, medical superintendent of Utica State Hospital. In
an address before the Association in 1897 he decried the too enthusiastic use of drugs, blaming here not only the fadism of the profession but also the blandishments of drug houses.

With respect to drugs, while we doubtless understand their action
better than our forebears, and realize that in their relation to the
corpus vile they are, like everything else in this world, subject to law,
we often exhibit a childlike faith that suggests the mysticism of the
Middle Ages. Our mail brings day by day a new claimant for recognition fresh from the press of the wholesale drug house, and latterly even
the Transatlantic pharmacist, not backward in his appreciation of our
craving for things European, thrusts his foreign envelope under our
noses to call our eager attention to some new remedy of strange name.
So we go on experimenting with this drug and with that, year in and
year out, groping, vaunting, doubting, spurning each by turn, till
finally we lose faith in the permanent value of any drug and run the
risk of ultimate entrance upon the stage of therapeutic nihilism.[25]

Blumer felt that labor and physical occupation were better for
the insane, because "exercise is indispensable to the proper development of the motor area of the brain." This concept was analogous
to one in moral treatment, where it was believed that brains were
only partially damaged in insanity and that therefore particular
care must be taken to prevent atrophy in other cerebral regions. In

the late nineteenth century, evidence was adduced for this position. J. Crichton-Browne, for example, wrote that

In persons who have been long bedridden by chronic disease and debarred from all muscular exercise, the whole motor area of the brain is, after death, more or less atrophied and waterlogged. It is unquestionably essential to the welfare of all motor centres, and especially of the large and complicated motor centres of the hand, that the parts with which they are immediately connected should be used in an active and varied manner.[26]

Individualized care implied far greater contact between staff and patients than had become customary. The superintendent was now asked to assume again a personal agency in the treatment of each patient. He was directed to

Discover the motives that lie at the root of his patients' conduct and set to work his ingenuity to correct these and direct them into right channels.[27]

He was to engage in

thorough scientific investigation . . . the closest study of the laws that control the action of the human mind.[28]

And, he was to create an appropriate course of therapy for each patient, determined not by abstract professional rules and directives, but by the exigencies of his own situation, and by his own ingenuity and insight.

The thesis of poor habits becoming imprinted in the brain led some late nineteenth-century psychiatrists, as it had early nineteenth-century alienists, to view the mental hospital as a school, in which patients might be resocialized and correct habits of will and action developed to replace disordered functioning. The role of the patient's own moral faculties in the process of his own recovery were stressed.

It would indeed be a startling proposition to assert that insanity is ever a condition voluntarily assumed, but . . . it is evident that particular symptoms of the mental disturbance are often amenable to control through the will of the individual affected, and if proper motives can be brought to bear to influence the direction of will activity, the clinical history of the case may be favorably modified.[29]

Psychiatrists therefore attacked those aspects of current hospital administration that specifically hindered this process. It was pointed out, for example, that the custom of prescribing chloral hydrate nightly for long periods fostered drug dependency but did not allow the patient to learn to sleep naturally. Similarly, it was said that the common management of incontinent patients merely confirmed their behavior, rather than gradually teaching control. As in earlier moral treatment, reconstitution was to begin by fostering whatever normal functions still remained. The patient was no longer to be a passive recipient of services; he was to be helped to mobilize his own strengths to combat disease.

There is no other rational method of moral control of the insane than to get hold of the personality of the individual, ascertain the lines along which the functional activity of his brain proceeds, take out of this whatever is normal, whatever is healthful, and on this establish our base of operations—going back to it for a renewal of power whenever we find that we have exhausted our store. In less mystifying terms, if there is in any insane person, any function of the brain that is normal in activity, if there is any direction in which there is healthy action we must seize upon this and from it start lines of activity by such an adjustment of environment, such an impress from other intelligences, as will bring still other centres of activity into normal action.[30]

It was believed that when proper behavior was elicited, this was a sign that the physical damage had been repaired, and that normality was gradually returning.

We can be assured that when the function is restored to a healthy standard, the physical sub-structure must be also healthy.[31]

Thus, physicians and attendants were urged to

So arrange the environing conditions that they will require on the part of the patient a daily exercise of volitional control or automatic action looking toward the betterment of his mental and physical state.[32]

A number of programs were launched, therefore, that attempted to stimulate gradual and correct development of mind and will. One of these was directed by Walter Channing of Brookline, Massachusetts, who set up a system for the physical training of the insane in gymnastics and games. His work was stimulated by the growth of interest in sports in schools and universities since the Civil War and particularly by the system of "Swedish Movement Cure" introduced to Boston by Dio Kewis in the 1850's, in which localized defects were attacked by special exercises. In 1867, Worcester State Hospital had established regular gym classes, complete with flannel uniforms for patients, and led by teachers from the local public school. Channing's program, however, was more specialized. He directed mixed classes, of patients and staff, in a three-year graded course of exercises, in which individual participants were taught to persevere in order to gradually improve their own performance.

The principle of enlarging, improving, going forward to something better, can be steadily adhered to, and is the vital element of success in modern gymnastic work.[33]

Not only were such programs seen to have direct physical benefit, but also indirect moral effects, because they increased disciplined performance and the patient's own sense of mastery. Asylum reports now began to include references to the performance of hospital sports teams, indicating the extent of professional interest in these matters.

New concern with the role of the social environment in insanity, the requirements of individualized care, and the criticism of reformers led psychiatrists to attempt to raise the caliber of attendants and nurses. This was done in part by trying to inspire pride of calling by providing uniforms and by raising salaries. It was also done by creating new programs to train nonmedical personnel, leading to the granting of a certificate of proficiency. During this period, a number of institutions, led by McLean Asylum for the Insane in Massachusetts, opened schools for attendants. Classes covered such topics as the major classifications of insanity; the properties and toxic symptoms of various drugs; elementary anatomy and physiology; first aid; and various other useful subjects.

There were those who felt, however, that this was not sufficient, that employees must be sensitized to the nonphysical aspects of insanity and to the moral methods of modifying patient behavior. Moreover, their own moral characters must be raised.

He should study and search out the small remaining spark of reason and virtue, and on it fix as the starting point for the restoration of his patient. He should be active, industrious, prompt, fearless. He should be patient, level-headed and firm. He should be without affectation, kindly sympathetic, plain spoken and honest. Himself implicitly obedient, he should cultivate that nice tact that will teach him just how far obedience from his patient should be enforced. Above all he should exhibit to the disordered but more or less discriminating judgment of his patient, sound reasoning and goodness of heart. He should understand that insanity is disease, its subject the victim of disease, and however repulsive its features, the object of his charity and sympathy. His patient should not be coerced but firmly led. I mean by this that the impression left upon the patient should not be that he has been compelled against his will to obedience but that he has been impelled by a belief that the action required must be done for his own best interests.[34]

The attendant, like the psychiatrist, was to study the idiosyncrasies of each case and to make each patient his friend.

Training schools were found to have many benefits, but one of the most significant was the feeling by some psychiatrists that they could now trust the discretion of nonmedical personnel sufficiently to decentralize their asylums. This removed a major obstacle to hitherto rejected notions that various cottage systems be established, in which patients with different needs might be placed in a number of separate buildings at varying distances from the central institution.

Another by-product of the schools was that they brought the medical and nonmedical staff closer together. Edward Cowles, Superintendent of McLean Asylum, noted,

One can not meet his people, even somewhat formally in the lecture-room, every week for a series of months, without being more keenly moved by a sympathetic interest in each of them,—in their troubles, their good efforts, and their attainments. They discover this feeling, of course, and there is soon a community of interest, a union of purpose, and a mutual confidence that brings good to the common cause.[35]

This combination of more individualized care, more solicitude on the part of the medical staff, and better trained attendants was found to markedly reduce the need for mechanical restraints, until members of the Association were able to repudiate the stand of their predecessors. They held that the propositions on this subject were products of "sentiment and the outgrowth of routine and custom." One psychiatrist, W. W. Godding, added in 1888,

Today that resolution does not, in my opinion, fairly express the sentiment of this Association. A change has come over our American psychiatry. We have learned that labor and outdoor exercise may in a majority of cases replace mechanical restraint and seclusion to the advantage of the mental health of the patient. Recognizing this fact the Association now relegates the great mass of the restraining apparatus that was so lately in use in our hospitals to the limbo of closets and attics.[36]

Moreover, several classes of patients, whom asylums were obliged to accept by law, and who were earlier considered undesirable, were now found cooperative if treated under this new humane program. E. P. Elliot, Assistant Physician at Danvers State Hospital in Massachusetts, for example, suggested that alcoholics were not such unrewarding patients as had long been claimed.

When I first entered the hospital service, I naturally contracted the prevailing prejudice . . . I can only say that, upon better acquaintance, I have found the poor drunkard not so black, by half, as he has been painted. . . . If put upon his honor, and at the same time made to feel that he is under a certain amount of constant supervision, he can be trusted to a very considerable extent. If treated as a man and a brother, instead of being told that he is a nuisance on the face of the earth (and more especially in a hospital), he is as a rule obliging and helpful, and is often willing to work as steadily and conscientiously as a hired man.[37]

By the late nineteenth century, therefore, there was a surprising return, among certain psychiatrists, to the theories and practices of moral treatment. American psychiatry was changing. Superintendents were beginning to experiment again. Their various discoveries, however, like the late-blooming intimations of moral management, affected only a few select cases in each asylum, and contributed little to ameliorating the fate of thousands of others.

NOTES

1. *The American Journal of Insanity*, XLII (1885–1886), 7.

2. *The American Journal of Insanity*, XLIII (1886–1887), 78.

3. *The American Journal of Insanity*, XLVI (1889–1890), 13.

4. *Ibid.*, p. 4.

5. *Ibid.*, pp. 8–9.

6. *The American Journal of Insanity*, XLV (1888–1889), 10.

7. William James, *The Principles of Psychology* (New York: Henry Holt and Co., 1890), Vol. I, p. 112.

8. *The American Journal of Insanity*, XLVIII (1891–1892), 498.

9. *The American Journal of Insanity*, XLIX (1892–1893), 4.

10. *The American Journal of Insanity*, XLV (1888–1889), 10.

11. *Ibid.*

12. *Ibid.*, p. 11.

13. *Ibid.*, p. 12.

14. *Ibid.*

15. *Ibid.*, p. 380.

16. *The American Journal of Insanity*, XLVI (1889–1890), 11.

17. *Ibid.*, pp. 186–187.

18. *The American Journal of Insanity*, XLV (1888–1889), 13.

19. *Ibid.*, pp. 379–380.

20. *Ibid.*

21. *Ibid.*, p. 377.

22. *The American Journal of Insanity*, XLVII (1890–1891), 13.

23. *The American Journal of Insanity*, XLV (1888–1889), 123.

24. *The American Journal of Insanity*, XLVI (1889–1890), 11.

25. *The American Journal of Insanity*, LIV (1897–1898), 157–158.

26. *Ibid.*, p. 159.

27. *The American Journal of Insanity*, XLV (1888–1889), 16.

28. *Ibid.*

29. *Ibid.*, p. 11.

30. *Ibid.*, p. 16.

31. *Ibid.*

32. *The American Journal of Insanity*, XLIII (1886–1887), 421.

33. *The American Journal of Insanity*, XLVI (1889–1890), 171.

34. *The American Journal of Insanity*, XLV (1888–1889), 14.

35. *The American Journal of Insanity*, XLIV (1887–1888), 191.

36. *The American Journal of Insanity*, XLVII (1890–1891), 14.

37. *The American Journal of Insanity*, XLVI (1889–1890), 55.

Chapter 25

NEW ENTHUSIASM FOR
INNOVATIVE TREATMENT
AND RESEARCH

The feeling of liberation and adventure in the Association of Medical Superintendents at this time gave rise to a new spirit of daring. Not only were the old propositions of the Association abandoned as unduly constraining a younger generation but also abandoned was the earlier cautious treatment of patients, in which all risks were avoided, that dated from the era of Dorothea Dix's influence. Instead, risks and experiments were advocated to dispel the scientific and therapeutic stagnation of most institutions. At the 1890 annual meeting of the Association, for example, the outgoing president, W. W. Godding, medical superintendent of the Government Hospital for the Insane in Washington, D.C., said that, because only one third of patients ever recover, while the rest are doomed, "Let us resolve to leave nothing undone" that might aid recovery.

I would say to our young men entering upon hospital work, while there is nothing so inexcusable as recklessness in medical service, you are justified in thoroughly testing all legitimate forms of active treatment in your efforts to effect a cure in the acute forms of insanity. It will not do to let the man go down into dementia without putting forth every effort to save him from that death in life that there is some reason to think may be averted in the early and active stage of his disease.[1]

Godding urged his colleagues to learn new advances in brain

surgery and never to neglect trepanning in suitable cases of epilepsy, even if the case be old. Of even newer methods he said,

Will hypnotism aid us in our treatment of mind? I do not know; try it. It probably belongs to the mere driftwood of science, but to throw to a drowning man anything is better than nothing.[2]

At times Godding's advice seemed alarmingly reckless:

Where the paroxysm of mania is traceable to ovarian irritation is Batty's operation justifiable? Insanity that is otherwise hopeless justifies anything. But would it not be well to try potassic iodide, counter irritation, active purgation, strict regimen and a few other things first? In the eyes of the modern surgeon the operation is so simple, so comparatively free from danger that womanhood is shorn away with as little compunction as were the enlarged tonsils in the times of our fathers.[3]

Of electricity he noted,

Try it and persevere in trying it on suitable cases up to any point short of fatality.[4]

The public, however, objected to a number of these innovations. In 1892, for example, the *American Journal of Insanity* reported that state Senator Mitchell of Oregon

has introduced a bill into the Senate making hypnotism, electromagnetism or mesmerism a crime, punishable by death. The bill was introduced at the request of a distinguished lawyer who is convinced that magnetic or hypnotic influences are responsible for many crimes.[5]

There was also a rash of cases in which doctors, like W. H. Baker of Boston, were sued for removal of ovaries, a practice that, the *Journal* admitted in 1892, had become much abused.[6]

A variety of new treatment schemes appeared during this period. There was the "photochromatic treatment of insanity," in which the mentally disordered were exposed to sunlight filtered through colored glass. There was musical therapy, of which G. Alder Blumer wrote in 1891,

It is impossible to measure the precise value of music in our armamentarium. It cannot be placed on a par with drugs in this respect, and one must be content to speak of its therapeutic value in more general terms.[7]

It was observed, however, to have an effect on such functions as the circulation of blood.

In Danvers State Hospital, in Massachusetts, musical therapy became so popular that an orchestra played during meals. A typical selection for breakfast and dinner was listed in the *Journal:*

Breakfast—George Weigand, March, "The Lenox"
  F. Schubert, Overture, "Rosamunde"
  V. Herbert, Selections from "The Serenade"
  Hymn, "Old Hundred"
  Sousa, March, "Stars and Stripes"
Dinner—T. Moses, March, "The Puritan"
  F. V. Suppe, Overture, "Morning, Noon and Night"
  T. Tobani, Selections, "Hungarian Fantasia"
  Haydn, Andante from "Surprise Symphony"
  Chopin, Valse in E Minor
  Hymn, "Old Hundred"
  E. Levi, March, "U.S. March" [8]

In the same vein, an anthropologist, Aleš Hrdlička, in an 1898 article on "Art and Literature in the Mentally Abnormal," announced his findings that poetry is bad for the insane; that epileptics prefer religious songs; and the "Insane criminals manifest some liking for the dance." [9]

A great deal of interest was shown at this time in physical therapy. There were, for example, various schemes of massage to "arouse and stimulate all the vital functions" and a variety of Turkish baths, showers, and other forms of hydrotherapy. Great emphasis was also put on special diets, and a number of studies were made during the first decade of the twentieth century on the composition of gastric fluids in various forms of insanity. Deficiencies in digestive enzymes were corrected, and this was found to improve mental health.

There was renewed interest in pathological research, in part inspired by the example of Adolf Meyer who, in the 1890's, began to publish in the *Journal,* and was acknowledged early as the leading figure in American psychiatry. The influence of German psychiatry was also growing; and there was much interest in the latest classifications of insanity according to the system of Kraepelin and his contemporaries.

Some exotic forms of classification were advocated. William Krauss of Buffalo, New York, for example, read a paper on "The Stigmata of Degeneration" before the Buffalo Medical Club in 1896. He held that all forms of insanity produce deformities in the cranium, face, and body that may be used in diagnosis. Such "stigmata" included asymmetry in the two sides of the face, squints and tics, and an improper slope of the face. Ears might be excessively large, small, folded, asymmetrical, irregularly shaped, or have no lobes; there were twenty-two kinds of ear deformities listed. Other danger signals included disorders of hard and soft palates and abnormalities of the teeth, such as persistence of milk teeth, abnormal length of canine teeth, abnormal shape and position of teeth, and so forth. Eyes might be too large or small, or improperly placed; a high proportion of criminals, Krauss noted, were left-handed; insanity might be seen in a sallow, pallid, leathery skin, in a face "prematurely wrinkled," in early gray hair, hairy moles, and in the "absence of hair over the chest in adult males." There were also, Krauss pointed out, "moral stigmata."

These individuals have no conception of the meaning of the terms justice, honesty, friendship, virtue; the only rule of their life is the gratification of one or other of their perverse propensities. . . . They are cunning, revengeful, untruthful, relentless, and prostitute all their mental powers to the gratification of their morbid desires and their deep hatred.[10]

Establishing insanity by such physical criteria, so reminiscent, by the way, of the old science of physiognomy, apparently became familiar to the public. In *Billy Budd*, for example, Melville proved that Claggard, the villain, was a psychopath by noting that he had violet eyes and a receding chin.

One of the areas that psychiatrists began to examine with interest by the 1880's and 1890's was that of the possible existence and functions of the unconscious. This field had long fascinated American writers from Hawthorne and Poe to Melville and Henry James. Most major European authors of the nineteenth century were concerned with men in society, but their American colleagues, feeling that a new, egalitarian nation furnished scant material for stories of class struggle and the playing out of great events of church and state, turned instead to examine the interior life of the individual—the border land between waking and sleep, between reality and illusion that becomes reality. They dealt with dreams, hypnotism, repression, and sexuality in a way that makes them highly interesting to twentieth-century psychiatrists.

Attention was drawn to the unconscious by the work of psychologists and philosophers like William James. Its existence was suggested by the effects of hypnotism, particularly in hysteria, and by the phenomena of sleep and dreaming. Psychiatrists were interested in a variety of mysterious phenomena—the fact that there seemed to be a threshold for perceiving sensory stimuli, when hitherto unfelt nerve reactions became conscious; the fact that customary actions, once requiring conscious thought, can become habits requiring no thought at all, so that the original cerebration needed for their completion must take place at a lower level of consciousness; the fact that problems that cannot be solved before going to bed may be solved in a dream; the fact that people can wake at a prearranged time; the fact that people forget the actions they perform in an epileptiform state; and so forth.

An interesting paper on the unconscious appeared in the *Journal* in 1892. Charles W. Page, medical superintendent of the Danvers Lunatic Hospital wrote an article, "The Adverse Consequences of Repression," in which he examined the case of an angelic young girl who had gone mad and had begun to use foul words that nobody had realized she knew. Page explained the case as an upsurge of mental energy, usually kept out of the conscious mind by the forces of rationality.

As rational efforts weaken, emotional effects become prominent. Surprising volumes of subjective feeling arise, and stimulate mental action. A multitude of ideas well into the patient's consciousness, succeeding each other too rapidly for complete verbal utterance.[11]

Page noted that, although it is usually impossible to find the source of many of these insane utterances, many of them seem to be the effect of earlier repression.

A resolution to banish certain trains of thought, or to shun all reference to particular things, recognizes their existence, magnifies their objective reality, and brings the whole unwelcome topic into the closest relations with deep feelings of personality.[12]

When such repression occurs, the individual endows the idea with added mental energy; thus, paradoxically, he is more likely to remember it. Page felt that such a mechanism frequently confounds "those who early conceive a high standard of moral duty and anxiously strive to fulfill the letter of the law, too mindful of their personal weakness."

It is thus no wonder that when Freud came to lecture at Clark University in 1907 he was welcomed so enthusiastically and that the United States has since become the bastion of his theories. Not only did his ideas fit with those of psychologists like William

James, and with those of a segment of local psychiatric opinion, but they dovetailed with a native intellectual tradition of introspection and analysis of the "soul."

The impression one draws from psychiatric articles of this period is one of great diversity and ebullience. The *Journal* published a wide range of papers and had no dominant theme. Articles on brain pathology, with impressive pictures of microscopic sections, or clinical descriptions of Korsakoff's psychosis, dementia praecox, or tertiary syphilis mingled with accounts of esoteric treatment schemes, analyses of bodily fluids, the hobby-horses of strange splinter groups, and a controversy on whether female nurses should be used on male wards. American psychiatry, at least on the surface, appeared lively.

Perhaps one of the clearest indications that psychiatrists themselves expected significant changes in the practice of their profession may be seen in the relief of a number of superintendents that new advances, unlike the old, appeared to be the products of evolution, not revolution; that they were based solidly on experience, not on fad. It was noted with pleasure that they had arrived quietly and discretely, without the public fanfare of past panaceas or the pressure of guild edicts. Godding, for example, noted that the new emphasis on nonrestraint had luckily not created any claims of golden ages dawning, or of popular hysteria; rather, it had been a quiet, gradual, and hence, perhaps, a lasting advance.

Yet the golden age has not fully materialized [with the end of restraints]. As to each one of us grown wary of watching for ships, which with priceless freights are being wafted over the seas, so to this old, toiling world, sin beset and sorrow laden, the millenniums that are always coming are invariably sidetracked in the coming. Somehow of late I have not heard as much of these public bonfires being used as the popular guarantee of successful hospital management; it is believed that a private crematory will accomplish all that is needed in this direction.[13]

Nevertheless, dramatic changes were far away, for the problems that had dogged American psychiatry throughout the nineteenth century had not abated. In spite of early optimism psychiatrists, during the first decade of the twentieth century, were sadly acknowledging the fact that their system had not yet been jolted out of stagnation.

The refrain of leaders of psychiatry at the turn of the century was still "research," but there seems to have been some confusion about the form such investigations should take. In 1907, for example, Charles G. Hill, attending physician at the Mount Hope Retreat in Baltimore, said in his presidential address to the Association,

I am convinced that the dead-house has had its day, and that prae-mortem, rather than post-mortem studies should engage our attention. The revelations of the autopsy avail us little in the treatment of our patients and the study of the living is far more profitable than the study of the dead. We must get away from the growing of pumpkins, the rearing of pigs, and the planting of potatoes, close up our old textbooks, always ten years behind the times, and study the latest clinical diagnosis, physiological and pathological chemistry, bacteriology, toxicology, and metabolism. If we grow tired of these and cannot find solace in Benjamin Rush, Esquirol, or any of these old writers, let us improve our diagnostic acumen by reading Shakespeare, Sherlock Holmes, and Kipling; and lastly, to broaden our philanthropy, ennoble our aims, quicken our sympathies, and gild the edges of the volume of useful knowledge we have accumulated, let us take down from our shelves that priceless little gem, The Bonnie Briar Bush, and read and reread the story of Wellum MacClure.[14]

A paucity of scientific research was caused not only by a lack of professional focus but also by some persistent and familiar problems, endemic in the asylum system. Political jobbery continued to be destructive, causing the summary dismissal of such leading advocates of the new system of patient management as Richardson of Athens, Ohio. It also discouraged young men from attempting any work outside the hospital routine, because they knew that their promotion would not be accelerated by extra effort. Lack of money meant that new plans remained on paper and staffs were often cut with little notice.

Some practitioners felt that the poor showing of American psychiatry was due to the caliber of those engaged in the profession. In 1904, C. B. Farrar, of the Sheppard and Enoch Pratt Hospital, wrote,

One of the causes of slow advance in this field, which has even today to be reckoned with, is the fact that too often the choice of men to whom the observation of the insane is entrusted has been, to say the least, unfortunate. . . . We have thus to do with the lamentable situation of *the most difficult problems which science has to present being left in the hands of men the least able to solve them.*[15]

Farrar urged his colleagues to study not diseases, but individuals, to take not an arbitrary norm, but the idiosyncratic psychology of individuals, which "cannot be profitably tossed into a half-dozen text-book categories." Asylums should establish laboratories of experimental psychology, modeled on that which Kraepelin established in 1890 in Heidelberg, to bridge the gulf between psychological medicine and psychology. Farrar thus called for psychiatrists and social scientists to labor together in "one of the broadest and most important departments of medicine."

Various methods were advocated to improve the scientific work of the profession. Hill, for example, suggested that prizes might be awarded to those making discoveries. He urged that the *Journal* be made into a monthly periodical so that there might be a greater exchange of ideas; and he advised hospitals to educate their chiefs to a better appreciation of laboratory work.

One of those who actually instituted a program to promote interest in scientific investigation among his personnel and to combat the stultifying effects of hospital routine was Edward Cowles, Superintendent of McLean Asylum in Massachusetts. He established the "seminary method," a system of staff education, in which there was to be an integration of clinical observations, laboratory work, and reviews of the literature. The staff met periodically in seminars to present papers on these important issues.

In innovative patient care, as in research, the basic problems remained. Some of the early critiques of asylum architecture ruefully noted that hospitals were large public investments and could not be replaced when professional advances revealed their shortcomings. Above all, there was overcrowding, which defeated all efforts at large-scale individual care and diffused the attempts of physicians to treat, investigate, and administer a community of insane adequately. As W. W. Godding said in his 1890 presidential address to the Association,

All my term as superintendent I have known no hospital but a crowded one. Erecting buildings all the time, the incoming flood has still kept in advance of construction. I have had dreams of classification of which the thronged wards would never permit the realization. Day by day, year after year, I have seen the individualized treatment of special cases swamped by the rising tide of indiscriminate lunacy pouring through the wards, filling every crevice, rising higher and higher until gradually most distinctions and landmarks have been blotted out. Twenty years I have battled with this flood. Like the gnomes in the German story trying to bring water, it will whelm me at last, but there are younger men just entering the outer edge of the inundation to whom the warning of my drowning cry may not come too late. We must arouse the public to the great wrong they are doing to us and to their own kindred whom they commit to our care.[16]

The suggestion for solution remained the same: build ever more asylums to contain the mentally disordered with as little delay or frills as possible. Full state responsibility for all insane was demanded, for all those held in unsuitable county asylums and those still at home, because only public authority, no matter what shortcomings its regulation might have, could shoulder so large a burden.

Finally, psychiatrists remained fearful of critics of their own new plans, who might claim that they still smacked of sentiment and unscientific reasoning.

Let it not be understood . . . that we are to be simply kind-hearted humanitarians called upon to provide physical comforts and a safe protection for our patients. Such a narrow and unscientific view of our work is not to be countenanced. . . . I do not wish to be understood as belittling the influence of medicinal agents . . . but I do protest against any such view of the treatment of insanity as limits the scientific aspect of it to such narrow boundaries.[17]

Nevertheless, the basis for important advances remained, particularly the idea of forming special provisions for the acute insane, which would produce psychopathic wards and institutions. And a basis was also established for individual initiative and experiment in scores of asylums, which contained a potential for growth.

NOTES

1. *The American Journal of Insanity*, XLVII (1890–1891), 11–12.

2. *Ibid.*, p. 12.

3. *Ibid.*

4. *Ibid.*, pp. 12–13.

5. *The American Journal of Insanity*, XLIX (1892–1893), 540.

6. *Ibid.*, pp. 513–514.

7. *The American Journal of Insanity*, XLVIII (1891–1892), 361.

8. *The American Journal of Insanity*, LV (1898–1899), 774.

9. *Ibid.*, p. 393.

10. *Ibid.*, p. 84.

11. *The American Journal of Insanity*, XLIX (1892–1893), 377.

12. *Ibid.*, p. 379.

13. *The American Journal of Insanity*, XLVII (1890-1891), 14-15.

14. *The American Journal of Insanity*, LXIV (1907-1908), 8.

15. *The American Journal of Insanity*, LXI (1904-1905), 439.

16. *The American Journal of Insanity*, XLVII (1890-1891), 6.

17. *The American Journal of Insanity*, XLV (1888-1889), 16.

Chapter 26

TENT TREATMENT

At the end of the nineteenth and turn of the twentieth centuries, a series of enthusiastic articles and notes appeared in the *American Journal of Insanity* on "tent treatment," hailed by its practitioners as a much-needed addition to the psychiatric armamentarium. It was purported to be a highly effective method of improving mental and physical health in a wide range of patients, including the tubercular, the demented, the filthy, and the convalescent, by housing them in the fresh air, "where they were surrounded by abundant shade and were constantly swept by breezes." [1] It is a good example of the more imaginative methods of patient care that were tried at this time, and the almost chance way in which they rose and fell.

Tent treatment as a publicized venture started as a public health method. In 1901, A. E. Macdonald, superintendent and medical director of Manhattan State Hospital East on Ward's Island, fearing an epidemic of tuberculosis in his overcrowded wards, ordered the erection of isolation tents on the hospital grounds because no other facilities were available. The danger of mass infection was thought particularly acute because it was believed that serious mental disorder increased susceptibility to tuberculosis.

There were at least two precedents for using tents. In 1884, T. S. Armstrong, superintendent of the Binghamton Asylum for the Chronic Insane, had been permitted by the State Board of Charities and by the trustees of his hospital to erect tents in order to alleviate gross overcrowding. The results of this venture were similar to those obtained at Ward's Island; but it was the staff of the latter, nearly twenty years later, who were first to realize the therapeutic value of tent treatment, although the program at

Binghamton was not publicized until 1903, when much interest had already been aroused.

On June 5, 1901, forty tubercular patients at Ward's Island were moved into two large tents, each with a capacity of twenty beds, which were pitched on dry, elevated ground overlooking the East River. In keeping with contemporary views on the importance of fresh air in the treatment of tuberculosis, ventilators were let into the tent walls, and the sides were kept open as much as possible "so that the interior was literally flooded with pure air." [2]

In order to ensure complete isolation, all necessary facilities were provided at the camp site. Food was cooked in the central hospital kitchen but was served in the dining tents; and, again in accord with current ideas on treatment of tuberculosis, a "varied and full diet" [3] was provided. In order to further reduce the possibility of contagion, scrupulous cleanliness was maintained. The walls and floors were scrubbed; and every hour the air was sprayed with an antiseptic that, whether or not it destroyed the germs, was found to have providentially killed all the insects.

The results of tent life startled and delighted the physicians. Physical and mental improvement were so marked that on July 16, 1901, a tent was pitched for twenty nontubercular patients, a heterogeneous collection, 60 per cent of whom were bedridden, and most of whom were seriously regressed and filthy.

In keeping with the emphasis on physiological factors at the turn of the century, the weight of patients was taken as one index of mental health. It was here that some of the earlier gains of tent treatment were demonstrated:

Their weight was taken on admission and about every subsequent three weeks. Eight of the patients weighed less than 100 pounds, the lowest weighing only 88 pounds. At the second weighing, three weeks later, it was noticed that every patient in the camp showed an increase in weight except one and he weighed exactly the same. [4]

There were other dramatic improvements, particularly in the habits and deportment of the regressed patients.

At the end of three months there were only three patients who might be called filthy, and these had shown a marked improvement since admission. The majority had become accustomed to attending to the calls of nature and would voluntarily use the commode chair. [5]

A number of case histories were cited as evidence of the efficacy of tent treatment, such as the following descriptions of nontubercular cases:

A patient aged forty had been an inmate of the hospital for nineteen years and was in a condition of terminal dementia, secondary to melancholia. For the last two years he had been very dirty and filthy in his habits, soiling his bed and clothes, and exhibiting no interest whatever in his surroundings. . . . At the closing of the camp it was noticed that he had gained seven pounds during the three months. He was brighter and more appreciative. While he was still considerably demented, a decided improvement, both physically and mentally was noted. He had begun to appreciate the necessity of attending to the calls of nature, and at the end of three months, was not what could be called a filthy patient.[6]

Another remarkable improvement was in a man twenty-two years of age. He had been a patient only seven months and on admission was extremely depressed and demented. At the time of admission to the camp, he was dull, and very filthy in his habits. An almost immediate improvement was noted. He began to brighten, became more appreciative and steadily gained in weight. On admission he was greatly emaciated and weighed only 93 pounds. . . . At the time of breaking up the camp, this young man had made the remarkable increase in weight of 50 pounds. With the gain physically, a mental improvement, almost as remarkable was noticed. He was bright and appreciative and was one of the most valuable assistants about the camp, helping the more feeble about and attending to the distribution of the food. He became absolutely clean in his habits and in every respect a well-conducted and orderly person. Suffice it to say that this patient has since been discharged, and undoubtedly is now a useful member of society.[7]

Camp life was free and interesting. Most of the patients left their beds to wander about the lawn. They watched the steamers and excursion boats passing along the river "and listened to the music with interest." They read papers and magazines and played games, "and all showed a greatly increased interest in their surroundings." [8]

At the end of the summer, all but one tentful of the most serious tuberculosis cases were returned to the wards. The results were noted with interest. "Several of the patients have been closely observed since the breaking up of the camp, and it is noticed that the inclination of those who were formerly filthy is to relapse into their former habits." [9] Another observer working in the t.b. camp, C. F. Haviland, reported, "As a commentary on the comforts of this plan of living, it may here be mentioned that had the patients' wishes alone been considered, it would have been necessary to continue the use of both large tents." [10] When the camp was reopened the next year, Haviland noted,

Ten patients who were sent into the wards last autumn, when the capacity of the camp was reduced for the winter and who were at that time in a comfortable physical condition were again admitted to the camp this spring. Without exception all showed a physical failure, although when formerly in the camp they had all made a progressive improvement.[11]

Meanwhile, most of those left out all year in an elaborately winterized tent continued to thrive.

Tent treatment was publicized the following year in several detailed and enthusiastic articles. These were illustrated with photographs of groups of men and women seated near their tents under the trees on benches and garden chairs with two or three nurses standing behind them. These photographs were a rare feature for articles in the *American Journal of Insanity* at that time, because most plates showed brain dissections or abnormal tissue formations.

An interesting feature of these articles is that in spite of the meticulous recording of events and of case descriptions, only vague and fleeting inferences were drawn about possible reasons for the unexpected success of tent treatment. Haviland felt that improvement was due to "the influence of the sun-light and the greater diversity of event." [12] O. J. Wilsey, the physician in charge of the Long Island Home, who reported Armstrong's experiences at Binghamton, attempted to be somewhat more specific:

While giving full credit to ventilation, fresh air and sunshine—the hospital has them all—I wish to emphasize the point that it was, in my opinion, the complete change in the whole existence of the patient that was the important curative agent. The listless monotony was broken . . . the mind was aroused, and the patient started, as it were, on a new life.[13]

Tent treatment removed patients from wards containing one to two hundred inmates and placed them in circumscribed groups of twenty. Patients performed housekeeping and nursing chores for each other; and units developed an *esprit de corps*. In a 1905 article, it was reported that, before an athletic field-day, the patients insisted on decorating their tents with flags and bunting so that the camp would be attractive when inspected by visitors.[14]

The tents also provided other benefits. Staff was assigned to a small group, so that many obstructions encountered by patients trying to contact doctors were removed. There was more individual attention, particularly when these former hopeless, backward patients became the show pieces of the hospital. Even the taking of group photographs shows the hospital's sudden pride and interest and probably served as a further stimulus to group cohesion.

Many of the serious inconveniences of ward life were alleviated. Magazines, papers, and games were made available, which contrasted with the idleness and boredom on the ward. There were also sufficient bathroom and toilet facilities in the camp, which may account for the miraculous improvement in habits of personal cleanliness noted in all these groups. In 1907, G. A. Smith, superintendent of Central Islip State Hospital on Long Island, published an article, "Application of the Cottage System to the New Hospital," in which he noted,

I would like to lay particular stress on the necessity of having a sufficient number of lavatories and closets. The rush, crowding, and clamoring of patients to reach the closets and lavatories, which are inadequate to meet this sudden onslaught, during the early morning or getting-up hour, is the most distressing sight that occurs during the entire hospital service. There is too much centralization of lavatories and closets for economy's sake. . . . It might do for prisons but not for hospitals.[15]

In the years following the initial articles on tent treatment, the movement expanded. By 1904, the Ward's Island camp for non-tubercular demented had been enlarged to 260 patients. This was not only an indication of the high regard in which tent treatment was held, but it may also have reflected the fact that, during that summer, Manhattan State East was so overcrowded that the insane pavilion at Bellevue was asked to reroute all cases to Central Islip on Long Island.[16]

Meanwhile, Ward's Island opened another camp, this time for a particular class of convalescents, those for whom

The prognosis for rapid convalescence was exceedingly unfavorable and the outlook for the restoration of the patient's mental health very uncertain. The patient's lack of insight into his past alienation . . . deters the physician from recommending the patient's discharge, it being argued that this lack of appreciation of his past condition on the part of the patient will lead to complications in his future business and social relations with his friends and relatives, when he leaves the hospital.[17]

Here, as elsewhere, there was commendable avoidance of selecting only "good cases."

It would have been an easy matter to fill this camp with cases which had a very favorable prognosis for recovery and thus to have been able to return statistics for the period (June 1 to December 1, 1903) with probably 80 per cent recovered and discharged. But such a policy would not only have indicated a desire to produce spectacular statistics, but would have subverted the true sphere of the camp's usefulness.[18]

All cases with an excellent prognosis were kept on the wards, and only those whose period of convalescence was judged unduly long or who were suffering relapses were put into the camp. This, however, may not have been done exclusively in the interest of science, because the reluctance of ward staff to relinquish good workers was a constant problem in hospital administration, whereas there would perhaps be less objection to the removal of a relapsed or paranoid patient. Of 44 convalescent cases in the tents in 1903, 7 per cent were discharged, 16 per cent were expected to be discharged in the near future, and most showed a "decided improvement." [19]

An application of what was felt to be the principal factor in tent treatment, "an abundance—a superabundance, as it were—of fresh air," [20] was instituted at Manhattan State East when it was decided to extend its benefits to ward patients, who were now to be kept out-of-doors as much as possible during the winter.

The old method of taking this class of patients out for a perfunctory walk around the grounds has been found deficient in many respects, especially during the winter months. Such mere "out-door-exercise," without end or aim, fails to arouse an interest in the patients; their attitudes suggest the most extreme apathy and listlessness. Many appear totally oblivious to their environment, walking on and on in a mechanical and automatic fashion, their mental torpor associated with a low ebb of physical vigor, as shown in their cold and cyanosed extremities.[21]

It was further noted that

The respiratory movements of patients in the wards are always more shallow than those habituated to prolonged residence in the open. Therefore, in devising an improved system of out-door exercise which will obviate the faults of former methods, the requirements of the individual patient must be noted and the indications met.[22]

It was suggested further that patients be taught to work together, first by passing a ball back and forth; then by participating in team sports; next by working in teams to pull lawn rollers and push wheelbarrows; finally the patient was to be graduated into a job at one of the hospital's shops or workrooms. The results of this treatment were highly encouraging.

By thus systematizing and grading the amount and character of out-door exercise for our patients, we have reduced the number of filthy cases to less than ⅕th of 1 per cent of the entire population of the hospital, excluding those patients habitually confined to bed from paralysis and allied disorders. During the past year nearly 25 per cent of the patients in the ward for extremely demented and uncleanly have been "graduated," through the efficiency of these measures, into our wards designed for the better class of chronic, demented, working patients. Some, indeed, passing further up the scale, are now taking their places regularly with the best class of shop workers.[23]

Although Manhattan State East published most of the articles on tent treatment, the participation of other institutions in what soon became a minor fad can be traced through the half-yearly summaries of the *American Journal of Insanity*. In 1903, for instance, Columbus State Hospital, Columbus, Ohio, opened a t.b. camp for 24 patients; in 1904, this was enlarged to accommodate 48 women in six tents and 36 men in two tents.[24] In 1906, with the institution much overcrowded, 150 cases were treated, and "almost without exception, the patients have shown quite marked improvement."[25] In 1905, Willard State Hospital opened a t.b. camp but was forced to close for a severe winter; however, they expected to open again in the spring.[26] In 1906, Illinois Asylum for the Incurable Insane at Peoria reported,

No improvement of the year has given greater satisfaction than the recently constructed tent colonies for consumptives.[27]

Mendocino State Hospital in Talmage, California, set up a tent colony for 15 t.b. patients in 1904 and for 45 nontubercular demented cases in 1905. Not only was improvement noted, but it was estimated that installing tents cost $60 a bed, whereas it would have cost $500 to $800 a bed to build new wards.[28] This may illustrate some reasons why tent treatment was adopted enthusiastically—the hospitals had to isolate their t.b. cases, they were short of ward space, and the initial investment for tents was comparatively low.

Two allusions to tent treatment show that it was much talked about at the time. T. J. W. Burgess, a Canadian, was elected president of the American Medico-Psychological Association in 1905 and in his presidential address described the history and problems of psychiatry in Canada. He remarked that he doubted whether tent treatment could be practicable in his country because of the rigors of the climate during the winter months.[29] A second allusion is even more illuminating. A. W. Hoisholt of California wrote a number of letters to the editors of the *American Journal of Insanity* on the aftermath of the San Francisco earthquake. In one of these he described the destruction of Agnew Asylum and the fate of its inmates, now housed on the grounds in tents and makeshift lean-tos, many of which the patients had erected themselves.

I was astonished to see how nicely the patients got along under the circumstances. Men and women who had been more or less constantly violent and untidy when confined in the building were now getting along peacefully, seldom quarrelling, and showing more desire to keep clean than they had done when restricted to the limits of the building and the airing courts. They all seemed more comfortable and contented in the tents and on the open grounds. . . . Immediately following the catastrophe . . . many worked like Trojans in the effort to rescue those caught in the wreck and in caring for the wounded. . . . The record of the patients' condition and conduct during the first two or three weeks of this enforced out-door life certainly speaks well for tent-treatment. Even the epileptics have had fewer attacks.[30]

Here was a case in which tent treatment had apparently been so publicized that the coincidental presence of tents, fresh air, and sunshine was given credit for improvements that we might be likely to ascribe to heightened morale following a catastrophe and to the patients' opportunity to perform necessary work.

Tent treatment, however, did not retain its prominence for long. It declined in large measure because its operative factor, the small group, was being eliminated, while the "superabundance" of fresh air and sunshine was scrupulously maintained. On the one hand, units were made too small, as when, at Ward's Island, one or two beds were placed in revolving tents that could be turned to face the sun or when pavilions were built at other hospitals that isolated bedridden cases in single rooms. On the other hand, camps were becoming much bigger, housing several hundred patients. In 1903, there were 175 cases in the Ward's Island camps; in 1905 it was expected that facilities would be enlarged to accommodate 300.

In most hospitals the problems and expense of heating, maintenance, and frequent replacement of structures led to the erection of wooden pavilions with large windows and sun porches instead of the orthodox canvas tents. In 1905, Ward's Island published an article declaring:

In the restoration of mental health, the effect of the unrestrained life in tents appears to be of vital importance, and it is our opinion that this freedom cannot be as satisfactorily obtained by the use of pavilions, either of a permanent or semi-permanent type, the tent system alone being competent to fully supply this want.[31]

In the half-yearly summary of 1906, it was announced that at Manhattan State East,

Plans have been drawn for the construction of two frame camps, somewhat similar to those already on the grounds of the hospital, to replace the old tents. These frame camps are habitable both summer and winter, and are permanent.[32]

In April, 1907, the following announcement was made:

Two wooden pavilions, built together in the form of the letter "T", at the end of the island, have been completed, the size of each being twenty feet by seventy feet, and will accommodate a total of seventy patients. These pavilions are similar to pavilions C and D, of which the sides are largely made up of windows, so that they may be raised or lowered at will, allowing plenty of light and fresh air. They take the place of tents A and B. These pavilions are for permanent use and will increase the capacity of the hospital to the extent of 70. There has also been built one sitting room pavilion, size 30 feet by 70 feet, with wide verandas surrounding it, also a contagious disease building, size 20 feet by 80 feet. A portion of this building will be used for laboratory purposes.[33]

Thus tent treatment had lost its distinctive features and was being absorbed into the rest of the hospital. The pavilions, which at first held 35, instead of the 20 patients housed in a tent, would soon hold 40 or 50. Staff and equipment shortages would follow; the patients would no longer be able to wander about the lawns because there would be doors and locks. The whole atmosphere of the improvisation, adventure, and group cohesiveness would disappear, as would the concern and pride of the staff and their special attention to individuals in a selected patient population.

In spite of the large number of articles and notes on the efficacy of tent treatment for nontubercular patients, many alienists continued to regard it primarily as a technique for isolating t.b. cases and as a temporary expediency at that. In the 1906 memorial notice on the death of A. E. Macdonald, superintendent of Ward's Island until 1904, it was noted that,

In 1901, he established the tent treatment of the tubercular insane, removing them from all communication with any unaffected patient. The principles underlying this undertaking are now universally accepted by the medical profession here and abroad.[34]

In April, 1907, the Asylum for Insane at London, Canada, reported,

Great efforts have been made to combat tuberculosis, but so far no special isolation has been built, the only provision that can be used for segregation is the use of a few tents in the summer months.[35]

The use of tents for isolation wards and the disregarding, in some hospitals, of its effect on the nontubercular chronic insane is hardly surprising, because one was a pressing and vital issue in every institution while the other was not. Asylums at this time often appear to have been primarily concerned with keeping inmates alive until bodily health, and hence mental health, might be restored; but there was little hope that chronic cases would ever be cured no matter what methods were tried. It was, therefore, a more practical investment in time and effort to forestall epidemics that would attack the curable as well as the hopeless and that would give the institutions a bad reputation, than to spend them on the severely demented.

NOTES

1. The American Journal of Insanity, LIX (1902–1903), 319.
2. Ibid.
3. Ibid., p. 320.
4. Ibid., p. 315.
5. Ibid., p. 317.
6. Ibid., p. 315.
7. Ibid., p. 316.
8. Ibid., p. 317.
9. Ibid., p. 318.
10. Ibid., p. 321.
11. Ibid., p. 324.
12. Ibid., p. 326.

13. Ibid., p. 635.
14. The American Journal of Insanity, LXI (1904–1905), 101.
15. The American Journal of Insanity, LXIII (1906–1907), 511.
16. The American Journal of Insanity, LXI (1904–1905), 490.
17. Ibid., pp. 99–100.
18. Ibid., p. 99.
19. Ibid.
20. The American Journal of Insanity, LIX (1902–1903), 639.
21. Ibid., p. 637.

22. *Ibid.*, p. 639.

23. *Ibid.*, p. 640.

24. *The American Journal of Insanity*, LXI (1904–1905), 729.

25. *The American Journal of Insanity*, LXIII (1906–1907), 269.

26. *The American Journal of Insanity*, LXI (1904–1905), 726.

27. *The American Journal of Insanity*, LXIII (1906–1907), 259.

28. *The American Journal of Insanity*, LXII (1905–1906), 345.

29. *Ibid.*, p. 32.

30. *The American Journal of Insanity*, LXIII (1906–1907), 131–132.

31. *The American Journal of Insanity*, LXI (1904–1905), 110.

32. *The American Journal of Insanity*, LXIII (1906–1907), 264–265.

33. *Ibid.*, p. 579.

34. *Ibid.*, p. 540.

35. *Ibid.*, p. 586.

Chapter 27

ALTERNATIVES TO

CLASSIC INSTITUTIONS

An issue which had long concerned nonpsychiatric critics was that of possible alternatives to the classic pattern of American institutions. It was thought that the adoption of various European models, such as the "free air" system of Gheel in Belgium, or the cottage system of Scotland, would maintain chronic cases in greater freedom and at less cost to the state than would the overcrowded wards and locked doors of custodial institutions. The majority of practitioners, however, opposed these plans strenuously, although some, like Pliny Earle of Northampton, eventually experimented with some of the ideas. Most alienists agreed with J. E. Browers of the Minnesota Hospital for the Insane, who declared in an annual report that he had little patience with those who advocate such "sentimental nonsense."

Ironically, the suggestion for finding alternative accommodations to overcrowded asylums had first come from psychiatrists. The need for more and cheaper facilities was recognized in the 1860's. In 1862, for example, John Gray had written,

Let us acknowledge that hereafter in the history of this nation—if indeed we can confidently anticipate a history for our distracted and debt-burdened country—public hospitals of palatial size and costly administration, for the demented and chronic insane, are out of the question. And he will be most deserving of honor who shall first demonstrate how, in local and simple buildings, to combine a proper cure with some provision for useful labor, in the decent and humane support of this class.[1]

After the Civil War, the problem became even more acute. It was estimated by such authorities as Pliny Earle that 30,000 to 35,000 unhospitalized insane existed in the United States.

Those advocating novel systems of patient care had first to contend with public preconceptions about what constituted a suitable asylum. In 1869, a Massachusetts board of insanity examining such alternative patterns noted:

In Massachusetts . . . the idea got lodgment in the public mind that the insane must be confined and guarded. The idea suggested that institutions for confining and guarding them should be built. Once built, they react to strengthen the popular idea. The thought of any other mode of treating them will not be entertained.[2]

Superintendents, moreover, were anxious to forestall the erection of separate chronic-stay institutions. Legislators hoped that these would be self-supporting through patient labor, reserving other asylums for acute, salvable patients. Most members of the Association of Medical Superintendents emphatically opposed this plan; and opposition was crystallized in the 1860's when New York proposed to build the Willard Asylum exclusively for chronic cases, retaining Utica State Asylum for active therapy. John Gray led the protest against such false economies, demanding,

What . . . are the items you would cut off or cut down? Is it in amusements you would cheapen their care? Perhaps it is in music—their ears are dull of hearing; perhaps it is in the ministrations of religion you would economize—they have no longer kind and thankful hearts, and do they need a preacher? Perhaps you will allow them no longer the visits of their friends, as they may not recognize them, and a little might be saved in attention! Is it in these you would cheapen? Perhaps it is proposed to cheapen in air? Crowding into little space without ventilation—or will you cheapen in warmth and clothing, or give them less cleanliness, that they may die off the sooner? Are you going to give them less sunshine? Oh, no! They may have an abundance of that, for you propose to turn them into the fields and make them earn their own bread. It is said they are to work for their own advantage, and this labor will be *the element peculiar to the system.*[3]

Gray advised a conservative stance, warning his colleagues to offer the public no clues on how to cheapen the hospital system, nor themselves to sanction any plans that might endanger the comfort of their patients.

In response to the threat of massive, centralized, custodial institutions, alienists adopted a resolution calling for small hospitals in each subdistrict of the state, accepting all types of cases, both acute and chronic. They also waged a propaganda battle against the New York State plan for Willard. One facet of their attack was the denigration of the value of patient labor and the denial that any mental hospital could be self-supporting.

Ironically, however, those promoting the erection of a special hospital for chronic patients in New York had the most humane of motives. They sought to abolish the corrupt system of county receptacles. It was hoped that by specifically designating the new asylum as a chronic-stay institution, the local facilities would have difficulty evading regulations ordering the transfer of their neglected patients to Willard.

Another alternative to classic institutions, advocated by laymen in particular, was modeled on Gheel in Belgium, a farm town that had been for centuries a haven for the insane who had come to beg the intercession of St. Dymphia. In this system, the central institution was virtually eliminated for all but the most agitated or infirm lunatics, while all other patients boarded with village families and worked the land.

The "free air system," as it came to be known, was scorned by most leaders of American psychiatry. Pliny Earle, Isaac Ray, and others opposed the plan in part because they had toured Gheel in the 1840's, before the Belgian government had ordered reforms, and they had seen enough abuse of patients by farmers, greedy for profits, to fear a decentralized and ill-supervised system. They also felt that, although the scheme might work in a village where it had been the tradition of centuries, it could not be transplanted elsewhere; otherwise, as Earle noted, similar institutions would have sprung up in the surrounding countries over the last thousand years.

Gheel is unique, a warning, rather than an example. It had no historical predecessor; and has had no competitor, nor imitator for a thousand years. It has answered a purpose for chronic cases amongst a people unwilling to change even by way of improvement, and remarkable for great simplicity of manners and habits of life. It is a cemetery of the living, where from infancy to old age, generation after generation has vegetated and dozed in a hopeless and unambitious monotony, with no other gift or aspiration except to feed, lodge, and care for imbecility, idiocy, and senility. The various attempts which have been made to combine that sort of treatment with modern modes do not warrant repetitions of such experiments.[4]

There was, however, popular support for a free air system. In 1867, the Massachusetts State Board of Charities suggested that harmless, chronic cases be boarded out with families. It was suggested that the State pay the board and lodging of these patients and that it supervise the foster homes to prevent abuse. This idea was raised by Samuel Gridley Howe, the chairman of the Board of Charities, who had just returned from a European tour on which he had visited Gheel, and had evidently been impressed by local conditions.

Another boarding-out system often advocated was the "family care" method of Scotland and France. Psychiatrists like Earle opposed this also as dangerously decentralized and as hence exposing patients to neglect and abuse. It was felt, moreover, that the public was too afraid of the insane to accept them in the community.

A family care system, however, was established in Massachusetts in 1885 and was administered by F. B. Sanborn, chairman of the Board of State Charities. First results were encouraging, and the plan appeared to be a success, until Sanborn was discharged from the board, and his place was taken by a successor who had no interest in the scheme. It limped on for twenty years and became a favorite program of Owen Copp, the executive officer of the State Board of Insanity in Boston at the turn of the century. The plan, however, had little professional support. In a series of articles in the *Journal*, Copp chronicled the failure of this scheme. It had never spread out of Massachusetts, in part, he felt, because of the still widespread fear of insanity in the community. He suspected that many had considered it a regressive step, because there had been so much propaganda in favor of institutional care for all the insane. The financial benefit of this program to the taxpayers was not immediately apparent; nor did the plan catch the imagination of asylum staffs

The institutional effect of family care does not appeal to self-interest. To be sure, boarding out a patient removes immediately or remotely a floor bed from crowded halls or corridors, but the coincident loss of a comfortable, perhaps helpful inmate, dampens the ardor of active promotion of the cause; while the altruism stimulating to discharge every patient whose happiness, welfare or mental state may allow, easily lies dormant in the busy preoccupation of the medical staff in other more pressing duties.[5]

In many local hospitals, such as Bridgewater, patients were used not only for janitorial duties but also as nurses' aides, giving massage and hydrotherapy. In such institutions, Copp reported, nurses refused to part with the quiet, stable patients who were suitable for family placement. He argued in vain with ward staffs that when "good" patients were removed, "bad" patients became "good" in a surprisingly short time.

Nevertheless, Copp wrote that, in the twenty years of the program, some gains had been made. 762 patients, chiefly women, had been placed in 465 families "without doing a serious act of violence and rarely attempting any." They had been accepted by the local general practitioners and by their neighbors. Finally, Copp insisted that the traditional pattern of hospitalization was not the only, or the best, method for treating all the insane.

While I am second to none in recognition of the beneficence of institutions in their ministrations to those in need, and hold firmly the belief that our attitude toward them should be sympathetic, promotive of instant reception of every suitable patient, insistent upon thorough examination and full treatment, and zealous in defense of the public safety and welfare, I am convinced that the bounds of their usefulness may be set within these limits, and that imperative duty requires, not merely acquiescence, but *insistence,* that every patient whose mental or other infirmity does not necessitate detention shall have his chance to regain and maintain his place in life under the most favorable conditions, and such assistance as family care and "after care" may afford, and that failure shall be accepted only after actual trial and defeat.[6]

A less extreme plan than "family care" was the cottage system, instituted at McLean Hospital in Massachusetts and adapted from the FitzJames Colony at Clermont, France. A central building housed the most disturbed cases, while quiet and convalescent patients were placed in small groups in cottages round the grounds where they could have greater freedom and might thus accustom themselves to normal life.

In 1905, T. R. Nicholas, of the North Texas Hospital for the Insane, outlined such an institution. He stressed that it should be placed near a center of population, easily accessible by railroad, that it should provide at least one tillable acre of land for each patient, and that the capacity of the hospital should not exceed 1,200 beds. It was to contain open wards; recreational facilities for patients, including mixed dancing; and work programs.

Psychiatrists had at first argued that all these alternative suggestions to mental hospitals not only endangered patients because supervision by the superintendent would be reduced, especially in inclement weather, and the shortage of attendants would be exacerbated by decentralization, but they were painfully sentimental and unrealistic.

There is something attractive and romantic about cottages and cottage life. We associate with them domestic love, roses, woodbine, and luxuriant ivy running over thatched roofs; larks and nightingales; lowing cows, bleating lambs, and browsing goats; early cocks, prolific hens, fresh eggs; neat-handed Phyllises, rosy milkmaids, sighing swains; and all sorts of pastoral delights sung by poets of dubious sanity, and better adapted to love than to lunacy. The poetry is admirable, when it does not pall; but the reality is apt to be very rugged prose. An insane person, chronic or pauper, is probably more sensitive to creature comforts of life than to all its embellishments; prefers nutritive diet, good attendance, kind care, and social sights and sounds, to all the rose and woodbines that may adorn any rude, lonely hovel that fancy exalts into a delightful cottage because of such outward show, without thinking of its scanty room, its smothering roofs, and its pretty windows obscured by leaves and thronged by noisome bugs and mordacious insects.[7]

Nevertheless, they came to accept and to even favor them by the end of the century.

One of the most interesting innovations in the classic mental hospital pattern was the development of ways of bringing the facilities of asylums closer to the public. This led to the creation of dispensaries and out-patient clinics in asylums, of psychiatric wards in general hospitals, and of psychopathic hospitals. These not only gave the public greater access to psychiatric help but also helped the profession by providing an escape from the isolation of mental hospitals and by exposing psychiatrists to a far-wider range of cases than those commonly admitted to asylums. So great was the hope placed in these new ventures that G. Alder Blumer, medical superintendent of the Butler Hospital, Providence, Rhode Island, proclaimed in his presidential address to the Association in 1903 that, because of these facilities, "The future is big with promise."

One reason for opening dispensaries, like that created in 1885 at the Pennsylvania Hospital in Philadelphia, was to treat incipient cases of insanity before they developed into acute breakdowns. It had long been lamented by psychiatrists that there was no place to treat such cases for whom hospitalization was not yet needed and who might be saved a lengthy illness if only they might receive treatment in time. The Dispensary in Boston was founded in 1897 by Walter Channing and Arthur Jelly. During the first four years of its existence, Channing reported that his clinic had observed and treated and, when necessary, had sent on to mental hospitals nearly four hundred cases:

Incipient cases have come to us which have been at once taken in hand and occasionally the attack has been averted; and by watching the cases, we believe that something has been done to guard the community against a source of danger. It has also been proved to my satisfaction that there are more cases of insanity in the community at large than is generally suspected.[8]

Channing noted further that his dispensary seemed a useful method of preventing overcrowding in mental hospitals, by getting patients treated as early as possible in the community.

Extramural practice of psychiatry had been advocated by many critics as a way of combatting the isolation of psychiatrists themselves and as a method of freeing them from nonmedical duties. As Channing wrote in 1901,

The narrowing effect of routine duties in a large hospital goes without saying. Little by little the hospital man becomes a routinist, unless by some means he is kept in touch with the world outside the walls of the institution. . . . I have come to think more and more, as I have had experience with my own mental clinic, that there is a big field for the psychiatrist outside the hospital.[9]

Psychiatrists in out-patient departments and dispensaries were now called on to deal with hitherto unfamiliar conditions. One of these was retardation in children. Channing and his colleagues soon realized that criteria for assessing and treating these children were lacking.

It is not difficult to ascertain both physical and mental defects, but it is difficult to set a standard for a physical average which can act as a control. It seems to be the fact that at present almost no physicians, in Boston at any rate, regard themselves as experts on the subject under discussion.[10]

In 1896, however, Lightner Witmer organized a psychological clinic at the University of Pennsylvania for disturbed and mentally retarded children. He established criteria for distinguishing childhood psychosis from mental deficiency.

Psychiatric wards in general hospitals, like the Insane Pavilion at Bellevue, were established to deal with acute disturbances in centers of population. Doubtful cases of insanity, drunkenness, suicide, and so forth, were admitted from the streets. Prompt medical care was thus made available to those who otherwise would have been jailed, or who might have journeyed unnecessarily to remote asylums. Patients were placed under observation for an average of five days, until it could be decided whether they might be sent home or referred to a mental hospital.

Most psychiatrists welcomed the opening of these facilities, which provided prompt treatment without the "stigma of insanity" and the formalities of certification. They also welcomed the use of general hospital facilities—the proximity of other medical specialists for consultation, and access to laboratories. Nevertheless, some feared that such wards might be abused, and by providing too much comfort for patients, might encourage chronic behavior.

A pretty large percentage of the beneficiaries of these clinics are persons who have become for the time being social parasites through self-indulgence. I refer to the cases of alcoholism and delirium tremens. Over 26½ per cent of the patients taken care of in Pavilion F (Bellevue) are of that class. During their incapacity they need skilled care and nursing, and they get it. Their pathway through the mazes of delirium is rendered as easy and pleasant as their condition will allow. Sometimes it is so pleasant that delirium tremens has comparatively little terror for them. They lose one of the strong incentives of self-restraint. If drunkenness is a punishable offense, why should not delirium tremens, which makes the person more dangerous to, and more dependent on, his friends of the community, be punishable in a greater degree? Why should not the patient, after recovering from his delirium, be fined or imprisoned for having had it? Unless in some way it is made disagreeable or disgraceful to acquire delirium tremens, such excellent care as these wards or hospitals can and will supply will only serve as a premium on self-indulgence to the point of personal incapacity and dependence on the public.[11]

NOTES

1. *The American Journal of Insanity*, XIX (1862–1863), 105.
2. Gerald N. Grob, *The State and the Mentally Ill* (Chapel Hill, N.C.: University of North Carolina Press, 1965), pp. 195–196.
3. *The American Journal of Insanity*, XXIII (1866–1867), 175.
4. *The American Journal of Insanity*, XXVII (1870–1871), 83.
5. *The American Journal of Insanity*, LXIII (1906–1907), 362–363.
6. *Ibid.*, p. 370.
7. *The American Journal of Insanity*, XXVII (1870–1871), 84–85.
8. *The American Journal of Insanity*, LVIII (1901–1902), 110–111.
9. *Ibid.*, p. 119.
10. *Ibid.*, p. 112.
11. *The American Journal of Insanity*, LXI (1904–1905), 220–221.

Chapter 28

SOCIAL DARWINISM

One argument in favor of psychopathic wards and hospitals was that they separated acute cases from the chronic insane in mental hospitals. At the turn of the twentieth century, many psychiatrists felt that there was an essential biological difference between the two classes of patients.

Insanity was seen, now more than ever, as evidence of unsound heredity. In 1885, for example, a psychiatrist noted that

The mass of chronic insane already accumulated in this country, and which is annually receiving large accession, draws most of its recruits from this (defective) class. It must be remembered that comparatively few of this class recover, for the reason, chiefly, that they did not possess in the first place the conditions of recovery. . . . How can reason and volition return to those from whom it never departed.[1]

This argument, that curable and chronic cases were essentially of a different nature, became professionally fashionable during the 1880's and 1890's. J. B. Bancroft, of Concord, New Hampshire, for example, wrote in an 1887 article on "Separate Provision for the Recent, the Curable, and the Appreciative Insane,"

There is a wide range of persons, conditions and character embraced in this division (of curable cases). . . . They come from all trades, callings and professions, and belong to classes in the community not wanting in character, consequence or self-respect. In health they bear their share of responsibility and public burdens, and exert their share of influence. In a word they are the average people, the stock out of which the future is to spring, worth curing, if possible, and restoring to society. These are not the people who have contributed unduly to swell the army of the chronic insane in this country, but those who will promise the best results of remedial treatment.[2]

Unlike the chronic insane, this "curable" class of patients

is not composed of the world's drifting, unstable, ill-conditioned populations, including the modern tramp, but of the settled, industrious,
home-loving and stable classes . . . [they] represent more nearly than
any other . . . the average population of half a century ago, before
the great influx of foreign blood and character, often bearing the
germs of weakness, poverty and disease. It is therefore characterized
by a higher average of good and sound heredity and power of resistance to disease, as well as freedom from the vices and habits which are
demoralizing both physically and mentally.[3]

Individualized care for these favored classes, Bancroft added, is
imperative because such patients must be preserved, to counter the
deterioration of the national stock.

In the midst of the many modern influences calculated to deteriorate
the quality of the population, it is wise to be economical of the old and
the best stock.
In view of the warnings of students of social science that the stock of
the country is deteriorating, it is wise as far as relates to the insane, to
give remedial medicine its best chance of success; to put in operation
the most carefully and wisely studied plans, methods and influences
preventive of mental disease, and all that knowledge and experience
can do to apply remedial agencies where it already exists.[4]

This view was evidence not only of xenophobia but also of the
impact of Social Darwinism on social science and welfare planning
in America at the turn of the century. The doctrines of this system
sound particularly chilling in the late 1960's, because they evoke
wretched episodes in modern history.
In 1901, for example, the *American Journal of Insanity* printed
an article on "An Anthropological Study of the Small Brain of
Civilized Man and Its Evolution," by Charles E. Woodruff, a U.S.
Army surgeon from Fort Riley, Kansas. Its major thesis was that

As civilization and brain development have gone on hand in hand, the
lower races which have not taken part in it are forever unfitted for
it.[5]

The brains of these "lower races,"

Though specialized enough to take up some few special employments
as an intruder civilization, . . . cannot carry on the advance by themselves. . . . The negro is a survival of men who migrated too soon and
whenever he is left alone he invariably reverts to ancestral life as in
Haiti. His color and physique bar him from the best parts of this

country where he quickly perishes, and the struggle in a civilized environment is causing such degeneration that he is producing a tremendous crop of degenerates in the south from bad food, bad habits and exposure. Crime, consumption and insanity increase and hasten the inevitable extinction. He is sure to become extinct.[6]

The "lower races," Woodruff held, have smaller brains, otherwise perfectly normal and adapted to their environment. Brain evolution ended in Asia before it did in Europe, so

that all Asiatics are jetsam of evolution. The only ones who went ahead were the restless ones who were forced into Europe from the teeming areas of the North of Asia—and who became the ancestors of the Celto-Slavic or Alpine stock who certainly have helped civilization as much as any other race, and who are part of the newest and most vigorous of moderns—Russia.

Our New York Indians are doing very well, as they had evolved a large brain and were really the pre-historic Aryans of the new world, yet they are not able to do anything towards the advance of civilization, though far in advance of Peruvians and Aztecs. Some of them are living about as the lower Italians, both survivors of lower races in a civilization built up around them by brainier intruders.[7]

The chief apostle of Social Darwinism in America was William Graham Sumner, Professor of Political and Social Science at Yale from 1872 to 1909. Sumner felt that all welfare provisions that unnaturally preserved degenerate members of society allowed them to propagate and endanger the race.

A law may be passed which shall force somebody to support the hopelessly degenerate members of a society, but such a law can only perpetuate the evil and entail it on future generations with new accumulations of distress.[8]

Insanity was felt to be a sign of degeneration, of nature disposing of defective stock.

In an 1891 article on the "Physical Education of Children," Walter Channing, of Brookline, Massachusetts, expressed a view that would soon become widespread.

As the amoeba represents the beginning of life, the earliest form of existence, the idiot represents the end, the final stage before extinction. While countless centuries of evolution have intervened between the beginning of life and man at his best, the descent to idiocy is more sudden, more abrupt. It constitutes, as it were, the fall of man from his highest to his lowest estate; from man a little lower than the angels, to man little higher than the beasts. It is nonetheless the end, however, as the amoeba was the beginning.[9]

Channing, like many of his predecessors, blamed the environment for this reversed evolution, because man and his industrial and social world no longer complement each other. Social welfare, in particular, synthetically preserved misfits that would become extinct in a state of nature.

Unlike nature, society has preserved everything, both good and bad. This is the highest form of humanity, but it must produce its effect on the physical type. Our jails, our alms-houses, our lunatic hospitals, our idiot asylums, do an immense amount of good from a humanitarian point of view; but they preserve and foster the weaknesses of defects, mental, moral and physical, of mankind, and are of course tremendously instrumental in perpetuating such weaknesses and defects.[10]

Unlike later Social Darwinists, Channing did not advocate abandonment of humanitarian institutions. He hoped with some restrictions placed upon misfits, and with attention to the community environment, the bad consequences of flouting evolution might be avoided.

The weak and the bad are to be cared for, and not destroyed. They are an incident to the evolution of something better, and in time the unfavorable tendencies which they keep alive and transmit will be modified or overcome, but they are a most important factor. The harm which they may do to society is not sufficiently understood or guarded against. If, for instance, marriages among the defective classes were only allowed under conditions strictly favorable, it is probable that in time crime, idiocy and insanity would show a decided decrease.[11]

The community was urged to further combat degeneracy by guarding against the physical weakness that lay at the heart of mental instability. Physical education was therefore urged for adults, and particularly children, because

the truth appears to be that insanity, idiocy, unstable nervous systems, and weak bodies in other directions, are the result of the conditions of the society in which we live. The strain resulting from these conditions is too excessive, and the body gives way at its weakest point—the nervous system.[12]

Other writers, however, disagreed with Channing's optimism. They held that, once decline started, it was transmitted through the generations with ever-increasing seriousness until that family was wiped out. Studies appeared at the turn of the century comparing the effects of good and bad heredity in medical, moral, and economic terms. One of these appeared in 1901, when E. A. Winship compared the descendants of Jonathan Edwards, the great eighteenth-century divine, with those of Margaret Jukes, a prostitute.

In about 170 years, the family of that wicked ancestress had cost the communities in which they had lived $1,250,000 as criminals and paupers. 310 of the descendants of Margaret Jukes had spent their days in almshouses or similar places; 150 were victims of loathsome diseases, or had wrecked their health; 60 were professional thieves, and 50 had gone to the lowest depths possible for women to go in life. Only 20 of the descendants had ever learned a trade; of these 20, 10 had learned their handicraft in prisons.[13]

Jonathan Edwards' descendants, on the other hand,

left on their day and generation and on succeeding generations, their mark for Godliness and civilization and nobility of life.[14]

285 had been college graduates, of whom 65 had been college professors and 13 college presidents. There had also been more than 100 lawyers and 30 judges.

Psychiatrists doubted that environment and education could correct such massive determinism.

Of course, it may be possible, by absolutely changing the environment, and throwing round him an atmosphere of purity and righteous effort for several generations, and excluding the noxious influences of criminal associates, that eventually the development of the brain may approach more nearly to the normal, but in the individual moral imbecile such development would be impossible. We are apt to lose sight of the fact that the tendency of heredity is to produce and perpetuate an environment in harmony with such abnormal development, and the child having constantly before it the example of vice and debauchery more readily plunges into the vortex of crime.[15]

In 1884, John Gray had attacked this trend to chronicle family degeneration.

I am . . . satisfied that undue importance is attached to heredity in connection with the causation of insanity. . . . Disease is not a law of our physical or mental being. No person has ever been born insane. No person ever became insane simply because his father or mother, or both, or his grandparents, were insane.[16]

Gray said that occupations or crimes that seem to run in families are simply the result of education and training. They are not born or inbred.[17]

Individuals in such families are perfectible, as may be seen among immigrants who have improved in America. The method of demonstrating degeneration, Gray felt, was specious.

A common method of showing "heredity," is to take some exceptional family, one in a thousand or ten-thousand, where several members have been insane. The numerical method does not take into account the accidental or incidental circumstances which develop or intensify the causes capable of producing insanity in each member of the family, without reference to relationship. Again, a family is taken where peculiarities are strongly marked and general family decay has set in. Such persons usually live differently from other people, and finally become eccentric and from depreciated health may become insane. To say that such persons become insane without the operation of the ordinary causes of disease, is unscientific, and these occasional families cannot be taken as evidence of the existence of a law of transmission of disease.[18]

This is an area, Gray concluded, in which there is far too much superstition.

Seeds of Social Darwinism can be traced back into the 1860's and were particularly exaggerated during periods of immigration and financial crisis, when hordes of paupers were committed to mental hospitals. Pauperism, for example, was linked early to innate weakness and insanity. As Edward Jarvis wrote,

There is manifestly a much larger ratio of the insane among the poor . . . and especially among those who are paupers, than among the independent and more prosperous classes. [Poverty is] an inward principle, enrooted deeply within the man, and running through all his elements. . . . We find that, among those whom the world calls poor, there is less vital force, a lower tone of life, more ill health, more weakness, more early death, a diminished longevity. There is also less self-respect, more idiocy and insanity, and more crime, than among the independent.[19]

The "inherent elements of poverty and insanity" were considered an "imperfectly organized brain and feeble mental constitution." Moreover, it was thought that the greater proportion of insane among foreigners rather than native Americans was due to innate weaknesses that made adaptation to life in a new country particularly hazardous. Such views linking poverty and insanity may not have been so farfetched in the early years of a frontier economy, when there was apparently unlimited opportunity for self-support by farming or trapping, and fresh starts further west.

Psychiatrists were urged by leaders of the Association to fight the perpetuation of degeneracy by warning the public against marriage with tainted stock and by lobbying for legislation to forbid the unions of defectives and to exclude diseased immigrants. G. Alder Blumer, for example, told his colleagues in his presidential address in 1903,

But do we not, lest we hurt somebody's feelings, constantly shirk our responsibilities as mental physicians when we stand silently by as witnesses of the union of two stocks that is bound to be the parent of nervous and mental disease in the offspring? For one ambitious mother who schemes to marry off her daughters, regardless of consequences, I believe there are ninety-nine (such is my faith in womanhood) who would listen to and not resent, even if they did not often act upon, a hint of hygiene from the family physician. To us alienists it is so reasonable to protest that no person of direct insane inheritance shall marry another of like taint that we wonder why the criminality of such unions does not occur to the man and woman, often of apparently average moral sense in other directions, who contract or countenance them.[20]

Energetic steps must be taken to prohibit improper marriages, Blumer continued, because

men and women of feeble intelligence are notoriously addicted to matrimony and [are] by no means satisfied with one brood of defectives. Not long ago an elderly man of melancholy mien came to consult me about his wife, whose insane conduct had made life a burden from the ill-fated day of their marriage a year previously. The history bespoke a chronic psychosis of many years' duration. "But this woman is not your first wife?" I queried tentatively, for the tell-tale dye of his mustache suggested the successful widower. "No, sir," came the reply, lugubriously, "she is my fourth wife, and I am her fifth husband." When such things are so, and when, to quote Solomon, whose exceptional experience constitutes a claim to cathedral utterance in this context, "Wisdom crieth without; she uttereth her voice in the street," is it not high time, gentlemen, that our legislatures should enact laws looking to the effective prohibition of the marriage of the unfit? Suggestions of this kind have been pooh-poohed as without the pale of practical politics, but it is evident that nothing short of legal prevention will accomplish the end we have in view.[21]

Propaganda of this nature was readily accepted by the public. Blumer, for example, read a letter from a maiden lady who had remained single because so many of her families had died of "softening of the brain" and other mental disorders. She wrote to say how glad she was to learn of the kindlier treatment now given the insane, because she might so expect to spend her own decline in relative comfort. Lord Bertrand Russell recorded in his autobiography that his family sought to prevent his first marriage, to an American Quaker. They therefore asked the family doctor to tell the pair that, because there was mental instability in both families, their children would almost certainly be defective. Russell continued that he and his fiancée decided, after much unhappiness, to marry and have no children; and, although he later decided to risk having children, only to find that his wife was barren, Russell showed how seriously these fears were entertained by educated people at the turn of the century. These fears also affected legislatures. During the early years of this century, a number of states passed laws ordering the sterilization of certain classes of insane, retarded, and criminal persons.

Another set of laws were passed in response to the supposed threat of degenerate immigrants. It was felt by many psychiatrists and laymen that the increasing rate of insanity was because of the fact that America appeared to have become a repository for the defective classes of Europe. At the 1884 annual meeting of the Association, for example, one member read the following passage from the *New York Herald* on "Pauper Immigration."

The action of foreign governments in exporting their paupers to this country is as ill-advised as it is impertinent. Hitherto perfect freedom of admission to life and labor in the United States has characterized our system of economy, but this never contemplated the emptying upon our shores of the contents of British or other foreign workhouses. The arrival by the City of Rome of forty or more persons thus described, should arouse the vigilance of the authorities, and they should at once be returned whence they came. The fact that in this instance heads of families have been supplied by the British authorities with a little money looks like an attempt to evade the strict definition of paupers while preserving the essential character. If there is probability of such persons being thrown upon our charities for their subsistence they should be considered paupers and treated accordingly. The act of sending them here is ill-advised, because it is not unlikely to induce such legislation at Washington as will materially interfere with all foreign emigration to this country, a course of action not to be desired on any account.[22]

By this time, defective immigrants were already being deported lest they overload American charitable institutions. In March, 1903, Congress formally authorized the exclusion of immigrants who had been insane up to five years before the date of their arrival. Moreover, individuals could be deported within three years of immigration if they were found insane, epileptic, or feeble-minded.

Incongruous as it may seem, the effect of Social Darwinism on American psychiatry was in many ways a variation on a pattern seen earlier in moral treatment. Like their predecessors, many late nineteenth-century psychiatrists held that environment changed not only the tissues of the person actually exposed, but that these mutations were then transmitted through the germ plasm to future generations. And, like earlier colleagues, Social Darwinists saw community-wide efforts at prevention as the major weapon against this growing evil. They therefore tried, once more, to win the ear of the general public, to mobilize laymen against alcohol, tobacco, masturbation, "irregular habits," and the dangers of urban life. They also lobbied for legislation to eliminate sources of pathology. And thus, once more, psychiatrists spoke to lay audiences and wrote for nonprofessional publications on a wide range of subjects because of their concern, as citizens, for the health of the entire community.

The focus of Social Darwinism, however, was quite different from that of the earlier system. Although alienists had sought to prevent insanity in order to ease the suffering of individual fellow men, the orthodox of the later group attacked a more abstract target, the enervation of the race. The insane were seen as an alien influence, creatures of another kind, now classed once more with other species of "degenerates": criminals, paupers, deaf mutes, retarded, and so on. All the groups were to be treated in the same way, by isolation and sterilization. Custodial asylums thus became instruments to segregate the mentally ill from the community; and laws were enacted to stop the insane from having children, who would, in turn, burden society by their dependency and might further pollute the blood of the community. This ideology dehumanized the insane, as it did other classes of dependents and a number of racial minorities. It further discouraged support of custodial asylums and reinforced the old prejudices of fear and shame.

NOTES

1. *The American Journal of Insanity*, XLII (1885–1886), 137.

2. *The American Journal of Insanity*, XLVI (1889–1890), 180.

3. *Ibid.*

4. *Ibid.*, p. 181.

5. *The American Journal of Insanity*, LVIII (1901–1902), 71.

6. *Ibid.*, p. 72.

7. *Ibid.*, p. 73.

8. Milton Greenblatt, "Beyond the Therapeutic Community," Annual Israel Strauss Lecture, Hillside Hospital, Glenn Oaks, New York, April 29, 1962, p. 3.

9. *The American Journal of Insanity*, XLVIII (1891–1892), 308.

10. *Ibid.*, p. 309.

11. *Ibid.*, pp. 309–310.

12. *Ibid.*, p. 320.

13. *The American Journal of Insanity*, LVIII (1901–1902), 252.

14. *Ibid.*, p. 253.

15. *Ibid.*, pp. 253–254.

16. *The American Journal of Insanity*, XLI (1884–1885).

17. *Ibid.*, p. 6.

18. *Ibid.*, p. 9.

19. Gerald N. Grob, *The State and the Mentally Ill* (Chapel Hill, N.C.: University of North Carolina Press, 1965), p. 165.

20. *The American Journal of Insanity*, LX (1903–1904), 20.

21. *Ibid.*, p. 14.

22. *The American Journal of Insanity*, XLI (1884–1885), 63.

Chapter 29

INTO THE TWENTIETH

CENTURY

In 1896, Richard Dewey of Chicago, in his presidential address to
the Association of Medical Superintendents, decried the isolation of
psychiatry from the community.

This separation from the ordinary, everyday life of our fellow men is
an evil. It was far better for us to enter more into the life of the
community in which we live, and despite the fact that our duties are
uncommonly exacting and engrossing it seems to me we ought to do
so. It is for us to change this atmosphere of doubt, ignorance, and
suspicion to one of confidence, respect, and intelligence, and, to my
mind, this is our greatest task, next to our professional duties, and,
indeed, is part and parcel of them.

By mingling more with our neighbors we not only share with them
in the matters of education, religion, politics, and what not, which are
universally important, and interesting, but they gain a view of us new
to them, wherein we and our work appear in a more natural guise.
Above all ought we to mingle more with our fellow practitioners in
medicine.[1]

There is no reason, Dewey continued, why a mental hospital superintendent could not be a Sunday-school superintendent as well.

By the end of the nineteenth and the beginning of the twentieth
centuries, American psychiatrists had begun to move back into
voluntary association with their communities. At the level of the
guild, this took the form of an attempted rapprochement with general medicine and with the two competing fields of neurology and
psychology. As a sign of new moderation, the Association itself
was expanded, and membership was given to assistant physicians

with five years' service or more. In 1892, the name of the organization was changed to the "American Medico-Psychological Association," a twelve-man governing council was created, and new grades of honorary and associate membership were formed. New by-laws were passed, and the organization resolved to encourage research more strenuously than in the past.

During the last years of the nineteenth century, the Association invited neurologists to address annual meetings. In 1897, B. Sachs, Professor of Mental and Nervous Diseases at the New York Polyclinic, began his speech by self-consciously alluding to the scathing address of Weir Mitchell.

In view of recent experiences, indeed too recent to be entirely forgotten, you have evinced considerable courage in inviting another neurologist to appear before you. Evidently you are not willing to concede that there is a "state of war" between neurologists and alienists. Far from being foes or even antagonists, we are struggling for a common cause and should be united against the common enemy—the diseases of the nervous system.[2]

Sachs linked diseases of the nerves to those of the mind, and thus stressed his kinship with psychiatrists.

I have no doubt that others, like myself, would never have entered the ranks of neurologists if they had not been impelled to the study of nervous affections by a special fondness for the analysis of mental conditions. . . . I am certain, now that an "entente cordiale" has been established, that you will be amiable enough to allow that we, too, heal a patient or two every now and then, or if we do not succeed, we are constantly engaged in making desperate therapeutic efforts.[3]

In 1896, Richard Dewey had noted to his colleagues in the Association that they and the neurologists were separated by an indistinct boundary, which caused border wars. Nevertheless, he added,

We have only admiration for their facile command of all that is new and much that is good in theory and practice, though we find them somewhat unpractical in the care of the insane.[4]

Dewey pointed out, however, that because neurologists live in the midst of the general population, they are more involved in contemporary life, while the fact that they work in a narrower field allows them to get results.

In 1900, Boris Sidis, associate in psychology and psychopathology at the Pathological Institute of the New York State Hospitals, was the first psychologist to address the Association. He also began his speech with a certain barbed jocularity.

Medical men and especially alienists seem to observe less strictly the law "not to admit an alien into the congregation of the Lord," and are willing to listen even to a psychologist.[5]

Proper communication, however, was still lacking. Sidis added testily that he had prepared a long lecture on "The Nature and Principles of Psychology," but had only just learned that his speech was to take only twenty minutes. During the first decade of the twentieth century, psychiatrists made plaintive speeches, asking for greater recognition by psychologists, whose high status was symbolized by their university appointments.

Psychiatry also began to edge closer to general medicine. In 1903, G. Alder Blumer announced that the Association had united with the American Congress of Physicians and Surgeons. This, he felt, would vindicate the profession in the eyes of critics who denigrated its contributions to science.

If there still be detractors here and there who allege that psychiatry is a laggard in the race of the specialties, the account which we may be permitted to give of our stewardship every three years will either furnish proof of their contentions or of our own claim to sit in this Congress, not by sufferance, not by virtue of seniority as the oldest national medical society on this continent, but solely by reason of good work well done. We may well rejoice, then, that we have this opportunity to come out into the open and show our colors.[6]

There were those who suggested that, in order to further lower barriers between psychiatric and general medicine, doctors should be informed more fully about asylum procedures. One move in this direction had begun in the 1870's, in response to critics who had attacked psychiatrists for their failure to bring medical students into their wards. In 1878, A. E. Macdonald told the annual meeting of the Association that he had successfully conducted tours of Ward's Island for students from Bellevue in spite of previous opposition to the scheme by some of his New York colleagues.

I gave four clinics within the walls of the Asylum, and had an average attendance of about eighty, many of whom were practitioners; and in the course of that time some three hundred patients were shown to them. . . . In all that time there was no accident or disturbance. The patients did not seem to suffer in any way from it, on the contrary, it seemed to afford them considerable pleasure, and since that time it has been quite a common occurrence on my going into the wards, to have patients ask me when they are going to have an opportunity of meeting those gentlemen again. The experiment was so far successful that I think it is now an established thing.[7]

A further plan for linking mental hospitals to the rest of medicine involved the training schools for nurses which were being founded in asylums at the turn of the century. It was suggested that, rather than confine the curriculum of these schools to psychiatric matters, a general nursing program be offered. Graduates would then be able to find work in ordinary hospitals when they left asylum service, and they would thus become advocates of asylums in the community.

Another method of contact between psychiatrists and their colleagues in other areas of medicine was put forward by Adolf Meyer. He suggested that general practitioners in the communities near the mental hospital be taken on tours of the asylum and that they be instructed in such matters as commitment procedures. Further, he advised psychiatrists to call in the family doctor who had sent a patient to the asylum, to join staff meetings about that individual; and if the general practitioner could not attend, Meyer suggested that he be kept informed about the case by letter or by later meetings with the psychiatrist.

Facets of both nineteenth-century moral treatment and late twentieth-century community psychiatry may be seen in the writings of Adolf Meyer in the first decades of the twentieth century. He bridged the era of preoccupation with exclusively somatic etiology at the turn of the century and the era of the emergence of psychoanalysis as a dominant system in the 1930's and 1940's. He taught his colleagues to take the most complicated view of each patient. In his youth, he had written in his diary, "I am glad that I have decided to study the whole of man"; and in his subsequent work, he emphasized the importance of seeing patients, not only as physical organisms, but also as social beings, the products of an idiosyncratic cultural environment and life experience.

This pluralism pervaded his work and may be seen, for example, in a 1921 article on "The Contribution of Psychiatry to Understanding of Life Problems." He first defined *insanity* as a disease of social functioning as well as a manifestation of a disturbed mind.

Our patients are sick not merely in an abstract mind, but by actually living in ways which put their mind and the entire organism and its activity in jeopardy, and we are now free to see how this happens—since we study the biography and life history, the resources of adaptation and of shaping the life to success or to failure.[8]

The patient could only be understood, Meyer felt, by studying his entire life, not by examining only circumscribed areas.

There are in the life records of our patients certain ever-returning tendencies and situations which a psychiatrist of exclusive brain speculation, autointoxications, local injections, and internal secretions could never have discovered.[9]

Man was to be studied within the context of his social ties and conflicts.

Psychiatry has opened to us new conceptions and understandings of the relations of child and mother, child and father, the child as a recipient to the relations between mother and father, brothers and sisters, companions and community—in the competitions of real concrete life. It has furnished a concrete setting for the interplay of emotions and their effects.[10]

Meyer's plans for prevention and treatment required the participation of the entire community and its institutions. There was to be active and substantive cooperation between the mental hospital and local government, general practitioners, and concerned citizens. Because psychiatrists had neither the numbers nor the ability to deal on their own with insanity, the community must remove sources of pathology by controlling prostitution, for example, which spread syphilis; or by educating ethnic groups with unusually high rates of alcoholism. Community help was also needed to collect all the relevant data on patients that Meyer required for a proper evaluation of any case.

He demanded, therefore, a coherent community, reorganized to define and attack problems.

The districting of our cities is at present carried out in different ways for different purposes. As far as I know, the political wards and the police and fire department districts, the school districts, the criminal and juvenile court districts, the districts of charity organizations, all are apt to follow different lines of division. The ideal will have to be an organization so made that as many districts as possible may form reasonably complete households within themselves. Such an arrangement would make it possible for more people actually to realize what the community has to make itself responsible for; and it might become practicable to have district problems, district committees, and district meetings, such as the political parties have long been shrewd enough to maintain in their wards.

However much of a dreamer I may be, I pride myself on having seen a good many of my dreams come true. Can you see the ward or district organization—with a district building instead of a police station? With policemen as constructive workers rather than as the watchdogs of their beats? A district center with reasonably accurate records of the facts needed for orderly work? Among the officers a district health officer, and a district school committee and a district improvement and recreation committee, a district tax committee, a district charity or civic work committee—a tangible expression of what the district stands for? [11]

In such a community, Meyer envisioned a mental hospital or psychopathic unit whose personnel would pass freely back and forth between it and the district. In his own practice, Meyer was already linking the intra- and extramural worlds. His wife acted as the first psychiatric social worker, gathering data about patients in their native environment. Of his administration of Manhattan State Hospital he wrote,

An effort is made in cooperation with the State Charities Aid Association to have an agent in direct contact with the physician and with the patient, and also with the relatives outside while the patient is at the hospital, so that efficient simultaneous work can be expected in the adjustment of the conditions under which the patient had become ill, with a purpose similar to that of a Board of Health in providing for disinfection and quarantine in the sphere of the diseases that come under the charge of a Board of Health. We thus attain a *collaboration beyond the hospital walls* which is all-important with diseases which take sometimes months to develop under conditions which, so far, the hospital has not considered it its duty to investigate. . . .

It is necessary to go to the root of the evil, even if we come too late for prevention in a special case, to straighten out the environment, and to prepare the patient to be able to meet reasonably those difficulties which cannot be removed. That must in part be the duty of the state, but it can only fulfill it in cooperation with the friends and with the community which must be taught to be or to become a healthy environment fit for anyone to live in, even for those with not especially favorable endowment.[12]

Meyer attacked the tendency of his colleagues and laymen to confuse words with action.

To simply deplore from year to year the increase of insanity, and to get into periodic panics over the necessity of building more hospitals, is not doing the work at the right spot, and to the best advantage. But to reach this modern goal, we have to make proper provision and *see that the work is actually done*. We *are* inevitably pushed to the conclusion that each hospital must be the center of organized work in its district, with the help of the profession and all those who will take an efficient interest in public and individual health.[13]

Thus, as American psychiatry moved into the twentieth century, it broke further out of isolation. Plans for community involvement put forth by leaders such as Adolf Meyer echoed the prescriptions of alienists earlier in the nineteenth century. As in the past, however, such proposals for integration were succeeded, during the following decades, by the retreat of psychiatrists with their patients into the sanctuary of their clinics and professional offices.

NOTES

1. *The American Journal of Insanity*, LIII (1896–1897), 197.

2. *The American Journal of Insanity*, LIV (1897–1898), 1.

3. *Ibid.*, p. 2.

4. *The American Journal of Insanity*, LIII (1896–1897), 201.

5. *The American Journal of Insanity*, LVI (1899–1900), 41.

6. *The American Journal of Insanity*, LX (1903–1904), 8.

7. *The American Journal of Insanity*, XXXV (1878–1879), 111.

8. Alfred Lief (ed.), *The Common Sense Psychiatry of Dr. Adolf Meyer* (New York: McGraw-Hill Book Co., 1948), p. 5.

9. *Ibid.*, p. 6.

10. *Ibid.*, pp. 7–8.

11. Eunice E. Winters (ed.), *The Collected Papers of Adolf Meyer* (Baltimore: Johns Hopkins University Press, 1952), p. xxv.

12. *Ibid.*, p. 34.

13. *Ibid.*

Chapter 30

EBB AND FLOW

As we have seen, the history of nineteenth-century American psychiatry is a chronicle of ebb and flow. The idea that environment is a major influence, creating and curing insanity, and the consequent efforts of professionals to mold hospital and community milieux, rose, fell, and rose again throughout this period. There were corresponding cycles of attempts by psychiatrists to join in the lay and general medical communities in order to promote preventive measures; to attack misconceptions about the mentally ill; and to assume the normal social prerogatives of citizens, free to mix with their fellows outside asylum walls.

In retrospect, this ebb and flow seems to have had little to do with the intrinsic value of these ideas. From our own vantage point in the late twentieth century and from our own bias in favor of community psychiatry, many of the practices that appear most enlightened and even revolutionary to us have generally fared badly. It might be valuable, therefore, to try to abstract from history the factors that might have determined this pattern.

Some of these factors are fairly obvious: a shortage of manpower to implement programs, which reflected not only inadequate training facilities but also the low repute in which psychiatry was held by the rest of medicine; shortage of resources, which mirrored both the economic state of the community and the low priority accorded the mentally ill by the public and their legislators; the mutual stereotypes and expectations of laymen and psychiatrists, which hindered collaboration; contemporary theories on the etiology and treatment of insanity, which governed the degree of optimism with which psychiatrists viewed their task and which determined whether young men would adopt an exciting new system such as neuropathology or psychoanalysis to the exclusion of all else.

Another factor was the naïveté of psychiatrists about problems of community dynamics and about obstacles that could arise as a result of social and political forces; thus, when they ventured into the community, they were apt to encounter insurmountable barriers, particularly after periods of migration had produced large and heterogeneous cities. Thus many early theories that we now find so similar to the concepts of present-day psychiatry were formulated in a vacuum; and during the last century and a half, because of the magnitude of the task and the handicaps under which psychiatry labored, they could perhaps only have been so proposed. Their very clarity is a product of the inability of their successive waves of discoverers to realize the myriad factors that would complicate their implementation. Many of these are external factors, accidents of a particular social, economic, and scientific milieu, which still persist in our own day, but which are readily identifiable and may, in time, be conquered.

There are other more serious points, however, that appear to have become ingrained characteristics of American psychiatry during the last century and a half. Although professional ideas rose and fell, these traits remained, in part, because they had survival value, enabling the profession to develop and endure.

One of these traits was the tendency of psychiatrists to embrace panaceas, to hail each change as the solution to all difficulties. The system was then oversold, both to the public and to fellow professionals; but as experience revealed the shortcomings of each "miraculous" discovery, there was a pendulum swing to the opposite extreme. The entire system was jettisoned. And even the parts that had proved to have real, though limited, usefulness were lost in the general revulsion.

Second, as theories became fads they were invested with all available manpower, often while entirely untested. Their limitations were revealed only in execution. This led, on the one hand, to wasted resources, to the disillusionment of psychiatrists, and to the resentment of the public; on the other hand, it froze development, because, by the time the shortcomings of expensive plans had been realized, so much propaganda and money had been spent that it was difficult to abandon or replace them.

Third, as public demands for service from much-vaunted treatment schemes and public complaints about the failure of optimistic promises increased, psychiatrists tended to deal with such outside pressure by evasion rather than by direct confrontation. The gates of mental hospitals were shut in the face of critics; obstacles like waiting lists and admission criteria were established to dam the flow of cases. During the nineteenth century, psychiatrists escaped further, retreating into their professional guild. The Association became an increasingly closed sanctuary, in which outside critics could be ignored or abused, and where members received praise from their colleagues for their work, which assuaged their reaction to the vilifications of the outside community. These various forms of evasion further inflamed the public. They also allowed psychiatrists to lose touch with the realities of community life. Thus, their ideas and programs grew in a vacuum and often proved remarkably unsuited to contemporary conditions.

Fourth, there was a tendency to confuse speech with action, to assume that saying something made it so. During the nineteenth century, psychiatrists proposed grand schemes for hospital administration or community action. These were discussed and attacked; men flocked noisily to banners for and against such movements and enrolled their institutions in one of the rival camps. But, in fact, very little, if anything, had actually happened. When one examines the documents, one realizes gross discrepancies, for example, between articles in the *American Journal of Insanity* or discussions at annual meetings of the Association, and the reports of asylums, and one sees that much controversy was only theoretical, though the participants, apparently, were themselves deceived. This meant that some movements in the history of nineteenth-century psychiatry rose and fell only in men's minds.

Fifth, the primary goal of psychiatry, of preventing and curing a significant proportion of cases of insanity, has always proved impossible to achieve with current methods, even with panaceas. Psychiatrists, therefore, tended to fall back on the attainment of secondary goals to measure their own performance. Such objectives included good asylum administration, frugality, cleanliness, controlling diseases of pigs and potato blights on hospital farms, and creating efficient sprinkler and laundry systems. More recently, they have included approved training and research programs, and maintaining "correct" staff procedures, as in the intake formalities of traditional child guidance clinics. Although such objectives were often undeniably important, they had drawbacks. They obscured and replaced the unattainable, primary goals to which they were often only tangentially related. Thus means became ends. More-over, they were essentially parochial, arbitrary criteria of crafts-manship determined by professionals and reinforced by the guild. They allowed psychiatrists to work with minimal reference to the needs and demands of the public and to changing contemporary values and ideas.

Sixth, American psychiatry, until the late 1950's and early 1960's, neglected its own history, and so failed to learn from past experience. As each generation rediscovered the ideas of its prede-cessors, it also repeated actions and attitudes that had previously doomed such programs.

One reason for not learning from the past may have been the way in which histories were written. They usually chronicled the careers and theories of great men, such as Phillippe Pinel, Emil Kraepelin, Paul Eugen Bleuler, Jung, Freud, and Adolph Meyer. This led to a narrowing of historical focus and a distortion of per-spective. The development of the care of the insane appeared as a teleological growth from the healing shrines of antiquity and the superstitious cruelty of the Middle Ages to the scientific and hu-manitarian attitudes of the nineteenth and twentieth centuries. This traditional focus on outstanding individuals implied undemon-strated connections between ideas and obscured the relationship between the men whom we now regard as enlightened leaders, and the prevailing practices and ideas of their own time. It often glossed over the interplay of philosophies, personalities, and cur-rent exigencies of economics and social life that have contributed to the pre-eminence of these men and not of others, or to the neg-lect by their contemporaries of individuals and ideas that to us seem so prophetic. Thus, by examining a series of historical vignettes, psychiatrists on the whole failed to explain the develop-ment of their own field, to account not only for its advances but also for its still grave deficiencies and for the fact that certain of the practices of their predecessors often seem more enlightened than their own.

As damaging as these characteristics of the culture of American psychiatry appear to have been, it must be remembered that they also had survival value. This perhaps compensated for their other-wise noxious influence. It is doubtful, for example, whether in the nineteenth century apathetic citizenry and legislatures in a frontier society, harboring traditional prejudice against the insane, would have sanctioned and supported any innovative and liberal reforms unless the friends of the mentally disturbed had so radically over-stated their case. It is doubtful whether a significant number of able men would have accepted careers of working for the insane, either directly in hospitals, or indirectly by marshalling community support and resources, unless they felt that their mission was bound to succeed in the near future. It is doubtful whether the few American psychiatrists in the last century, untrained, isolated in scattered asylums, and chronic victims of political, legal, and lay pressures, could have survived as a professional group, without the guild to give them cohesion, information, and comfort. It is doubtful whether members could have withstood even as well as they did deprivation of resources; constant public clamor; and the evidence of their own failure in overcrowded wards, recidivism, and the apparently ever-rising rate of insanity, without secondary goals by which success might be measured—without boundaries against the flood of pressures and without the fads that constantly injected hope and excitement, however speciously. Finally, it is doubtful whether psychiatrists could have studied their own history. Had they done so they would have been forced to realize that they had progressed little beyond the practice of their predecessors. The entire American society during the late nineteenth century was obsessed with the speed of change. Authors like Theodore Dreiser in *Sister Carrie* felt it necessary to record details of contemporary dress and custom because they were bound to disappear in the near future; and psychiatrists had also to believe that their field was keeping pace with history. Looking backward was painful, as a few who accidentally did so found out.

Thus, if a twentieth-century psychiatrist were to assess his own work in the perspective of the past, he would have to balance the benefits and liabilities of these characteristics of professional culture. Otherwise, he might oversimplify by deciding, for example, that overselling an untested scheme was *ipso facto* disastrous; for the lesson of the past is that, although overselling often leads to trouble, it is also a way of counteracting apathy. Investing large resources in an untested scheme has not only created the danger of disillusionment and waste but also has proved the only way to test the real value of a plan.

There was a greater "mistake" than overselling and reckless experimenting in the nineteenth century. This was stagnation, which resulted in part from purely theoretical exchanges between colleagues attacking and defending plans that did not then exist. This point is particularly significant today, when the merits of community mental health centers and their possible success or failure are being busily discussed without the benefit of evidence drawn from an evaluation of practical experience.

PART FIVE

Epilogue

Chapter 31

IMPLICATIONS FOR COMMUNITY PSYCHIATRY: PERSONAL REFLECTIONS

Gerald Caplan

Before becoming involved in this study of nineteenth-century psychiatry I believed that "traditional" American psychiatry was individual-patient-oriented and that the ideas of those of us who advocated a population-oriented approach represented an innovative, even a revolutionary, movement. This was because I, like most psychiatrists, limited my past time perspective to the memory of my own work plus the extra twenty years or so of the experience of my teachers and role models. I usually brushed aside information that might invalidate this view of tradition, such as the fact that most severely ill patients had always been cared for in institutions administered by governmental agencies; that the number of psychiatrists being trained was clearly related to planned governmental intervention through training grants and stipends from the National Institute of Mental Health; and that now and again I would come across curiosities such as turn-of-the-century chapters in the *Collected Papers* of Adolph Meyer, which discussed proposals for welding the operations of mental hospitals into a network of medical and welfare services to serve the needs of the mentally ill of the population living in their surrounding districts.

I now realize that traditional American psychiatry has been community and population-oriented from its beginning and that, with

all its undeniable assets, the individual-patient orientation of academic and psychoanalytic psychiatrists of the last twenty to thirty
years has been to some extent a withdrawal to a professionally controlled haven from the difficulties of grappling with the demands
made upon us by the society that sponsors our operations. Community psychiatry is not merely a bright new idea developed by some of
us in the 1960's as a reaction to our awareness of the shortcomings of
the individual approach but is a return to an orientation that was
our basic mandate from society when our profession was established and within the framework of which it has been developed.

In our democratic capitalist country, individual psychiatrists
have the freedom to decide how they will use their skills and make
a living, but as a corporate profession they must either be respon-
sive to organized communal demands to deal with formally recognized population needs or they will incur sanctions and eventually
be pushed aside in favor of some other profession, the development
of which will be fostered in order to deal with the neglected problem. In our own day we are witnessing such a process in the deflec-
tion of community resources in the field of mental retardation
from psychiatry to pediatrics, neurology, psychology, and education. This has been a consequence of the failure of psychiatry as a
profession to convince public opinion and its leaders that we have a
sincere commitment to the prevention and remedy of problems of
the mentally retarded.

It is exciting to believe that one is being innovative and is a
pioneer in a revolutionary movement, as has been recently claimed
by some community psychiatrists. Unfortunately there are some
significant drawbacks to such a self-perception, apart from its historical inaccuracy. It tends to stimulate in us a rebellious or crusading spirit in which we oversimplify our problems and expend our
energies on wasteful battles for the Forces of Light, or Right, or
Progress, against the Forces of Darkness, or Evil, or Reaction. In
the heat of polemic, we tend to become narrow and rigid and to
close our minds against anything sensible said by the opposition—
as demonstrated in several instances in this book. We also tend to a
global disavowal of the practices of our opponents. For instance, I
have been impressed by the regrettable tendency in some community mental health circles to see psychoanalysis or individual clinical practice or psychotherapy as "the opposition" that has to be
rooted out. Assuming that this could be achieved, nothing more
catastrophic could occur to American psychiatry. I say this, not

because of my vested interests as a practicing psychoanalyst and psychiatric diagnostician and therapist, who has spent much time and energy being trained and who continues to appreciate the professional rewards of practice in this field, but because I believe that a community psychiatrist who is not a competent clinician is unlikely to make an optimal contribution to community planning or action. His particular contribution, as a psychiatrist, to a field in which many other specialists are involved is his understanding of individual, family, and small group psychodynamics and psychopathology and his abiding special interest in discussing every community issue from the point of view of its implications for the reduction of the mental sufferings of individual people. The other specialists rely upon him to contribute the best current knowledge about mental disorder to their pool of information and to help them take into account the contributions of all mental health practitioners, of whatever school or orientation, in planning how to deploy available resources to lower the level of suffering in the population.

An understanding of the history of our profession, of the factors involved in the unfolding of ideas, and in the vicissitudes of theories and practices within the situational context of their times not only guards against the narrowness of naïveté and against the excesses and wasted efforts of devotion to doctrinaire movements, but it may also offer guidance on how to influence our own destiny. I do not believe that history repeats itself. Each moment in time and each situation is unique. But a study of the dynamics of past constellations of forces, with the advantage of hindsight in assessing outcomes, may sharpen our awareness of the significance of otherwise apparently irrelevant factors in our own current predicaments. This may improve our problem solving in the same way that a study of his own and other's clinical cases helps a psychiatrist deal more effectively with his future patients, even though each individual is uniquely different from all others.

Certainly, I feel that the privilege of being involved in my daughter's historical researches, of participating in her analysis, and of reporting her data has sensitized me to several issues to which I previously gave little thought. In the belief that some of my reflections about the lessons to be drawn for our own time may be of interest and value to other workers in the field, I am presenting the following points for their consideration.

Historical Swings

I am impressed by the ebb and flow pattern of historical development. This book documents the swings of interest in mental disorder over time among the public and their leaders, and the oscillations in their attitudes concerning the importance of providing significant resources for the care of the mentally ill. These wave-like changes appear to be linked in a complicated reverberating fashion to concomitant swings in professional attitudes and practices.

This leads me to the realization that it is hazardous to place too much emphasis on intermediate-range planning, which is based upon an assessment of the current situation of professional ideas and the interest and commitment of legislators and the general public to provide support for programs. The definition of "intermediate-range" can be seen in retrospect to have varied from time to time, but on the whole I would put it at five to fifteen years. In other words, I would be quite cautious in planning with any degree of clarity or commitment programs that must wait five to fifteen years for implementation, because currently unpredictable changes are likely to alter the situation so drastically that either what seems sensible now will not appear that way then, or present public support will be withdrawn. Many aspects of the recent antipoverty program provide a good example, and so do some of the plans for separate community mental health center buildings that are already beginning to seem out of step with current plans for comprehensive health and mental health centers. There are also hints of future developments leading to even more comprehensive human services centers that will incorporate physical and mental health units together with care-giving facilities in welfare, adult education, law, manpower, and recreation. I have the impression that many of the buildings at present being built on the basis of the 1963 Community Mental Health Centers Act may well be outdated by the time they open their doors.

Unfortunately, even in our technologically advanced society, it takes several years to plan and erect buildings, especially in the public sector. And once erected, the capital investment introduces a conservative influence, so that they will continue to be used for many years, even though by that time professionals and the public may no longer be enthusiastic about their rationale. I see no clear way of dealing with this except to collaborate with physical planners and architects to design buildings that can be used as flexibly as possible; but because the site of the building may be a major issue (that is, should the mental health unit be associated physically with a general hospital, a public health center, an educational and manpower complex, a multiservice welfare center, and so on?), flexibility in use of internal space, such as by using movable internal walls within the structure, is clearly only one of the problems to be overcome.

What is really needed is a method of construction that will provide us with movable buildings. I sometimes have the fantasy of buildings of the future that will be like the tanks of modern mobile warfare instead of like the fixed emplacements of a medieval castle or a Maginot Line. An alternative would be to design all public service buildings, such as schools, churches, clinics, hospitals, and office buildings, so that their basic structures are interchangeable. This would mean that when the changed situation made the site of a particular utility inappropriate, it could exchange its function with a unit situated in another part of the community. This has happened to some extent, but in an unplanned and relatively wasteful way, in taking over redundant tuberculosis hospitals by mental health departments.[1]

Unfortunately for the implementation of such professional ideas of cheap, movable public building units, which might one day become technologically feasible in the form of prefabricated structures like mobile army field hospitals, it appears that the culture of legislators and governmental planners demands something different. Perhaps this may change in the future, but till now it appears that the solidity and imposing immobility of a public building provides a lasting monument to its builders and is a visible validation to the public of the meritorious service of its leaders and public servants. I doubt whether these values will soon change.

On the other hand, perhaps we professionals can try to introduce a counterbalancing force by pressing for programs and services that are as little as possible linked to buildings and that derive their stability and the continuity of their organization from the functions they fulfill. Recent trends toward goal-oriented and evaluative program planning, such as the Program Planning and Budgeting System that is emerging from the Department of Defense into general use throughout the Federal Government and increasingly in state government, provide some basis for optimism.

Undoubtedly, however, we must also take into account another area of need conflict. Individual workers are constantly searching for personal job security and stability. This is usually provided if their job is linked to an enduring institution tied in space to a building and to an associated legislatively sanctioned budget. Although this budget is usually reviewed annually, it is likely to be renewed with its main outlines relatively unchanged because of the network of commitments and expectations in which it is held. This type of stability is no defense against the bad effects of the pendulum swings of history, as has been shown in this book, because the demands on the institution in regard to such matters as the number and type of clients or what it is expected to do for them may drastically change; and resources that were adequate for the previous period may now be so inadequate as to lead to degeneration. If, on the other hand, programs and jobs do not have the stable foundation of a building that more or less commits government to maintain some semblance of budgetary stability, if only to avoid obvious waste of capital resources, they become vulnerable to every shift in the economic and political winds. Professionals can obtain flexibility, therefore, only at the expense of personal insecurity.

Such considerations convince me of the need for a mental set in planning that focuses on an improvisatory short-term approach in which we deal pragmatically with problems posed and opportunities provided by the current situation, and thereby capitalize on the present state of the oscillatory forces in the economic, political, social, and professional fields.

Of course, we cannot operate entirely in the present or in terms of the short-term goals of one to five years from now. We must extrapolate to the intermediate and distant future. But our reading of history should temper our optimism about intermediate-range goals, and we should be prepared not to be surprised or disappointed if the swing of the pendulum puts them effectively out of reach.

On the other hand, if we have enough patience and staying power, we do not have to be too pessimistic about not achieving the intermediate range goals, because we can predict that eventually the pendulum will swing back, and then we will perhaps be able to continue our advance.

The crucial question is whether individuals or groups of workers in a field, or the field as a whole, can develop the guidelines and the staying power to make progress a little at a time whenever the cycle is in the flow phase, and to maintain some or all of the gains during its ebb. Perhaps my reading of history is overly optimistic, but I do believe that the mentally ill in this country are in fact better off now than they were at comparable phases of the cycle in former times—the oscillations continue, but the curve, as it were, is gradually rising.

Such long-term optimism in regard to the field as a whole should not blind us, however, to the need for caution in regard to the evaluation of the contribution of a particular individual or group. It should not lull us into a sense of complaisance about our own efforts *sub specie aeternitatis*. I believe that an examination of history provides us with some hints on how each of us may so manage his own professional work in regard to the likely ebbs and flows of the cycle that we can optimize our contribution to the general good and perhaps increase the gradient of the long-term rising curve, while achieving our shorter-term individual goals.

Beware of Equating Ideas with Accomplishments

This book has shown that repeatedly people have put forward ideas and developed them in journal articles and professional meetings in such a way that they have been accepted by others, although the plans have not been actually implemented in more than a token fashion. This was due to a vast number of economic, organizational, and social obstacles that were not originally envisaged and that could not be overcome with current resources of knowledge, skill, and manpower.

Repeatedly in American psychiatry our ideas have run too far ahead of our practice. The original idea may have been good, as, for instance, that of treating the mentally ill in individualized humanitarian ways and in therapeutic communities; but, before we had explored and overcome the obstacles to the implementation of such an idea, we began to operate as though we had already done this, and could go on to newer concepts.

This has been complicated by the common human tendency to oversimplify the "state of the union" and to fit "old wine into new bottles." By this I mean our habit of talking glibly of the "moral treatment era" or "the present period of the community mental health center," without taking stock to answer such questions as what proportion of the mentally ill in the United States were at any time being cared for by moral management? Which institutions were completely or partially organized along moral treatment lines—or, for that matter, as pure custodial institutions? In 1968 how many of the institutions built in accordance with the 1963 Act (P.L. 88–164) actually do anything different for the mentally ill in their communities than was done previously? Is this a quantitative or a qualitative difference? When we read statistics about the mental health consultation being done all over the country, what in actual fact does this mean—who is doing what with whom?

In the past, and at the present time, we have operated as though the answers to these questions were self-evident. They are not, and we have never devoted the resources to collecting even minimal data to answer them. Instead, we have assumed that accomplishments followed almost automatically upon concepts, and we went on to elaborate higher-order concepts instead of embarking on the painstaking and often humdrum process of finding out how to translate the ideas into action.

This involves the need to develop programs in which there is a quick feedback between concepts and practice, so that concepts do not get too far ahead of implementation capabilities and so that a focus on the realistic obstacles and unexpected side effects of innovative programs becomes a highly valued part of our professional culture. It also involves the need to define the elements of methods and techniques and to describe them so that other workers will recognize what we have done and be able to compare this with what they have done. Such "evaluation of process," that is, specification of the elements of what does and does not constitute a program based upon a particular idea, is an absolute prerequisite to surveying what is actually being practiced in a field such as that of late twentieth-century community mental health centers or nineteenth-century moral treatment institutions. Only after this has been accomplished can we proceed to evaluate the consequences of such programs in achieving specified goals for reducing the toll of mental disorder.

Otherwise, we will continue in the future, as in the past, to be subject to fads and fashions both in theory and in practice and to discard methods as useless with as little validity as we embrace what are the popular panaceas of the moment.

I realize that the technology of sophisticated scientific evaluative research in preventive and remedial psychiatry is still in its infancy and that it will be many years before we will be able to provide valid answers to the question of what beneficial results we can expect from a particular approach. But I believe that we already know enough to begin to describe and specify the elements of our practice, whether in mental health consultation or education, or day hospitals, or any of the other elements of a community mental health program named by the Regulations of P.L. 88–164, so that workers in different places can let each other know what they are doing, instead of assuming that they know because of the labels on their doors or the paragraph titles of their journal articles.

Implementation of Ideas Demands Adequate Climate and Resources

This book repeatedly documents the correlation of the resources made available for the implementation of a particular idea and the complex of professional, social, and political factors that combine to produce the current climate. Of particular importance are economic factors, and the overall availability of resources must obviously be limiting. However, the determination of what proportion of the public treasury should be allotted for capital outlays and operating budgets in the mental health field in relation to competing demands from other segments of public service will depend on the contemporary evaluation of the burden of mental illness, the public commitment to dealing with this burden through organized community action, and the belief that psychiatry will provide value for the money. The book also demonstrates the development of professional ideas that in retrospect can be seen to have been ahead of their time in needing more resources for their implementation or more public support to maintain them in the face of the erosions caused by sociopolitical or economic changes than was available at that period of history.

On the other hand, changes in the general climate can be seen to demand new professional ideas; and not infrequently we get the impression that psychiatry was pulled into ways of thinking as a reaction to developments in enlightened public opinion rather than engendering its own innovations. The climate demands the ideas as much as the ideas need the appropriate climate.

Sometimes the timely ideas are held back by professional reaction. Innovation is uncomfortable and promotes feelings of insecurity in individuals and groups because it is not possible to foresee the outcome of new ideas as easily as that of those to which we are accustomed. Sometimes, the new ideas are delayed or rejected because people say they are not new at all but have been tried by a previous generation and have been found wanting. In the 1880's there were those who opposed therapeutic milieux on the grounds that moral management had failed in the 1850's. In the 1960's some have opposed population-oriented community mental health centers because they say that population-oriented child guidance clinics failed in the 1940's. In such cases the opponents of the new ideas that the times demand are correct in saying that the ideas are only new in relation to the recent past but are repetitions of ideas that were developed by previous generations. It is fallacious, however, to decry them on the grounds that they failed in the past. They were never evaluated objectively, and they were not discarded because it was demonstrated that they did not achieve their stipulated goals. They were rejected when their time had passed, when they no longer fitted the current climate, and when their implementation proved impossible or too costly because the necessary resources were not forthcoming.

I suggest that, instead of opposing an idea that seems timely because its newness makes it uncomfortable or because it was proposed in the past and did not work, we should learn from studying the past history of an idea what deficiencies of resources and what conditions of climate impeded its implementation, and then see whether we can remedy these deficiencies in the present situation in order to give us a better chance of success than our predecessors.

On the other hand, we can also learn from the past to recognize field forces with overriding negative implications that are likely to frustrate our efforts as they did those of our predecessors. This should guide us in deciding to give up the struggle when the dice are loaded too much against us. An understanding of history should help us to judge when and for how long to fight for the implementation of an idea that seems to be in tune with the times, and when to conserve our efforts or explore a new avenue of approach.

Sanctuaries for Hard Times

When the tide of public and professional interest ebbs, all gains of the recent past are usually not blotted out. There are enough deviant individuals and institutions in our pluralistic and largely decentralized society so that we can rely on a goodly number refusing to go with the tide. They maintain their ways, even though their resources, their status, and their opportunities for major development are reduced. When eventually the tide turns, they emerge from relative obscurity, and the ideas and practices they have kept alive become part of the new trend and provide a basis for rapid progress.

Such a bastion of moral treatment ideas and practices was Northampton Hospital under Pliny Earle, as described in Chapter 17. In our own day, schools of public health provided houseroom for psychiatrists with a community orientation during the postwar era, when academic psychiatry was overwhelmingly committed to the depth-psychological focus on individual patients. When Erich Lindemann went from Harvard School of Public Health to Harvard Medical School in 1954, he had to devote his major energies to fostering the dominant individual-oriented philosophy and had a hard struggle to maintain some of his former community-oriented interests. When I made a similar move in 1964, I received a ready welcome precisely because I could bring a population-oriented research and teaching program into a medical school where this was now in great demand.

Although we can rely on the spontaneous continuation of secluded enclaves for the perpetuation of the old ways of thinking and practice, some of which will have lasting value for maintaining long-term development, I wonder whether we should not try to optimize this process in a planned way. By this I mean that, for example, during the current tidal flow toward a community approach we should try to make sure that some medical school departments of psychiatry should continue to concentrate on an individual-patient approach and that some psychoanalytic training institutes should be especially protected and fostered, so that in the helter-skelter rush toward the community we may continue to promote sources of creative thinking about the individual. I also mean that during these years, when there is such a favorable flow of money and trainees into our mushrooming population-oriented programs, some of us should be preparing for the inevitable ebb-tide. Readers of this book may agree with my prediction that, within a few years, possibly as soon as 1973 to 1975, psychiatry will be called to account for its accomplishments in obviating the scourge of mental disorder by means of community mental health centers and will be found wanting. The consequent public and professional disillusionment may by 1980 to 1985 lead to a global rejection of the approaches that currently are held in such high regard. Should we

not, therefore, at this stage give thought to how we can prepare for
that time and to what we can do to ensure the maximum protection
for those core people, ideas, and practices that eventually can continue to raise the level of community care for the mentally disordered after the next cycle?

Of course, in the absence of valid evaluative methods, we have
no way of being sure which of our current approaches is worth
saving for the future. Capacity for survival is often related to the
level of commitment of an individual or group to certain ideas and
to the strength, obstinacy, or conservatism of the workers in maintaining their values and traditions in the face of pressures to assimilation, and not necessarily to ultimate truth or to what will be
proved valuable by a future generation.

On the other hand, I believe that this book does provide some
rough guidelines for what by hindsight we can perceive to have
been useful in the past and that we can extrapolate for the present
and future. I will discuss some of these shortly, but whether or not
others agree with this list or develop a different one of their own,
what can we do, if anything, to increase the chances of the survival
of such principles of theory and practice when the tide turns?

I believe that at least a tentative answer lies in four concepts:
ideology, protected social structure or sanctuary, elite cadre, and
reference group.

By ideology, I mean a cohesive set of concepts and values—not
necessarily a system, but a systematic orientation, a way of looking
at things, and a correlated set of attitudes and personal commitments. My psychologist colleagues at the Laboratory of Community Psychiatry in the Department of Psychiatry at Harvard
Medical School, H. Charles Schulberg and Frank R. Baker, have
identified the existence of such a fairly circumscribed ideology
among mental health workers with a population-oriented approach
and have differentiated it from the ways of thinking about significant issues of individual-patient-oriented practitioners and researchers. They have developed and validated a test instrument, the Community Mental Health Ideology Scale, which can reliably define
the degree to which an individual or group is currently committed
to one orientation or the other.[2]

Such an ideological set or commitment, although possibly rooted
in basic characterological factors, is probably mainly derived from
life and professional experience, and in particular from education
and training. Therefore, I feel that one answer to our question lies

in fostering and protecting the continued existence and development of certain educational programs that promote this ideology.

In such programs the study of the history of psychiatric ideas—"psychiatric intellectual history"—should have a significant place, in order to provide students with a long-term perspective that overrides the temporary focus of the moment. On the other hand, the past should not be studied for its own sake, and as a way of escaping the harsh realities and frustrations of the present by the gratifications of dwelling on previous glories, especially those which have been retrospectively romanticized, but as a guide to the near and distant future.

The other characteristic of such an educational program should be the constant search for feedback between theory and practice, so that concepts are kept in line with externally based demands and with the realistic possibilities of overcoming the obstacles to their implementation in action. This means that the educational programs should be organized within the framework of a protected social structure or sanctuary.

The best place for such a sanctuary would probably be a university, because of its traditional role in this regard. It might also be a privately endowed institution, such as a private foundation or a mental hospital. McLean Hospital in Boston occupied such a role for many years. Institutions like the Menninger Foundation might also be appropriate sites. It is unlikely that institutions of Federal or state government would afford the necessary protection, but occasionally a concatenation of circumstances involving an influential person with long-term tenure in a key position might make even this possible, as shown by our example of the Northampton Hospital of the Commonwealth of Massachusetts.

The essential characteristic of the sanctuary is not that it walls its occupants off from contact with their surroundings. This usually leads to an ivory tower precious atmosphere that is the direct antithesis of what I am advocating. It is, rather, that the educators and practitioners are freed and protected from current trends of general public and professional opinion to work out their own solution collaboratively with their surrounding community so that whatever the dominant fashions, they can find out what their more limited local public appear to need and want, and negotiate a mutually satisfactory agreement with them, through personal confrontation and continuing dialogue. This replaces adherence to current professional or general political orthodoxy by the concurrence of

the client population, as a way of monitoring the continuing right
of a program or a worker to support. Because the opinion of clients
is influenced not only by their actual experiences of the program
but also by generally dominant cultural attitudes and values, this is
far from foolproof in affording the protection we are seeking. On
the other hand, history provides many examples of such localized
sanctuaries among circumscribed communities that have tolerated
professional or religious deviance from the overall culture of the
time.

My third concept, I am afraid, runs counter to dominant trends
in United States culture with its egalitarian anti-intellectual bias.
Nevertheless, because I am suggesting ways of minimizing the un-
wanted effects of this value system, which in general is so strongly
committed to progress, I hope I will be excused for suggesting that
in this country we should not be reluctant to utilize an approach
derived from aristocratic cultures, and to adapt it to the American
scene. I refer to the concept of an elite cadre—the recruitment and
education of a small carefully selected group of charismatic leaders,
who will develop and transmit the ideas and values of community
mental health to the next generation. The particularly American
contribution to this concept would be that members of this elite
group should not be recruited on the basis of family connections,
race, religion, or socioeconomic class, but on the basis of personal
qualifications and motivation. Preferably they should be young men
and women who show evidence of originality and of a capacity to
maintain an independent position without becoming unduly disturbed by pressure to conform to popular norms.

In order to provide stability to these educational sanctuaries, the
top leadership probably should have professional lifetime tenure. In
order to prevent their educational organization from getting progressively more conservative as the administration ages, efforts
should be made to ensure a continuing flow of younger educators,
each of whom would spend a few years in the unit and then move
on to key positions elsewhere in the field.

I am not advocating the organization of clandestine cells of reac-
tionaries, or a network of conspiratorial units plotting to over-
throw the establishment. On the contrary, these sanctuaries of
population-oriented workers, if they are to be successful, must
visibly maintain viable relationships both with their own surrounding community and with the general power structure of the profession and the public—at least sufficient to be allowed quietly to

pursue their deviant path as Pliny Earle did at Northampton. Another way of ensuring an open-minded approach to problems and the avoidance of reactionary dogma and discipleship would be to make multidisciplinary research a central core of their program, particularly applied and evaluative research. The development of a respected research reputation would help to attract a continuing flow of bright young people of different disciplines who would spend some time in these centers at an early stage in their postdoctoral careers, and help to counteract a natural tendency for such institutions to become ingrown, precious, reactionary, or monolithic.

The fourth concept, which complements the others, is that of the reference group. Not all the alumni of such sanctuaries will maintain their population-oriented traditions when exposed to the dominant values and pressures after they leave, particularly if the nature of their daily work does not foster the use of their community theories and skills. In order to withstand such pressures to assimilate to majority attitudes and practices there is the need for the development of a communication network and meaningful relationships among a sizeable group of those who identify with community mental health ideology, many of whom are, or were in the past, students or staff members of one of the sanctuaries. Such a group might be formally organized in a relatively small organization like GAP (Group for Advancement of Psychiatry), or it might convene informally when its members come together on committees or task forces of other organizations, or when they spontaneously assemble "where the action is" in relation to salient community issues in a variety of fields such as urban development, adult education, education, vocational training, social planning, and civil rights. Whatever their professional or institutional affiliations, members of this reference group will derive some of their status and self-respect from recognition by their fellows and will obtain guidance, counsel, and support from them.

I believe that measures such as the four I have outlined would constitute one feasible way of ensuring a quiet, persevering effort to keep ideas and practices of population-oriented community mental health alive during the period of ten to twenty years when they are likely to suffer from a reduction of general public and professional interest and support, so that when the tide turns we can more quickly and surely continue to go forward.

Danger of Inflated Promises and Therapeutic Claims

This theme is just as topical in the 1960's as it was in the 1840's and repeatedly in between. Careful study of nineteenth-century history reveals that the danger is not simply caused by individual vanity or wish-fulfilling self-deception of professionals, although such human failings are not less common among psychiatrists than other people. What often seems to happen is that, when the public and their leaders recognize some need and turn for help to professionals, they do so with the hope, often linked with irrational fantasies, that the latter will omnipotently provide quick and complete solutions to their problems. When they initially solicit the intervention of the professionals, both sides are ignorant of the very real difficulties of developing viable programs and of the degree of success that can be reasonably expected. The greater the urgency of public need, the more persuasive the appeal to the professionals, and the more seductive the situation in regard to bestowing and accepting a mantle of omnipotence. This situation is exaggerated by the fact that neither side as yet knows what an adequate program to satisfy the public's needs should cost; and therefore a bargaining relationship emerges in which the professionals try to get as much as possible, with the realization that their requests, mainly based on guesswork, are almost certainly for less than the job will demand, while the public exacts promises of marvellous results in return for their money. This easily leads to a situation of mutual stimulation and escalation, so that the professionals are tempted to make bigger and bigger promises, without being sure whether they can deliver anything at all, in order to obtain the resources that they hope will allow them to build a program sufficiently effective to redeem their claims.

Such a bad situation is often made worse if there are "middle men" involved, that is, friends or agents of the professionals, such as Dorothea Dix in the nineteenth century or the mental hygiene propagandists, fundraisers, and lobbyists of the twentieth century who are not inhibited by scientific caution and who judge success by the magnitude of the funds they are able to obtain from the legislators. The professionals gratefully receive the resources their friends have helped pry from the public treasury, but they later discover, often to their surprise, that during behind-the-scenes negotiations, they have been committed to produce impossible results in return.

Such an inauspicious beginning not infrequently is followed by the professionals discovering that lack of prior knowledge of the dimensions of the problem, such as prevalence of mental disorder, and of the expectable practical obstacles that will impede implementation of plans based on unsubstantiated theories, has made them grossly underestimate the resources they will need to do the job. Because they have now been committed to carrying out an assignment, they begin a struggle with the community leaders for more supplies. The leaders demand more assurances that the investment of increased funds will yield even more profit; and this sets the stage for a salesmanship atmosphere that leads to optimistic professional predictions of success and to inflated claims of cures. Before long it becomes almost impossible for the psychiatrists not to continue along this vicious spiral because they must now protect the whole edifice they have been building, including the job security of the colleagues whom they have involved in their enterprise.

Part of this problem seems related to the difference in culture of professionals and community leaders. The latter, drawn from the ranks of business, administration, and politics, are more oriented to a *quid pro quo* expressed in concrete terms. They expect to be told exactly what they are buying and to express the bargain in the form of binding contracts. Professionals such as psychiatrists, on the other hand, think in terms of doing the best job of which they are capable with current knowledge and skills. They are usually vague about the outcome, expecting hopefully that as long as they take care not to do harm they will probably make a useful contribution. Because the community leaders hold the purse strings, this culture clash has often been resolved on their terms; and the psychiatrists deviate from their customary mode, thus putting themselves in an untenable position.

I feel that the recognition of this issue and its hazards is one of the most significant lessons we can learn from the past. We must be alert to maintain our own values and posture when negotiating with community leaders and not to allow ourselves to be seduced either by their demands or by our own cupidity to promise more than we have good reason to believe we can deliver. I believe that we should make an intensive effort to bridge the cultural gap and to interpret to the community leaders the limitations of our approach. We cannot guarantee results; we can only undertake to work hard and to contribute our knowledge and skills to a concerted attack by the community on the problems with which it is confronted.

This does not mean that we will not accept responsibility, but that in doing so we should define both in advance and in clearly expressed progress reports our understanding of the realistic limitations of our capacities. We can offer the best that money can buy; but this must necessarily be less, and in certain cases much less, than what the purchaser may want or may dream of getting.

Such a clarification involves no easy process, precisely because the two parties do not speak the same language and because of the pressures of the needs of each. I believe that community psychiatrists should devote much time and attention to clarificatory discussions with community leaders on a continuing basis, and not dismiss the matter as soon as a contract or budget negotiation has ended. Because there are so many obtrusive affective elements on both sides to cloud memory and judgment, it is necessary to keep working at maintaining a consonance of expectations in the same way that a prolonged period of "working through" is needed to consolidate the mutative effect of an interpretation in the psychoanalysis of an individual patient.

A further complication of this process that is well documented in this book is the potential effect of guild pressure in exaggerating professional claims of potency. We must beware of developing doctrinaire positions regarding the merits of a particular preventive or therapeutic approach as a debating technique used by each side in trying to win higher status for its adherents within our professional organization. Being human, psychiatrists will inevitably coalesce into cliques and factions with differing theoretical and technical interests and will often compete with or oppose each other. It is important that the internal polemics and claims to have a better system than others within the guild should not be allowed to spill over into propaganda to the public that expresses itself in guarantees of preventive or therapeutic successes. An important message to be derived from this book is that we should self-consciously maintain a boundary between the intraorganizational clash of ideas and claims for merit and our communications with the public, which should be studiedly circumspect and modest—in keeping with our realization of the vast gulf between hopeful ideas and established accomplishments, as well as the great likelihood of unexpected and unpredictable obstacles to the implementation of plans that we deem reasonable.

Rather than relying on our native wisdom to maintain our realization of the inevitable eventual debacle when the public and its leaders remind us of our earlier promises and contrast these with our less-than-perfect results, I feel that we should place much more emphasis in the future on the importance of evaluative research. Most of us pay lip service to this; but in fact very little research has been carried out to evaluate the goal accomplishment of any program or technique in our field. This is in part due to the difficulties and expense of carrying out valid studies with our present inadequate research technology. It is in part a reflection of the pressure of community leaders and professionals to get on with the service job because of obtrusive needs of suffering people. Because there are usually inadequate funds and staff available even to operate minimal preventive or remedial programs, evaluative research may be seen as a luxury that cannot be afforded.

If we professionals were to maintain a stand that we will never be in a position to determine whether or not public money has or has not been profitably expended unless a significant proportion of it is spent on evaluation, I feel that we will build a safeguard to keep our promises and predictions in line with expectable reality. It will be difficult for us to maintain simultaneously the contradictory positions that we can promise good results and that we cannot know which results are good or bad without valid evaluative research. If we go on to tell the truth also about the latter, namely, that it will be many years before we can perfect the evaluative techniques needed to give a definitive answer to our questions, and that we must meanwhile struggle towards closer and closer approximations, we will still further intensify the atmosphere of professional caution that we must try to communicate to the public. I do not believe that community leaders will be alienated, even though they may be disappointed, by such an approach. On the contrary, I believe that they will be impressed by our honesty and will feel more confident that they are getting the best value for their money in the present state of the art.

We Must Accept the Realities of Political Life

If we organize or participate in programs that are administered
or financed by public bodies, particularly state or local government, we must be prepared to accept the political framework
within which the support is given. In addition to the inevitability
of phasic swings, this usually means that there will be political
strings attached in the form of a demand for surveillance and some
measure of control on the part of the governing body. This must
be seen as legitimate and not as "lay interference." This in turn involves working out communications between the professionals and
the community leaders so that they will share a common semantic
framework to allow the two sides to collaborate for the benefit of
the mentally ill. The essential issue is for both sides to recognize
that they do not initially speak the same language and that a special
effort must be continually made to communicate.

Another issue that is likely to lead to difficulty in the future, as it
has so often in the past, is that each side has special interest goals in
addition to those of serving the mentally ill. The professionals are
interested in research, theory building, and professional development, as well as in the more mundane goals of making a living and
achieving status. The community leaders are interested in building
up their political party and furthering its general program; in obtaining some control of public funds for patronage, both to repay
political debts and to further their influence; and in promoting
their public image among voters so that they will be re-elected or
move up to positions of higher power.

It appears to me that in the past our colleagues have felt more
comfortable in pursuing their own unstated goals at the public expense because they have judged them compatible with the public
good, than in agreeing that the politicians should achieve theirs. In
fact, I get the impression that psychiatrists sometimes feel that in
contrast to their own "pure" motives, the party and political ambitions of community leaders are somehow selfish and nefarious, and
opposed to the public welfare. This viewpoint is sometimes validated by pointing to the excesses of a particular politician or party
in grossly exploiting a public trust by using the spoils system to introduce manifestly unsuitable candidates into key positions. I am
not exonerating such wasteful nepotism. Such excesses are, however, a matter of general concern in organizing community affairs,

and professionals are one group among many who should be working to maintain safeguards against individuals or political parties misusing public funds, as well as to reform situations that get out of hand.

I am, however, advocating learning from history that we psychiatrists can easily fall into the human trap of taking our own vested interests for granted while being oversensitive and overrighteous in projectively suspecting the worst from the politicians. This is exacerbated by our rebellious feelings against those who control us by holding the purse strings, so that our insecurity makes us overreact to issues that could be relatively easily handled if taken quietly in our stride. Often a politician will recommend a friend or a constituent for a job as a matter of form. All he wants is that we should see his candidate and take him on if we judge him suitable. If we reply that we have sympathetically considered his man, the politician will usually be satisfied that his constituent will feel that he has been helped by his sponsor. If we do not then give the man the job, the responsibility will be ours and not the politician's.

Likewise, if a community leader refers a member of his family or a constituent for "special treatment" as a patient, I see no reason why we cannot accept this case and give it as much attention as it intrinsically deserves, plus use the extra leverage of the politician's power position to open up channels in the management of this case that could be useful in dealing with cases of this type in the future.

The point I am making is that during periods of history when psychiatrists were not frightened of or resentful toward politicians they were able to work out ways of accommodating to their styles and constraints, and the ensuing collaboration led to the betterment of the lot of the mentally ill. On the other hand, when the differences between the two groups polarized into mutual anger and distrust, each side legitimated only its own vested interests and sought no accommodation with the other, the chief sufferers being the mentally ill over whose bodies the battle waged.

The Importance of Confrontation
Between Psychiatrists and the Public

This is a crucial issue. It follows from all that has so far been said in this chapter. This book clearly documents the tendency of psychiatrists to withdraw from interaction with the public and its leaders when the going gets rough. Such withdrawal exacerbates

bad relationships by facilitating the development of negative stereotypes on both sides that still further increase mutual distance. This
vicious spiral not only prevents the psychiatrists from trying to en-
list the support of the political leaders, even though the latter ultimately hold the purse strings, but it prevents an adequate flow of
information from the public to the profession about currently felt
needs and about people's reactions to professional practice. The
guild turns in on itself and replaces realistic criteria for evaluation
of accomplishment based upon satisfaction of publicly expressed
need by the unreal measures of guild values and traditions. The latter are peculiarly susceptible to bias by wish-fulfilling fantasies, a
process made all the more likely by consensual validation in a
closely knit reference group.

The lesson for our times seems to me to be that we should make
every effort to build into the structure of all our organizations,
programs, and institutions measures that will force us to confront
our publics—the community of patients inside our institutions, the
community of our potential patients in our locality, the local and
state leaders who provide our resources, and representatives of general public opinion that influences all of us.

Five principal purposes should be served by these continuing interactions, and I believe that some of the difficulty in the past has
been caused by confusing these. First, we psychiatrists must communicate with legislators or others who distribute community resources, such as directors of community chests, in order to persuade them to allot to us an appropriate share of such resources in
competition with representatives of other groups and interests. We
must be aware of this competition and admit the validity of other
claims, realizing that resources are limited and that if our special interest group gets more, others get less. In addition, we must ensure
that we accept accountability for reporting to the donors on what
we have accomplished with the resources we have received.

I have the uneasy impression that some psychiatrists at the
present time who are moving from institutional or private practice
into community mental health centers perceive the population base
of a catchment area as a new-found stratagem to obtain welcome
additional funds "for service." There is even some competition in
certain localities between psychiatrists who wish to stake out claims
to populations for the purpose of obtaining building and staffing
grants from NIMH and state governments. They appear to feel
that the population of the catchment area is "theirs" and represents

a kind of property equity, so that they compete with other psychiatrists or institutions for domain and engage in boundary disputes. They do not appear to realize that the essence of the catchment area concept is not that the bounded population belongs to them but that, on the contrary, they belong to it, that is, they are receiving the share of local community or Federal funds in return for their assumption of responsibility to satisfy the mental health needs of that population. The acceptance of the obligation to serve the population should lead to the establishment of adequate accounting practices, not only to ensure that funds are not misspent, but that there are regular and meaningful reports and reviews of what is being achieved with these funds. In the hurly-burly of public life, with its frequent changes of leadership and the pressure to exercise surveillance over vast service areas, psychiatrists have in the past been able for long periods to avoid a meaningful accounting to community leaders. This has been aggravated because it is so difficult to establish valid and concrete criteria for measuring accomplishment, and so easy to use statistics of numbers of patients seen, or visits made, or beds occupied, or patients discharged as apparent evidence of achievements, buttressed by a few case examples of human interest success stories. Fortunately for the mentally ill, and unfortunately for us, the day of reckoning inexorably arrives, even if delayed. In our times this is likely to happen more quickly than in the past, because the amount of money involved is larger. This puts psychiatry in the political "big leagues," and makes it a prime target for politicians who can utilize investigations likely to reveal lack of appropriate benefits from the use of public funds as ways of attacking or undermining the influence of their legislative opponents who voted this money.

This leads me to advocate that psychiatrists should by careful design ensure periodic meetings with community leaders, at which they should do more than go through the motions of justifying their good work. They should instead attempt to expose to joint critical scrutiny what they have and have not accomplished. In such discussions both they and the politicians should examine what their best efforts have produced and try to elucidate ways of improving the situation.

The second purpose to be achieved by interaction with community leaders is to influence social policy planning. Nineteenth-century history emphasizes the lesson that is equally obvious in our century, that public policies in dealing with the mentally ill are

part and parcel of the total approach of the community to the satisfaction of human needs and to the organization of public services
in education, welfare, health, manpower, corrections, and so forth.
In our times, increasing population, increasing affluence, and the increasing complexities attendant on technological progress and the
concentration of the population in huge metropolitan conglomer-
ates make it obvious that meaningful social policy decisions are
more and more taking place at Federal, state, and regional levels,
rather than at city and local levels. The important question is
whether these decisions will be made with sufficient wisdom to
provide direction, guidelines, and standards, backed by appropriate
supplies and sanctions, within which localities can develop services
that are sufficiently tailored to the idiosyncrasies of local needs,
values, and traditions so that at the level of the consumers the services can be delivered in a humanistic and individual-sensitive manner. The larger the system and the more centralized, the bigger the
danger of dehumanization and of consequent alienation of consumers who feel impotent in molding their own fate. Awareness of
this problem has in recent years stimulated the development of
local groups who demand control over their neighborhood or area
services and who rebel against domination by city hall, not to mention the state house and Washington. I believe that some measure
of local control is essential in combatting dehumanization and
alienation, but I feel that inevitably the major decisions on social
policy will be taken not at the local or city level but at state and
particularly at Federal levels. Examples are the major advances in
services for the mentally ill at the end of the nineteenth century
produced by the comprehensive reform legislation in New York
and the recent promising surge forward in response to Federal legislation in the mental health, medical care, welfare, and education
fields.

The implications of these considerations for psychiatrists are that
we should not expect to influence social policy development by in-
teracting with our local publics and their leaders.

These individuals and groups must inevitably be frustrated in
their ambitions to exercise major control over their own destinies.
Instead, either we, or the leaders of our profession, should arrange
to develop relationships of mutual trust and respect with legislators
and influential figures at the state and Federal levels, so that our
views and experience, based upon our mission in reducing suffering

from mental disorder, can be taken into account in organizing services to satisfy the needs of the people.

On the other hand, by also working closely with citizens and civic leaders at the local level, we can help them formulate their demands and communicate these through appropriately amplifying channels to the central decision makers. This will ensure maximal impact in improving the consonance between centrally determined social policies and their eventual implementation at the neighborhood and family level.

From this it follows that I advocate a multilevel series of continuing interactions between psychiatrists and civic leaders, city, state, and Federal legislators. Such contacts would have the goal of helping to improve the articulation of the series of decision makers so that policy decisions will provide sufficient latitude to allow maximal control by the consumer population, while preventing the narrowing and rigidity or the distortions likely to arise from overgeneralization in country-wide or statewide policies from the idiosyncratic experience or needs of localities or special interest groups.

The third principal goal of confrontation of psychiatrists and their publics is that of monitoring salient needs to which mental health services should be addressed and of finding out how to utilize nonpsychiatric resources in the community to extend the impact of the mental health professionals. This demands a continuing dialogue at the local level. I agree wholeheartedly with the views expressed by Jarvis and the practitioners of moral treatment in the 1840's and 1850's, as well as by Adolph Meyer at the turn of the century, that this issue can only be dealt with effectively on a neighborhood basis. Even a catchment area of 75,000 to 100,000 is probably too big a population unit for adequate interchange regarding local needs and resources. What is essential is for the mental health workers to divide their area up into relatively homogeneous or naturally bounded units and then to build continuing communication links between these and separate teams of professionals. The goal is for each side to obtain valid information from and about the other, so that the mental health workers confront the realities of the needs and indigenous resources of their population and so that the people dissipate their fantasies about the psychiatrists and their services and learn what they have to offer and how to invoke their aid when this might seem appropriate.

The fourth principal goal is that of feedback from the recipient population to those providing mental health services. Expression of opinion by the local population about the relevance of the program to their current needs, and whether they feel that users of the service have benefited, is a method of evaluation that is admittedly crude. It is, however, not subject to the one-sided bias of the self-appraisal of the practitioner or of his reference group. Particularly significant are the opinions of dissenters or critics, even if they are deviants and emotionally disturbed grumblers. This book has documented that the voice of dissent among the general public or among deviant groups or individuals, even though motivated or distorted by mental disorder, often carries messages of fundamental validity and importance. We should learn from this to listen with particular care and to control our own defensiveness, when somebody grumbles or negatively criticizes our programs. We should also try to amplify the voice of dissent by establishing mechanisms whereby we send people into the community to search for critics or discontented consumers, particularly among the deprived and the inarticulate, whose voices are quiet or whose language it is hard for us to understand.

The fifth function of confrontation between psychiatrists and the public is to obtain sanction for our activities. A large measure of formal sanction is obtained from legislation that defines our duties and responsibilities and from legislative and nongovernmental appropriations of funds for specified services. In addition, we need to consolidate and maintain this sanction at successive levels of the community power structure. This includes the caregiving agencies and formal and informal influential community figures, as well as the families and individuals who are our potential patients, and those who might advise them to turn to us. Once again we in our day can turn for guidance to the pioneers of the early moral treatment era, who realized the importance of a continuing dialogue with the public and who maintained their own integration within the general intellectual and cultural framework of their times. At present, this issue of obtaining and maintaining wide public sanction is rendered easier by the development of the mass media, particularly radio and television. Psychiatrists working in community programs should allot a significant portion of their time to meetings with the press, and especially to contributing to audience participation panels on television and radio, not only for the purpose of general mental health education, important as that undoubtedly is in its own right, but in order to inform the public about our plans and services and to explore with them the degree to which they approve or support what we wish to do.

Finally, the most important lesson about confrontation I have learned from this book is the ever present danger of retiring into our own professional group and reducing or interrupting communication with the public and its leaders when they criticize or attack us or when they say things we do not like to hear. This danger is increased by the tendency of any reference group to wall itself off and to replace ideas based on externally derived information by an internally produced mythology. I have no definite suggestions on how to combat this danger, except to keep reminding ourselves of the difficulties demonstrated by our historical experience and to make a special effort to maintain and promote communication with our critics. In addition, we should welcome any opportunity to structure regular continuing contacts with a variety of citizens' groups, especially those whose membership we cannot control, and to invite critics and antagonists to come into our staff meetings or to meet with us informally in order to explain their point of view. I would like to see our profession develop a tradition whereby psychiatrists would achieve merit and status in the eyes of their professional peers by demonstrating their sincere interest in searching for and listening to the voice of criticism and dissent.

The Crucial Importance of a Multifactorial Open Systems Approach to Theory and Practice

My reading of nineteenth-century psychiatric history has brought me to the conclusion that periods of professional innovation, vigor, and productivity, as well as active collaboration between psychiatrists and the public, have coincided with the dominance of multifactorial theories of the etiology of mental illness and an open systems ecological approach to preventive and remedial practice. Likewise, periods of professional stagnation have been linked to espousal of etiological theories that have focused exclusively on one mode or parameter of noxious influence, whether a hereditary taint, a structural alteration in the brain, a particular psychological defect, or an environmental constellation. Such periods have also been characterized by the dominance of one type of treatment to the virtual exclusion of all others.

This leads me to the conclusion that, in our complicated and confusing field, where truth is so elusive and evaluation of accomplishments so difficult, we can reassure ourselves that our current etiological theories and remedial practices are probably leading in a productive direction if they are based upon a multifactorial open systems model of some kind. Moreover, any sign of overconcentration upon a single parameter, such as organic, psychosocial, or sociocultural factors, whether in theories of etiology or of treatment, along with neglect or rejection of the others, should alert us to the probability that we are beginning to oversimplify our grasp of the field of reverberating forces to a dangerous degree. I am not saying that all researchers and practitioners must be equally interested or skilled in all parameters, because experience teaches us that some professionals have temperamental biases that make them more interested in one area and less in others, and most skilled in particular preventive or remedial techniques. Not all of us can be universal men. What I am emphasizing, however, is that we should all subscribe to a basic philosophy that sincerely admits the importance of the other factors and accords respect to those studying and working with them. I am also suggesting that we should realize that we are part of a vast complex of remedial influences and that we should take special steps to search out other workers with different viewpoints and coordinate our activities with theirs.

The Need for High Quality Workers

This book convinces me that good ideas and techniques, a balanced comprehensive philosophy, and an organizational structure that guarantees continuing confrontation of psychiatrists and their publics are a necessary but not sufficient basis for an effective approach to solving the problems of mental disorder. What is needed to complete the picture is an adequate supply of high quality workers led by innovative and charismatic leaders, who will ensure that the potentialities of our resources are translated into the actual delivery of services in the community. Perhaps as an educator my final conclusion, after studying this book, is the reassurance that my own work is important—a point of view that is hardly unbiased. On the other hand, there does appear to be objective evidence that the quantity and quality of psychiatrists during any particular period did exert a profound influence on the unfolding of events. Once again, there seems to be a reverberating interaction between this and the other factors in the system, so that during periods of narrow oversimplified theory and practice and professional isolation from community confrontation, the quality of human input into psychiatry deteriorated, and low caliber leaders and followers contributed to a further demoralization and degeneration of the profession. The eventual pressure of external reformers not only shook up the psychiatric system but also stimulated an influx of higher caliber candidates and fostered an atmosphere that supported the continuation inside the ranks of the profession of bright young men who previously would probably have left in disgust.

From this I draw the conclusion that our profession should devote particular attention to the recruitment and selection of exciting and talented young men and that some at least of our academic institutions should make a special effort to educate them in ways that by design develop their capacity for innovative leadership. Returning to the first point I made in this chapter, I feel that our inability to predict the nature of the problems and opportunities of our field ten to fifteen years from now should persuade us to focus some of our educational efforts not merely upon giving our students the opportunity to become proficient in current theory and practice skills, important though such a thorough grounding undoubtedly is; but also to help them acquire a body of basic principles and the ability to deal in an innovative manner with unexpected and unfamiliar problems that are today at the periphery, or actually beyond the accepted boundaries, of our domain. Experience in a variety of educational settings, including our own Laboratory of Community Psychiatry at Harvard Medical School, has proved that it is feasible to help students improve markedly their capacity to cope constructively with novel situations; to persevere in problem solving despite the confusion and frustration of not being able to understand the field of forces and their own role; and, when the latter has been clarified, to negotiate a generally acceptable contract for their operations within the system. Such an educational experience is burdensome both cognitively and affectively and demands a high level of native talent and staying power. But this acts catalytically on those who have the quality we are seeking, and they in turn attract those with similar talents and interests into our field.

Once again in this, as in the other areas I have discussed, a historical overview reassures me that progress will occur, even if only in fits and starts, whatever we do. Nevertheless, I believe that by design we can speed up this forward motion, and to me this is one of the benefits of studying books such as this.

NOTES

1. When I discussed the idea of interchangeable service units with my daughter she informed me that Jeremy Bentham had developed a similar scheme in England in the middle of the nineteenth century.

2. *Community Mental Health Journal*, III (1967), Number 3, 216–225.

BIBLIOGRAPHY

Primary Sources

BOOKS

Clifford Willingham Beers. *A Mind That Found Itself*. Doubleday, Doran and Co., New York, 1939.

Amariah Brigham. *Observations on the Influence of Religion upon the Health and Physical Welfare of Mankind*. Marsh, Capen, and Lyon, Boston, 1835.

Amariah Brigham. *An Inquiry Concerning the Diseases and Functions of the Brain, the Spinal Cord, and the Nerves*. George Ablard, New York, 1840.

Samuel Butler. *The Way of All Flesh*. The Modern Library, New York, 1950.

Charles Dickens. *American Notes*. Hazel, Watson and Viney, Ltd., London, 1927.

Pliny Earle. *A Visit to Thirteen Asylums for the Insane in Europe*. J. Dubson, Philadelphia, 1841.

Pliny Earle. *History, Description, and Statistics of the Bloomingdale Asylum for the Insane*. Egbert, Hovey and King, New York, 1848.

Pliny Earle. *Institutions for the Insane in Prussia, Austria and Germany*. New York State Lunatic Asylum, Utica, New York, 1853.

Pliny Earle. *An Examination of the Practice of Bloodletting in Mental Disorders*. Samuel S. and William Wood, New York, 1854.

Pliny Earle. *Medical Opinion in the Parish Will Case*. John F. Trow, New York, 1857.

Pliny Earle. "Psychologic Medicine: Its Importance as Part of the Medical Curriculum." Address to Berkshire Medical Institute, November 24, 1863. Roberts, Book and Job Printers, Utica, New York, 1867.

Pliny Earle. "The Psychopathic Hospital of the Future." Address delivered at the laying of the corner stone of the General Hospital for the Insane in the state of Connecticut, June 20, 1867. Roberts, Book and Job Printers, Utica, New York, 1867.

Pliny Earle. "Prospective Provision for the Insane." Address before the Massachusetts Medical Society, Boston, June 2, 1868. Roberts, Book and Job Printers, Utica, New York, 1868.

Pliny Earle. *Memoirs of Pliny Earle, M.D.* F. B. Sanborn (ed.). Damrell and Upham, Boston, 1898.

Charles E. Goshen (ed.). *Documentary History of Psychiatry*. Philosophical Library, New York, 1967.

Richard Hunter and Ida Macalpine (eds.). *Three Hundred Years of Psychiatry, 1535–1860*. Oxford University Press, London, 1963.

Henry M. Hurd (ed.). *The Institutional Care of the Insane in the United States and Canada*. Johns Hopkins Press, Baltimore, 1916, Vols. I, II.

William James. *Principles of Psychiatry*. Henry Holt and Co., New York, 1923.

Edward Jarvis. *Proper Provision for the Insane*. Government Printing Office, Washington, D.C., 1870.

Edward Jarvis. *Relation of Education to Insanity*. Government Printing Office, Washington, D.C., 1872.

Maxwell Jones. *Social Psychiatry in the Community, in Hospitals and Prisons*. Charles C Thomas, Springfield, Ill., 1962.

Alfred Lief (ed.). *The Common Sense Psychiatry of Dr. Adolf Meyer*. McGraw-Hill Book Co., New York, 1948.

Charles Robert Maturin. *Melmoth, the Wanderer*. University of Nebraska Press, Lincoln, 1961.

Isaac Ray. *Mental Hygiene*. Ticknor and Fields. Boston, 1863.

Benjamin Rush. *Medical Inquiries and Observations Upon the Diseases of the Mind*. Hafner Publishing Co., New York, 1962.

J. G. Spurzheim. *Observation on the Deranged Manifestations of the Mind, or Insanity*. Marsh, Capen, and Lyon, Boston, 1833.

Eunice E. Winters (ed.). *The Collected Papers of Adolf Meyer*. Johns Hopkins Press, Baltimore, 1952, Vol. IV.

JOURNALS

The American Journal of Insanity, Vols. I–LXIV (1844–1845 to 1907–1908).

American Journal of Medical Sciences, Vols. LXXVII–LXXX (1879–1882).

American Journal of Medical Sciences, Vol. LXXXIX (1885).

(New Series.)

The American Practitionery, Vol. XXVI (1882).

Cincinnati Lancet and Clinic, Vol. V (1880).

Cincinnati Lancet and Clinic, Vol. VIII (1882).

Secondary Sources

BOOKS

Franz G. Alexander and Sheldon T. Selesnick. *The History of Psychiatry*. Harper and Row, New York, 1966.

Gay Wilson Allen. *William James*. The Viking Press, New York, 1967.

Robert Blake. *Disraeli*. St. Martin's Press, New York, 1967.

J. S. Bockoven. *Moral Treatment in American Psychiatry*. Springer Publishing Co., New York, 1963.

Norman Dain. *Concepts of Insanity in the United States, 1789–1865*.

Rutgers University Press, New Brunswick, N.J., 1964.

Albert Deutsch. *The Mentally Ill in America*. Columbia University Press, New York, 1945.

Milton Greenblatt. "Beyond the Therapeutic Community." 1962 Annual Israel Strauss Lecture. Hillside Hospital, Glen Oaks, New York, April 29, 1962.

Gerald N. Grob. *The State and the Mentally Ill, A History of Worcester State Hospital in Massachusetts, 1830–1920*. University of North Carolina Press, Chapel Hill, 1965.

Oscar Handlin. *The Uprooted*. Universal Library, New York, 1951.

Oscar Handlin. *The Americans*. Atlantic-Little, Brown, Boston, 1963.

G. R. Hargreaves. *Psychiatry and Public Health*. Oxford University Press, London, 1958.

Richard Hofstadter. *Anti-Intellectualism in American Life*. Vintage Books, New York, 1966.

Denis Leigh. *The Historical Development of British Psychiatry*. Pergamon Press, Edinburgh, 1961, Vol. I.

R. C. McGrane. *The Panic of 1837, Some Financial Problems of the Jacksonian Era*. University of Chicago Press, Chicago, 1924.

William Miller. *A History of the United States*. Dell Publishing Co., New York, 1958.

Nina Ridenour. *Mental Health in the United States*. Harvard University Press, Cambridge, Mass., 1961.

George Rosen. "Social Stress and Mental Disease from the Eighteenth Century to the Present: Some Origins of Social Psychiatry." Lecture, July 8, 1958, Institute of Psychiatry, Maudsley Hospital, University of London.

Gregory Zillboorg and George Wiltenry. *A History of Medical Psychiatry*. W. W. Norton and Co., New York, 1941.

INDEX

moral treatment (*cont'd*)
ernment involvement, 63–71; and
guild, 106–115, 117–124; and immigrants and paupers, 72–77; Northampton under Pliny Earle, 169–175;
professional attitudes toward insane,
143–153; and professional membership; 98–104; psychiatric theory of,
126–140
morbid brain pathology, 250
Mount, James Leonard, on dehumanization of insane, 148
music therapy, 265

national census of 1840, 58
National Committee for Mental Hygiene, founding of, 179
Negroes, insanity among, 58–59
nepotism, in asylums, 206
nerves, linked with mind, 304
neurologists: acceptance by Association
of Medical Superintendents, 304
Newcome, Nancy J., 214
New York, as model for reform, 234–
240
Nicholas, T. R., 288
Nichols, Charles H.: on catchment
area, 54–55; on isolation of guild,
113; lauding guild, 114
Nims, Edward, 174
nonmedical staff, schools for, 259–260
nonrestraint, 268
Northampton under Pliny Earle, 169–
175; changing patient body, 174; condition of, 170; economic success, 172–
173; lay leaders and, 173–174; standards of, 173–174; success of, reasons
for, 171
nutritional deficiencies, and insanity, 139

open systems approach, to theory and
practice, 345–346
organic diseases, and insanity, 138–139
out-patient clinics, 289

Packard, Elizabeth, 109, 191, 193
Packard Law, 191
Page, Charles W., on consequences of
repression, 266
pain, insensitivity of insane, 148–149
parent education, for prevention of
insanity, 15–18
Parigot, J., on overburdening of superintendents, 70
parole, 241
patient care: changes in, 247–261; public outcry against, 179–188
patients, *see* insane
paupers: classes of, 73, 81; overcrowd-

ing and cultural dissonance, 72–77;
prejudice against, 80–81; *see also* immigrants
Personal Liberty Law, 191–192
"photochromatic treatment of insanity,"
264
phrenology, and moral insanity, 120–
122
physical brain damage, correction of,
258–259
physical therapy, at turn of century,
265
physicians, attack of, on psychiatrists,
200–201
physiologists, theories of, 132–133
Pierce, Franklin, on wilderness land for
insane, 83
Pinel, Phillippe, 5, 6, 35, 119, 313; on
insanity and poetry, 42
Poe, Edgar Allan, 266
poetry and insanity, 42
political appointment of superintendents,
204–205
political patronage, 218
politics and community psychiatry, 338–
339
poor, hospitals for, 61
Poor Laws, 65
population-oriented approach, 319–320,
333
population problems, and early nineteenth-century psychiatry, 19
prejudice against asylums, 195, 215–216
pressure groups, for reform, 199–200
Prince, William Henry, 167, 169
Pritchard, James, on moral insanity,
119
private practice, merits of, 52
"psychiatric intellectual history," 331
psychiatric wards in general hospitals,
291
"psychiatrist," use of, 135
psychiatrists, *see* psychiatry; Association of Medical Superintendents
psychiatry: acknowledgment of faults
in, 217–222; alternatives to classic institutions of, 284–292; approach to
theory and practice, 345–346; attitudes, change toward insane, 143–
153; burden on, 69–70; climate and,
327–328; and community, 306–309;
community pressures, resentment of,
212–213; confrontation with public,
339–346; as corporate profession, 320;
corruption in, 205; courtroom behavior and, 117–124; criticism, fear
of, 212–217, 219–222; detachment of,
from patients, 156–157; diagnostic
emphasis of, 157; difficulties with